DATE DUE

CREATIVE PUZZLES OF THE WORLD

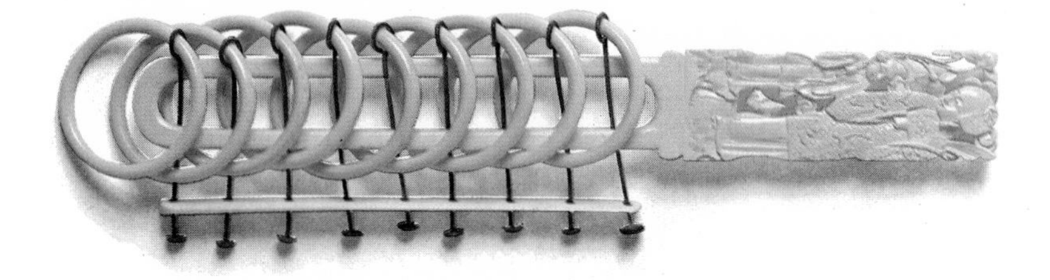

Pilton maze in England, covering two-thirds of an acre, is a puzzle on a giant scale. This wonder was begun in 1971 and took a year to dig. The maze consists of over a mile of trenches, varying in depth from 18 inches to three feet. Although over 25 people at various times took part in digging it, the greatest part of the work was done by the designer of the maze, Greg Bright. His passionate enthusiasm for designing and making these intricate patterns has earned him an epithet, the Maze King.

CREATIVE PUZZLES OF THE WORLD

By Pieter van Delft and Jack Botermans
Introduction by Prof. Dr. Ir. W. L. van der Poel
Text by Chris Cooper and Charmian Murley
Special Consultants: Prof. J. H. de Boer,
Prof. Dr. C. J. Bouwkamp, Stewart T. Coffin, and
Prof. Dr. Ir. W. L. van der Poel

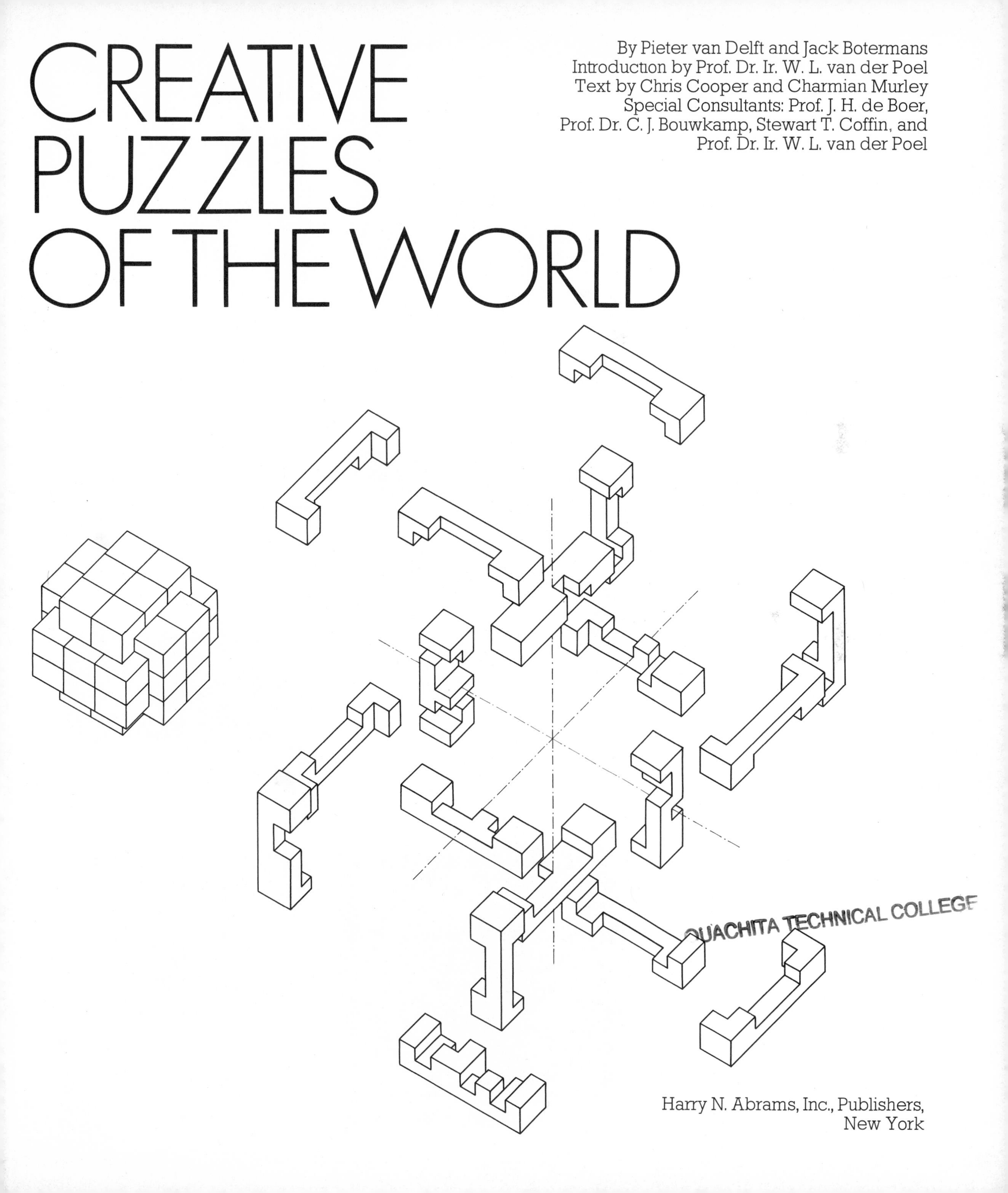

Harry N. Abrams, Inc., Publishers,
New York

Created by:
Pieter van Delft and Jack Botermans,
ADM International bv, Amsterdam,
Netherlands

Editor: Edith M. Pavese

Harry N. Abrams, Incorporated, New York

Library of Congress Cataloging in Publication Data
Delft, Pieter van.
Creative Puzzles of the World.
I. Puzzles. I. Botermans, Jack, joint author.
II. Title
GV1493.D4 793.7'3 77-80234
ISBN 0-8109-0765-8
ISBN 0-8109-2152-9(pbk)
Library of Congress Catalog Card Number: 77-80234

Printed and bound in the United States
Typesetting: Kleij Zetterijen bv, Den Haag
Lithography: Nefli bv, Haarlem

Contents

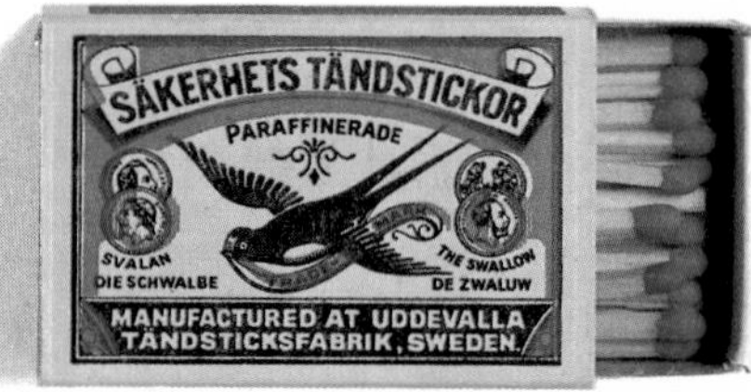

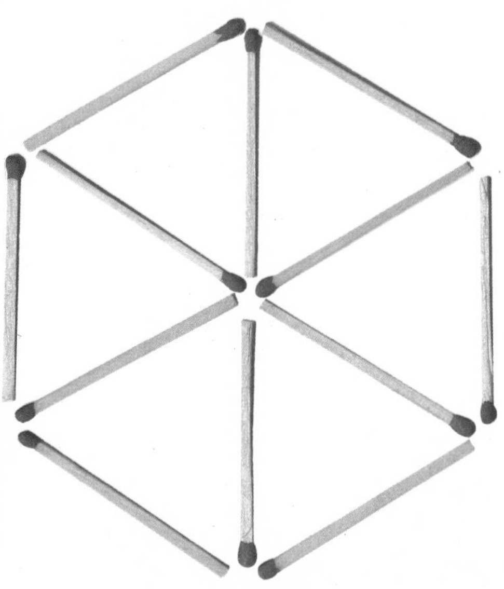

Domino Puzzles

These puzzles give a new twist to an old game. In some you are asked to form patterns with the dominoes in which numbers match where tiles meet, just as in the familiar domino game. In other puzzles you must make patterns in which numbers balance, or you must set up arithmetic problems, and so forth. These puzzles can be accomplished with an ordinary set of dominoes.

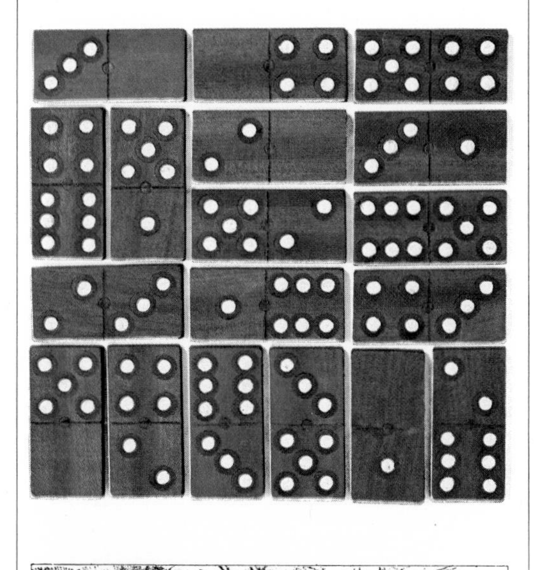

Construction Puzzles and Packing Problems

The construction puzzles in this section are as attractive as they are baffling. Assembled from interlocking wooden or plastic pieces that make a firm structure, there seems no way of taking them apart. The packing problems present the kind of challenge familiar to anyone who has ever packed a suitcase — fitting a number of oddly shaped items into a neat rectangular space. Complete instructions for making the pieces for these puzzles are included.

Magic Squares

Even if you do not believe in magic, you will find these number squares fascinating. In a magic square the rows, columns, and diagonals of numbers all add up to the same total. Even before becoming expert at creating magic squares, you can tackle the puzzles included at the end of this section. Nearly all of these puzzles require no equipment except pencil and paper.

Ring-String-Ball Puzzles 97

These puzzles are more common in Africa and China than in the West. The intricacy of the metal, string, and wood components belies the essential simplicity of their construction. The amateur puzzle maker can easily construct most of these puzzles from readily available materials. The puzzles are a delight to handle, but the challenge to move key components into new positions can be quite baffling.

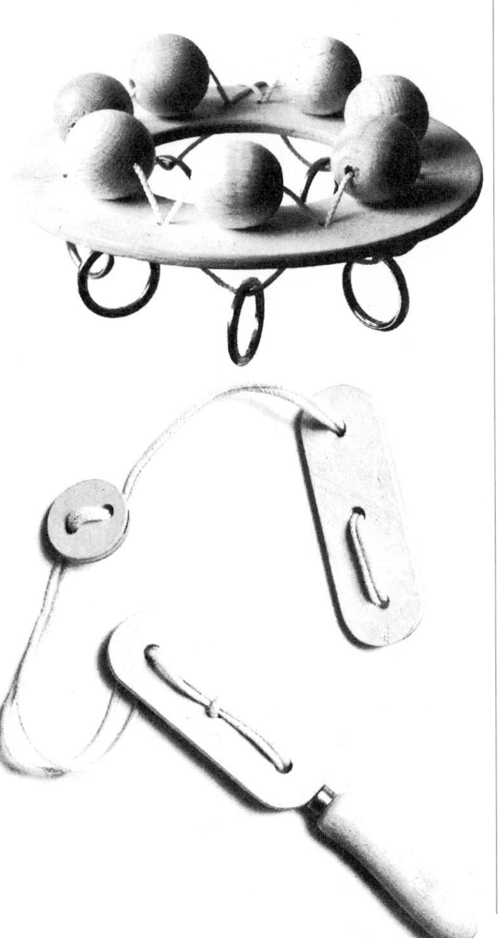

String Puzzles 117

Tricks with string and rope are part of every magician's bag of illusions. Here are some amusing puzzles and stunts in the same tradition for you and your friends. You can make string mysteriously pass through fingers, clothing, or pencils, or you can make amazing escapes in Houdini fashion. Also included are games known as string figures or cat's cradle — pattern-making games with string that have delighted adults and children around the world. Some of the puzzles will need the help of a friend, but elaborate equipment is not necessary.

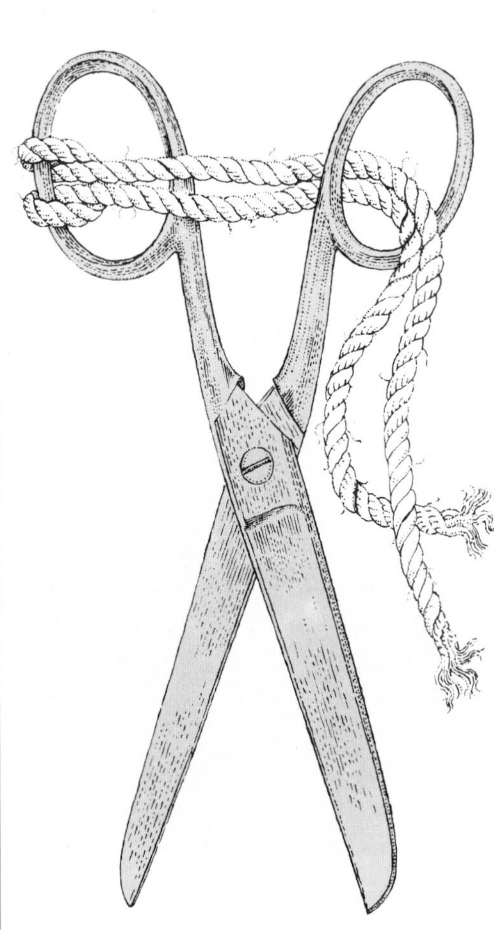

Mazes and Labyrinths 124

For millennia, mazes have held mystical significance for mankind — both inspiring terror and giving pleasure. Many of the mazes in this section are ancient designs. Some were made on church floors with tiles, and symbolized the journeyings of the soul. Some were cut in the turf of village greens and were threaded by villagers for sport. Others were hedge mazes planted in ornamental gardens. Yet some of the mazes in this section are mind-twisting modern designs. You need nothing but a pointer, such as a matchstick, to start threading these mazes.

These elegant puzzles are made of chromed welding wire, often mounted in brightly painted wooden handles. You can amuse yourself and your friends with the problem of separating the components and then joining them together again. The person who makes these puzzles will gain almost as much pleasure in constructing them as those who are successful in solving them. The cutting and shaping of the wire components are explained in detail.

School arithmetic and logical thinking are all you need for most of these puzzles. You can also learn how to make a punched-card computer, mind-reading cards, and a color-matching puzzle.

In these puzzles the objects to be positioned range from checkers and pencil dots or lines to imaginary railroad cars and ferry passengers. Many of these puzzles can be solved with pencil and paper. Others must be constructed as handsome wooden puzzle sets.

Above: The fascination of puzzles has been cleverly used in advertising. In the 1930s a brand of metal polish was publicized with this puzzle. The ring, which contains a narrow opening, must be removed from the disk. The ring must be worked through the holes until it reaches the edge.

Top: Most of us encounter our first puzzles as childhood toys. This toy, made in Germany in 1860, consists of a picture made up of movable blocks. It is a very simple example of a moving piece puzzle. A section of this book is devoted to more sophisticated puzzles of this particular type.

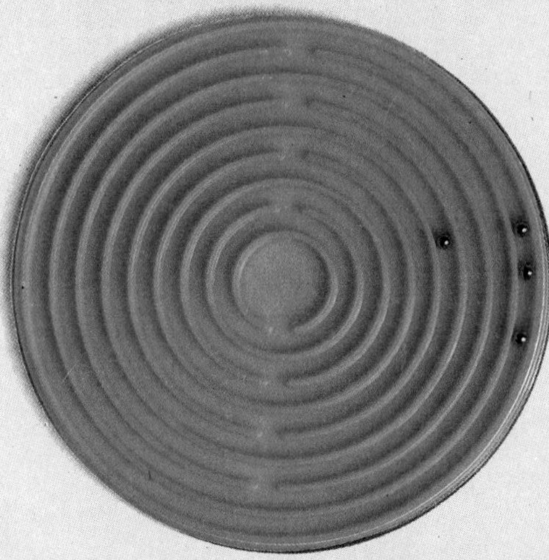

Above: A maze puzzle of this type caught the imagination of the public when it was sold as a children's toy in the late 19th century. It was called Pigs in Clover, and the aim was to roll all of the balls through the passages to the center. It is as popular today as it was then.

Left: This jigsaw puzzle delighted German children toward the end of the 19th century. The jigsaw is a perennial favorite with people of all ages, for an unlimited variety of pictures is available, and each puzzle can be very simple or enormously complicated.

Introduction

An intricate set of toy building blocks, made in Germany around 1900. The budding architect could build a church, a town hall, or a palace with this abundance of bricks, pillars, tiles, and even clock faces. Building blocks are among the most creative of toys, for the child can create and solve his own problems by making original building designs. Replacing the pieces in their box is also a challenging and enjoyable puzzle — a packing problem rather like those on pages 81-85.

Nearly all human beings love to test their wits on puzzles. In solving them they are exercising skills that are characteristically human, shared to only a small degree by other species. Consider one of the most impressive demonstrations of animal problem-solving. In a classic experiment the German psychologist Wolfgang Köhler confined a hungry chimpanzee to its cage and put a banana on the ground outside the cage just out of the animal's reach. After several efforts to reach the banana, the chimpanzee suddenly picked up a stick that Köhler had deliberately placed in the cage, reached through the bars with it, and pulled the banana within reach. For the chimpanzee the solution was original. It was very high in the scale of animal abilities. Yet a normal six-year-old child could equal it.

Many of the puzzles we encounter do not require great originality to solve them, for past experience gives us methods of approaching them. Gathering such experience is often fascinating. But for me a puzzle can lose its charm when a foolproof method of solving it is available. Perhaps the most satisfying kind of puzzle is one whose solution comes only with a change of viewpoint when the usual approaches have been completely exhausted.

There is an old tale about a young woman who in a flash of insight solved an apparently impossible problem. Her father owed a large debt to an evil moneylender and had no hope of paying it. The moneylender offered to release the father from his debt if he agreed to a wager. The moneylender would place a black pebble and a white one in a bag and the daughter would take only one from it. If her luck was good and she retrieved the white pebble, the moneylender would make no claim against the father. However, if she took the black pebble, she would have to marry the moneylender. With no other choice available, the father and daughter agreed to the wager. The moneylender picked up a handful of pebbles from the hundreds that were lying around. He dropped two into the bag — but the sharp-eyed daughter saw that they were both black. Her dilemma was terrifying. If she exposed the moneylender as a cheat, he would certainly have her father sent to prison for nonpayment of a debt. On the other hand, if she took a pebble, she would be compelled to marry the hated moneylender. Trying to find the daughter's solution should be quite tantalizing to the reader.

The girl turned the moneylender's trick against him in an ingenious way. She quickly took a pebble, fumbled in feigned nervousness, and dropped it before anyone could see its color. It was immediately lost among the myriad pebbles on the ground. "It's all right," she said, "we can easily find out what color it was, for it was the opposite of the pebble that is still in the bag." Thus she was able to "prove" that the pebble she had taken was actually white.

The heroine's shift of attention from the pebble she was to select to the pebble that would remain is perhaps typical of what happens when we have a flash of insight into a problem. The horse and rider puzzle on the next page requires a similar shift for its solution. The puzzler is presented with two separate pictures, A and B. (You can copy the outlines of the pictures on separate pieces of tracing paper in order to try the puzzle.) Without cutting either of them, place B on A so that each cowboy sits on a horse. After a few attempts, you may be convinced that the puzzle is impossible to solve. But by shifting your point of view, you may hit on an unexpected solution.

Here is a small puzzle that I invented. Again, a surprising answer can be found when the usual approach would indicate that the puzzle cannot be solved. Imagine that you have an unlimited supply of model railroad switches, all of them left-handed. Can you lay these down and join them up to form a closed network with no free ends left unattached?

A little experimenting with left-handed switches shows the puzzler that there is no way to make a length of track that curves around to join up with itself with no free ends branching from it. One can easily decide that the proposed network is impossible.

Lewis Carroll, mathematician, logician, creator of children's stories, and fervent lover of puzzles. Carroll published a book of mathematical puzzles that he devised while lying sleepless in bed, and a book of puzzles that he first made up for a children's paper. His love of paradox and word play, which delights the readers of his Alice books, is typical of many puzzle enthusiasts.

But while thinking about the problem, one may notice that it is simple to make two parallel stretches of track linked to each other at regular intervals by the branching arms of the switches. Since the earth is round why not lay such a pair of tracks around it so that they join up on the far side? But frustrated puzzlers may reject this solution as being cheating!

How are puzzles invented? Let me answer with reference to the type that interests me most — the construction puzzle made of interlinking wooden blocks. I am first struck by some attractive external appearance that a construction puzzle could have; for instance, it could resemble a cube divided into eight smaller cubes by three perpendicular cuts. Then I ask myself how the internal surfaces can be shaped so that the puzzle is a firm structure and yet not too easy to put together or to take apart. In reference to the cube mentioned above, I produced a design some years ago, but I cannot make the puzzle, for it requires very accurately cut dovetail joints that are beyond my skill as a carpenter.

The drawings that I make when constructing a puzzle merely document a design that I have thought out beforehand. Many puzzle enthusiasts are fortunate in being able to visualize a puzzle and work on it in their imagination without the use of a model or pencil and paper. Lewis Carroll, author of *Alice in Wonderland*, published a book of mathematical problems, some of them very complicated, that he had devised and solved in his head while lying sleepless in bed. Readers of the present book who cannot picture problems so vividly may take comfort from the fact that Carroll discovered that his ability to visualize improved as he worked on more and more problems.

The hundreds of puzzles described in this book range in complexity from those that require only pencil and paper or a box of matches, to intricate constructions that call for a few hours' work by a fairly skilled carpenter. The book is unique in the detail and comprehensiveness of the instructions it offers to the amateur puzzle maker, while readers who do not wish to construct puzzles will find many that they can attempt immediately. The book is a welcome addition to puzzle literature.

Willem L. van der Poel
Delft, Netherlands

A highly paradoxical object figures in the detail (above) from an engraving entitled *Belvedere* by the Dutch artist M. C. Escher. There is nothing remarkable about each part of the cubical frame viewed separately, but combined they suggest an impossible object. The strut held in the man's right hand seems to be vertical; yet it also seems to connect the far and near corners of the frame. To make such an object would be an insoluble puzzle.

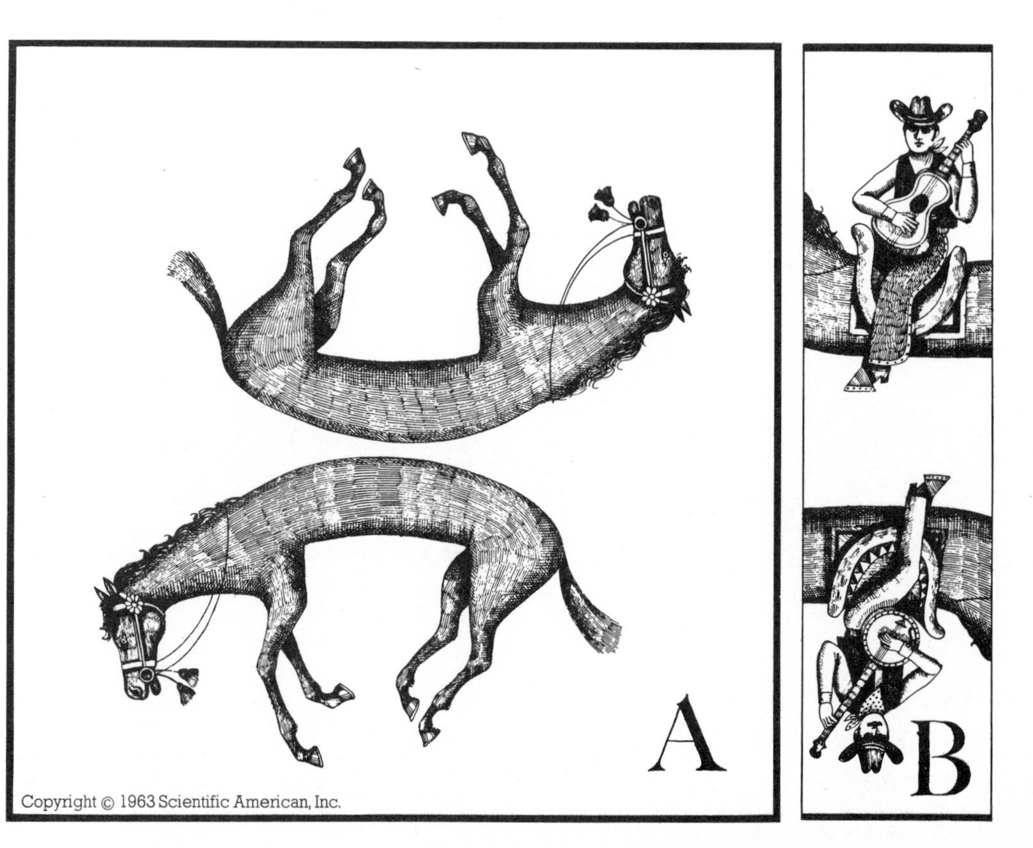

Pictures A and B (right) are on separate cards. The problem is to put each rider on his own horse. The solution appears on page 182.

Geometrical Problems

This exquisitely carved ivory tangram set was made in China in the 19th century. The pieces could be formed into two smaller squares to fit in the box.

The magic egg puzzle described later in this section normally hatches out birdlike shapes. Here it forms a lady with baggy sleeves and large feet.

One of the most ancient dissection, or "cutting up," problems was proposed and solved in the tenth century by Abul Wefa, a Persian mathematician. This problem can be duplicated by drawing three squares of equal size and then cutting them into nine pieces that can be reassembled into one large square.

This puzzle is similar to those found in practical situations encountered in everyday life. If you wanted to use three square pieces of a particular material — for example, cloth, wood, or veneer — to make a larger square without any waste, it might be helpful to know Abul Wefa's solution to the problem.

Here are two dissection puzzles proposed by the English puzzler Henry Ernest Dudeney. You begin with a 25" square. First Dudeney proposes that the square be dissected into four pieces that can be reassembled to make two squares, one 20" square and the other 15" square. Then he asks that a way be found of dissecting the original square into four pieces that will make two squares that are different sizes from the original two but again have sides that are a whole number of inches. (Solutions to all these problems are on page 182.)

As the last example shows, simple arithmetical thinking may be needed to solve such problems. In other cases geometry is needed. Invariably solving these puzzles takes a great deal of trial and error. Solutions may be suggested by doodling with pencil and paper or by cutting up paper into various shapes. However, the final solution must be exact; there must be some kind of geometrical proof that pieces match up.

The person who has developed the most sophisticated methods of attacking dissection problems is Harry Lindgren, an Australian who broke more records in solving this type of puzzle than anyone else. Numerical facts about the sides, diagonals, and angles of squares, Maltese crosses, and other shapes were always in his mind when working on a puzzle. In addition, he built up a set of standard procedures with names like P slides, TT dissections, and so forth. These enabled him to perform a variety of geometrical feats quickly and easily, such as changing a parallelogram into another desired shape. By these means Lindgren achieved many virtuoso dissections, such as cutting a square a hexagon or an equilateral triangle. into nine pieces that could make either All this may sound a little discouraging to the person without a mathematical mind, but many dissection puzzles require no skill in mathematics. Furthermore, in this field the experts are rarely certain that the best possible solution to a problem has been achieved. The amateur often contributes new and improved dissections, and his best aids are diligence and ingenuity.

In the next section dissections of the geometrical type are presented as puzzle sets made of wood, plastic, or any other attractive or practical material. Since in each case the dissection has already been done, the problem is one of reassembly into the alternative shape.

Moving-Piece Puzzles

This section is taken up with a type of puzzle involving a freer use of pieces. The archetype of these is tangram, a Chinese puzzle that is at least a few centuries old. A fine set, made from ivory and ornately carved, is shown on the left at the top. The pieces that are used in tangram are obtained by dissecting a square into various geometric shapes. The aim of the game is not to assemble a given geometric shape, as with geometrical dissections, but to create figures of people, animals, objects, symbols, letters of the alphabet, Chinese ideograms — in fact, almost any shape that can be imagined. The game becomes a puzzle when you try to copy figures that are given in the form of silhouettes. In this chapter we give hundreds of puzzle figures that can be made with the tangram set and with other puzzle sets that have differently shaped pieces.

The richness of the figures that tangram and similar games can yield is amazing and delightful. On the left is a figure created from the magic egg puzzle described on page 23 — a graceful lady. It is surprising that she should appear from nine pieces of arbitrary shapes — the more surprising since the magic egg generally specializes in hatching birds. Tangram-type puzzles also lend themselves to abstract shapes. As we see, the artistically inclined person can find as much of interest in moving-piece puzzles as the mathematically inclined.

Tangram

In the early part of the 19th century a new craze swept Europe and America. It seemed that suddenly everyone was playing the "Chinese puzzle game." The pieces used for this new pastime were seven shapes obtained from a square cut in a certain way. They could be assembled to form figures of people, animals, and everyday objects, as well as new geometrical shapes, numbers, and letters. The game could be played alone or in competition. Later in the century it acquired the obscure name "tangram." Its popularity continues almost undiminished to this day.

It is not known when tangram was invented; it seems certain that it was already old in 1813, the date of the earliest Chinese book known on the subject. This work contains over 300 tangram figures. Many Chinese tangram sets are very beautiful, made of ivory, bone, or lacquered wood and often inlaid with delicate carving.

In Europe tangram puzzles were published in books or on sets of cards, like those shown on these pages. The outline figures were often elaborated with pictures of the persons or objects that they were supposed to represent. Often, too, they would be set in landscapes in the hope that this would stimulate the imagination of the puzzle solver.

Nineteenth-century European and American publishers sold their tangram wares with the brashness typical of the times. One collection was advertised thus: "For young and old, for men and women and for the nobility and all other classes. It is, in addition, edifying, and you cannot, as you often can with other games, lose your money." Then, as now, parents could be induced to buy with the assurance that the game was educational. A teacher published *New Mathematical Demonstrations of Euclid rendered clear and familiar to the minds*

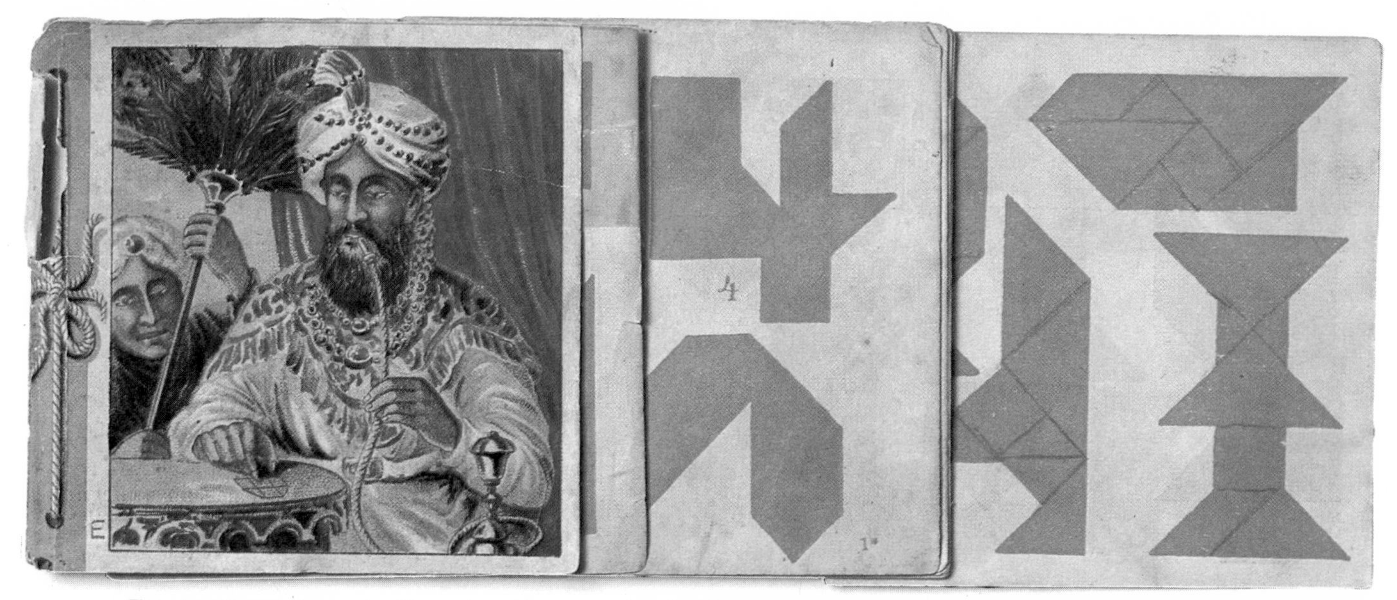

This stonelike tangram set with puzzle cards was produced in Germany around the turn of the century and sold for three cents.

of youth, which utilized no equipment other than the tangram pieces. Tangram was even peddled with verse:

But nor Poet, nor Painter, though
  giving free scope to
The visions of fancy, when fancy
  is warm,
Let them do all they can, yet they
  never could hope to
Surpass the queer figures your Puzzles
  can form.

The standard tangram puzzle challenges the puzzler to produce a given silhouette using all of the pieces. It can be tantalizingly difficult, but it can also be correspondingly satisfying when the pieces fall into place. It can even be thrilling when you invent a new form, whether abstract or figurative. Yet such discoveries are rare and usually result only after much trial and error.

That the seven pieces of the tangram, sometimes called tans (which consist of only five triangles of various sizes, a square, and a rhomboid), can imply a complex figure is quite amazing. Even the slender legs of a stork or the masts of a yacht can be suggested by a clever placing of the stubby pieces.

The subject of tangrams was enriched by the great American puzzle inventor Sam Loyd. His classic *Eighth Book of Tan* contains over 600 patterns, many of them invented by him. These are woven together with a tongue-in-cheek commentary that describes a completely bogus history of the game. According to Loyd, the 4000-year-old game was invented by the god Tan and was described in the ancient *Seven Books of Tan,* august works in each of which a thousand designs were listed.

These hand-painted tangram cards are part of a set published in Europe during the first half of the 19th century. The player's task was to duplicate each outline using all of his tangram pieces.

Sailboats lend themselves to tangram pictures. The simple variants of a basic pattern below are only a small sample of the possible nautical designs.

In Loyd's words these designs "illustrate the creation of the world and the origin of species upon a plan which out-Darwins Darwin, the progress of the human race being traced through seven stages of development up to a mysterious spiritual state which is too lunatic for serious consideration." According to Loyd: "It can be proven that Archimedes, Pythagoras, and Euclid must have known of the second book of Tan."

This hoax is supported with such a mixture of spurious references to real and fictitious authorities that Loyd spread a fog over the history of tangrams that still lingers. Scholars and philologists, who should have realized that Loyd's yarns were "too lunatic for serious consideration," set to work combing Chinese literature before concluding his history was baseless.

Tangram was not named after a god. The origin of the name is unknown. It might be a corruption of the obsolete English word *trangam,* a puzzle or trinket (it was misspelled as *trangram* in Samuel Johnson's dictionary of 1755). Or it might be a combination of *Tang* (the name of one of the greatest of Chinese dynasties) with the Greek suffix *-gram,* meaning "writing." Yet it might be taken from the name of the *tanka* people. These river dwellers were great traders and an essential link in the chain of opium smugglers. At night Western sailors would often be entertained by *tanka* girls, and among

(See solution page 182)

their more innocent diversions may have been the ancient Chinese puzzle.

Apart from keeping pedants harmlessly occupied, Loyd pointed out new aspects of tangrams and proposed some paradoxes. One type is illustrated by two figures of a man, identical except that one has a foot that the other lacks. (They appear on page 16.) Since both of these figures must be made using all of the tans, it needs some thought to see how the foot can be grown and absorbed.

Loyd was also interested in the way in which a tangram's illusion is enhanced by its context. A somewhat unconvincing figure of a cat seems more feline if there are one or two better-formed figures nearby. Loyd also liked to make figures that could be read in quite different ways when turned. An example of this appears on page 16.

Playing Tangram
Each figure must use all seven tans. All must touch without overlapping. The simplest, although possibly the most challenging, way to play is to experiment with the tans and form new shapes freely. You will reinvent many old designs and perhaps some new ones.

The result is more definite when you try to copy a given silhouette, like those shown here and on page 16. There is added excitement if you compete with someone else to see who can make a given design first.

Finally you can set yourself the task of making specific letters, numerals, geometric shapes, or particular figures in a story. For example, how many differently shaped triangles can you make? Or characters from the Cinderella story — prince, ugly sisters, and coach?

Are the energetic silhouettes above and at left performing the Charleston, a frenzied Cossack dance, or strenuous *Tai chi* exercises? Give your own titles to their actions as you try to piece the figures together, using all seven tans.

The dancers above are so lively that you can almost see the grins on their faces. In the 19th century tangram publishers would provide assistance to the puzzler with detailed pictures such as those of the young ladies below, bearing only slight resemblance to the corresponding puzzle shapes.

(See solution page 182)

The triumphant husband in the 19th-century French cartoon below is exulting in his achievement: after hours of effort he has solved a tangram puzzle. His wife does not seem very happy for him, which is understandable since she has been working on the same problem without success. They are now into the small hours of the morning, the baby has been neglected, and the warming pan has cooled off. Tangram has that effect; beware of insomnia as you tackle the puzzles on the next page.

Materials
Plywood, acrylic, or cardboard about 1/4″ thick and 4″ × 4″ square. With plywood, varnish is also needed.

Tools
Ruler and pencil; fretsaw and sandpaper (for wood or plastic); knife and steel straightedge (for cardboard).

How to Make the Puzzle
You can easily make a tangram set from cardboard or wood with the aid of the diagram below. After you have selected the material, cut it to a square exactly 4″ × 4″. With ruler and pencil draw in the grid lightly, making 16 squares, each of which should be 1″ square.

Then mark in the heavy lines. First join E to L and G to K. Then join A to the point CG (the midpoint of line EL) and continue the line until it meets line GK at point DH. Finally draw in the short lines connecting G to the point DF and the point BH to DH.

Cut along these heavy lines. Use a fretsaw if your material is plywood or acrylic, or a utility knife and a steel straightedge if you are using cardboard. You will end up with five triangles (two large, one medium-sized, and two small), one rhomboid, and one square.

If the tans are wooden or plastic, smooth them down with medium-grain sandpaper. Finish them with a coat of shellac or varnish. If the pieces are cardboard they may be painted or neatly covered with pieces of colored plastic tape cut to the respective shapes.

Make a scaled-up copy of this figure, and then cut along the heavy lines to make your tangram set.

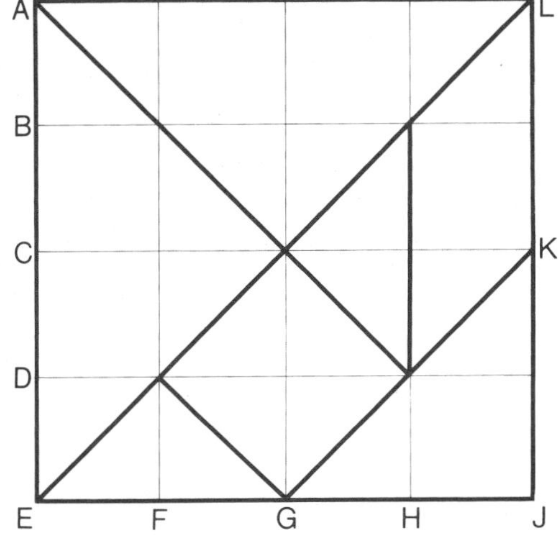

Smiles and frowns on human faces, the evil look of carrion crows, the complacency of a hen — all of these, as well as shapes of beautiful symmetry, can be detected among the silhouettes above. When you study these designs, you find the tans behaving most strangely. The lady bowing on the right, for example — isn't she familiar from elsewhere on this page? The two gentlemen next to her — how can one of them have an extra foot when both figures are made from the complete set of tangram pieces?

(See solution page 182)

Circular Tangram

The straight lines and severe angles of the classical tangram are considered a restraint by some players, who consequently prefer moving-piece games that include some curves. The one shown on the right was sold in the last century. Its pieces are obtained by the dissection of two disks.

The shapes that can be made with this puzzle have a softer or more fluid appearance than the jagged tangram figures. They often seem easier to solve, too, perhaps because of the greater distinctiveness of some of the pieces. For this reason, the circular tangram puzzle seems especially suitable for younger players. The same kinds of puzzles can be engaged in as with normal tangram: free invention, copying a given shape, or representing a specific object.

Materials
Two squares of plywood, cardboard, or acrylic, 4" × 4". Varnish (for wood).

Tools
Ruler, pencil, and compasses; fretsaw and sandpaper (for wood or plastic); knife and straightedge (for cardboard).

How to Make the Puzzle
Draw two circles each with a 2" radius. Draw a diameter on one of these. On the other copy the diagram below. (To draw arcs CAD and AE set the compasses to a radius of 2", and put the point on B and C respectively.) Cut out the pieces. Wood and plastic must be sandpapered, and wood needs varnishing or painting on both sides. Paint cardboard or stick colored tape on it.

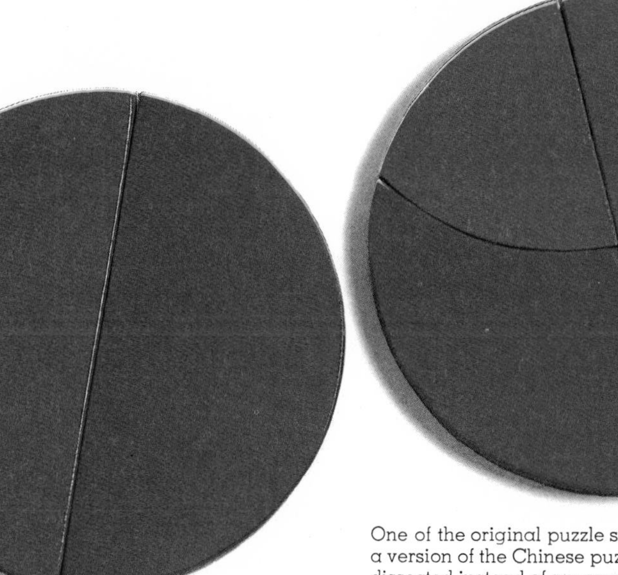

One of the original puzzle sets for circular tangram, a version of the Chinese puzzle in which circles are dissected instead of squares.

Pieces sometimes have to be reversed to make these shapes, some of which are distinctly creepy-crawly.

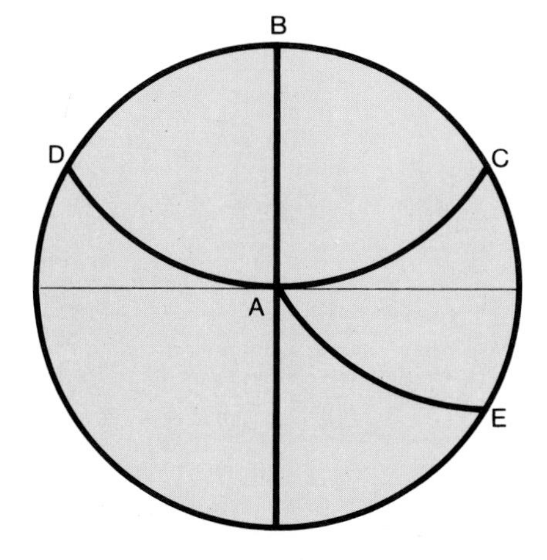

One disk is sliced along a diameter. The other is cut up along arcs and a straight line, in this way.

(See solution page 183)

Pythagoras

Most of us have vague memories of the Greek philosopher and mathematician Pythagoras from our schooldays — obscure stuff about triangles and squares and those fabulous beasts hypotenuses.

This moving-piece puzzle has all of these although it is doubtful whether Pythagoras himself could have proved his famous proposition with its aid alone.

Rest assured that knowledge of geometry is not called for in doing this puzzle. The orginal makers were F. A. Richter and Company, who manufactured many puzzles with moving pieces based on tangram. Evidently the name was prompted by the puzzle's hint of school geometry. The set below is one of Richter's products made at the end of the 19th century. Again the aim is to reproduce the outlines provided.

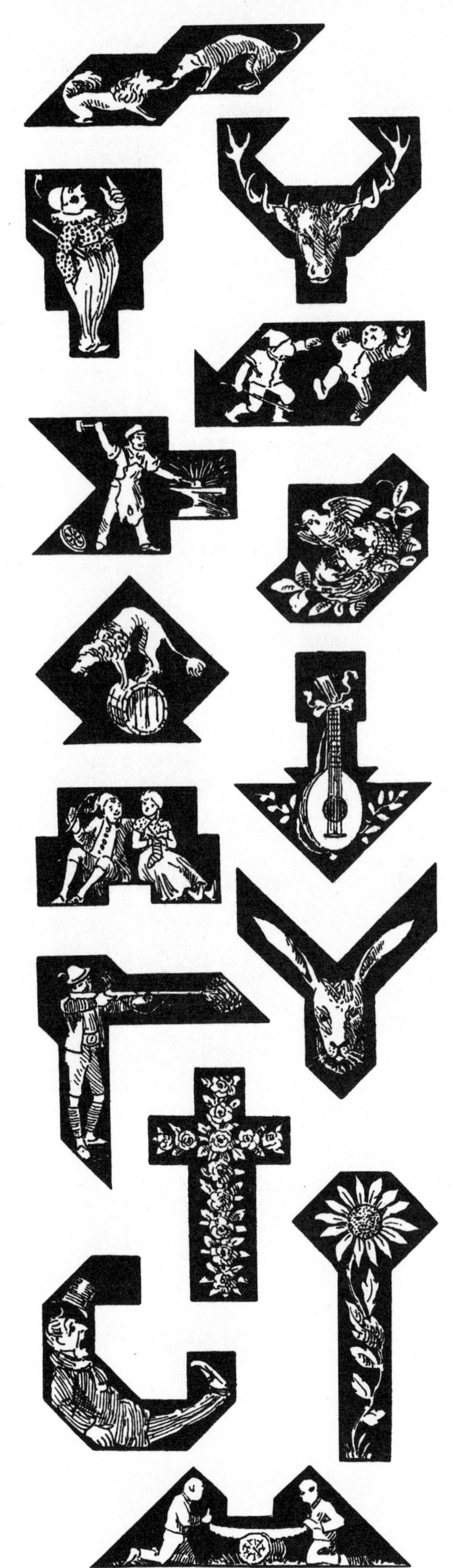

Before television, people had other means of entertaining themselves. This beautiful puzzle set was one way of passing a pleasant evening.

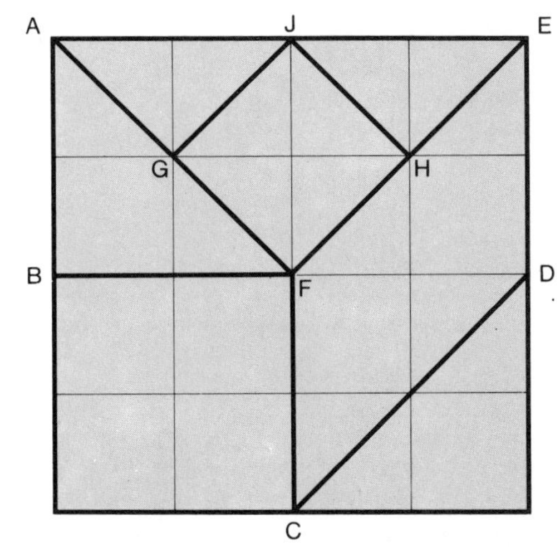

Copy this diagram to make your Pythagoras puzzle.

Materials

One square of plywood, cardboard or acrylic, 4" × 4". Varnish (for wood).

Tools

Ruler, pencil, and compasses; fretsaw and sandpaper (for wood or plastic); knife and straightedge (for cardboard).

How to Make the Puzzle

Lightly draw the grid, consisting of 16 squares, each 1" × 1". Draw in the heavy lines from the sides to the center, AF, BF, CF, and EF. Mark the centers G and H on lines AF and EF respectively. Mark J and D, which are the respective midpoints of the square's top and right-hand sides. Finally draw CD, JG, and JH. Cut out the pieces. If you are using wood, sandpaper and varnish or paint the pieces. Plastic needs merely to be sandpapered. Cardboard can be painted, or covered with tape.

Perhaps it is to be expected that a puzzle with the name of Pythagoras should lend itself to making geometric shapes. But the artist has shown how, with a little imaginative license, the mind's eye can see people and animals within the severe outlines.

(See solution page 183)

The Circle Puzzle

There is an almost endless number of ways in which one can take a pleasing shape, slice it up and put the pieces together again into attractive or expressive figures. The character of the patterns that can be created is strangely variable according to the original shape and the way it is dissected.

Compare the figures that are produced by moving-piece puzzles on the previous and following pages. Looking at these, you may decide that some are more to your taste than others, and you might consider making those puzzle pieces first. But a set of several puzzles, constructed in similar sizes and in uniform materials and colors, can be a pleasing thing to have in the house.

There have been people (especially the original makers) who believe that in playing with these puzzles you do yourself and your children a world of good. They are convinced that much is to be gained by testing one's brains on these problems. Toward the end of the last century F. A. Richter and Company marketed these puzzles, which were accompanied by booklets filled with the figures to be copied. The booklets often quoted a number of enthusiastic buyers. Among these was H. K. Tiemann, a pastor in Brandenburg, who admitted that occasionally, "being fatigued in spirit from the affairs of my office I often retire to a true recreation, making beautiful designs with the stones." Another "eloquent appreciation" received by these enterprising puzzle merchants came from a Mr. Holst of Amsterdam, who asserted with confidence that "these ever-popular toys are among the most developing means of education that one can put into the hands of a child."

Despite these solemn commendations, children and adults have found hours of pure delight in these puzzles. Again the aim is to use all of the pieces with none overlapping to duplicate each silhouette shown on the facing page.

The name "Circular Puzzle" appears in five languages on the lid of this old puzzle box, an indication of its wide popularity.

This original circle puzzle was made of a tough lightweight mineral mixture, pleasant to handle.

Materials
Plywood, acrylic, or cardboard about ¼″ thick and a little more than 4″ × 4″. The plywood will need varnish.

Tools
Ruler, pencil and compasses; fretsaw and sandpaper (for wood or plastic); knife and straightedge (for cardboard).

How to Make the Puzzle
Draw a circle with a radius of 2″. Draw a horizontal diameter AC and a vertical diameter at a right angle to it. Mark the points B and D on the vertical diameter, each point 1″ from the center. Draw the lines AB, BC, CD, and DA. Finally draw the line through D parallel to AC. Cut out all of the pieces. Wood and plastic will need to be sandpapered; in addition, wood will need varnishing or painting on both sides. Cardboard can be painted or covered with colored plastic tape.

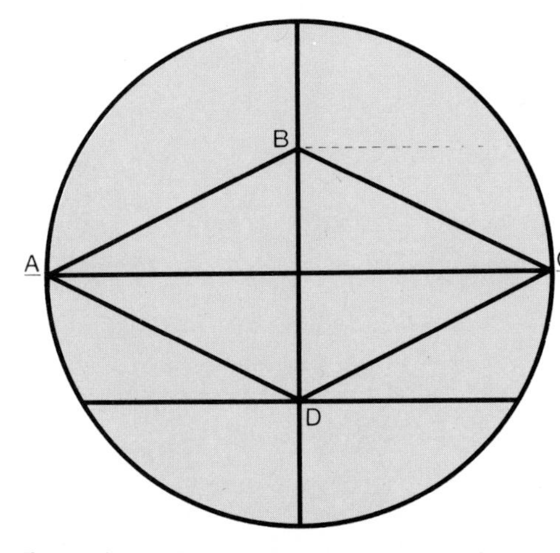

Follow the markings of the guide diagram above when making your circle puzzle pieces.

The forms and figures above are just some of the many possibilities that you can explore when working with a circle puzzle. Some are relatively easy to construct, others moderately hard, and others are definitely on the difficult side. Using the ten segments of the puzzle, try reproducing the forms that appeal to you most. When you have gained some experience with these, you could try competing with others to see who can make a given form fastest. Or you can see who is first to make a reasonable figure representing a specified person or object.

(See solution page 183)

The Broken Heart

The heart that gets broken will not be your own, but the nine-piece puzzle form below. The figures and shapes that can be assembled from the pieces display some interesting angles and curves, although few of them seem to be particularly romantic.

Broken hearts can be mended, and this one can be put together in all the ways shown on the right.

Materials
One square of plywood, cardboard, or acrylic, 3″ × 3″. Varnish (for wood).

Tools
Ruler, pencil and compasses; fretsaw and sandpaper (for wood or plastic); knife and straightedge (for cardboard).

How to Make the Puzzle
Draw the grid of 1″ squares shown. Mark the circles, radius 1″, centered on A and B, and then the heavy lines. Cut out the pieces with the fretsaw. Wood and plastic need to be sandpapered; wood needs to be varnished or painted on both sides. Cardboard can be painted or covered with colored plastic tape.

Use this diagram to make the broken heart puzzle.

Copy these figures, and then make some new ones of your own, reversing the pieces if necessary.

(See solution page 183)

The Magic Egg

It is a well-known fact that birds come from eggs. It should come as no surprise, therefore, that when this egg puzzle is taken apart and reassembled, it has the tendency to hatch one of the numerous varieties of birds on the right.

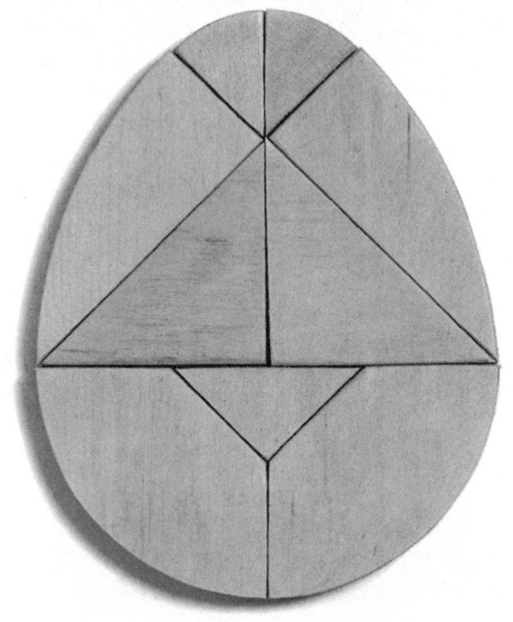

How many birds can you hatch from the magic egg?

Materials and Tools

The same materials and tools are needed as for the broken heart puzzle.

How to Make the Puzzle

Draw a circle with a 2" radius, and mark diameters AB and HJ at right angles. Draw the lines AH and BH and continue them about 2". Draw the arcs BD and AC (parts of circles centered on B and A) to meet these straight lines. Draw a circle centered on H that touches, but does not intersect, the larger circles at C and D. With the compasses at the same setting put the point on J and mark E; then draw a circle centered on E. Draw EF and EG. Cut out the pieces.

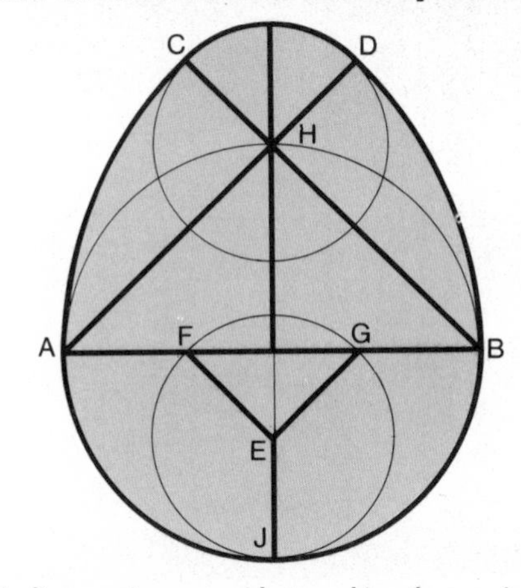

This diagram is your guide to making the magic egg.

The multitudes of flying creatures above include some species unknown to ornithologists.

(See solution page 183)

The Cross Breaker

The reasons for the strange activities of the two small gentlemen below are, alas, unknown. There are several possibilities. Perhaps these little men are stonemasons who have discovered a defect in one of the headstones they have produced and have decided to turn it into crazy paving. Or perhaps they find it easier to transport their products by breaking them up and reassembling them into the neat rectangle shown at the right. This would leave the client with the interesting problem of forming the pieces in the shape of a cross before use.

It is more likely, however, that this picture gives a whimsical glimpse of the activities inside the factory of F. A. Richter and Company, the original creators of the cross breaker puzzle.

Although it is not immediately obvious, these snugly fitting pieces are formed by breaking up a cross.

The illustration below accompanied the early cross breaker puzzles. If this was the normal way of making the pieces, wastage must have been high.

In that case, the employees are to be congratulated on the skill with which by means of a few hammer blows they made the puzzle set shown here, with its smooth edges and accurate fit. It is not recommended that you attempt the same method of making the puzzle but rather that you cut up a square according to the directions that follow. Then see how many of the shapes that are reproduced here you can make and how many new ones you can devise.

Materials

A piece of plywood, cardboard, or acrylic, 4″ × 5″. Varnish (for wood).

Tools

Ruler, pencil; fretsaw and sandpaper (for wood or plastic); knife and straightedge (for cardboard).

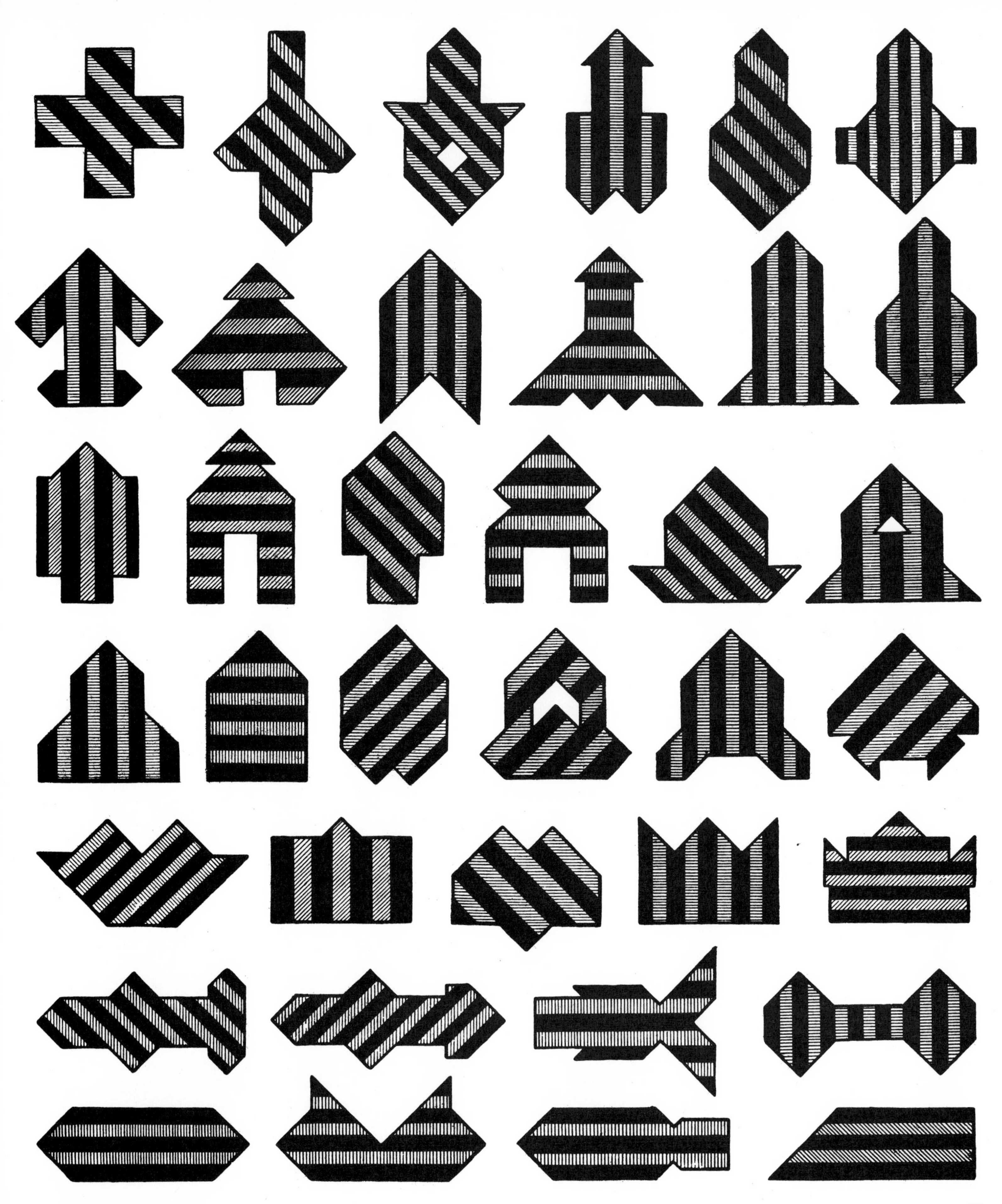

(See solution page 184)

How to Make the Puzzle
Draw a grid of 1" squares as shown in the guide diagram given here. Mark in the heavy lines, and cut out the pieces. Wood and plastic must be sandpapered, and wood needs varnishing or painting on both sides. Cardboard can be painted, or it can be covered with colored plastic tape — again on both sides, so pieces can be turned over.

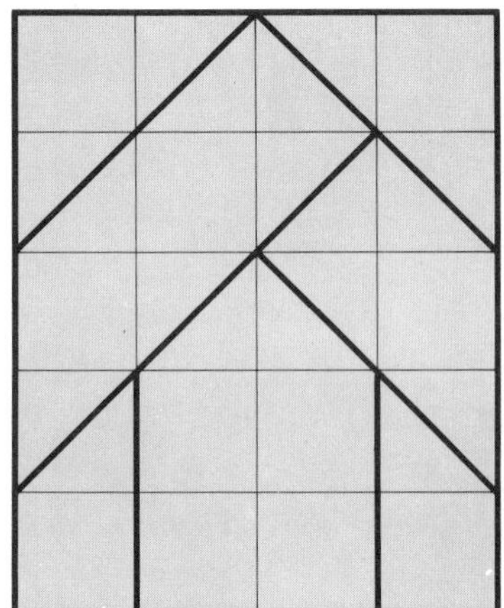

Use this diagram to make the cross breaker puzzle.

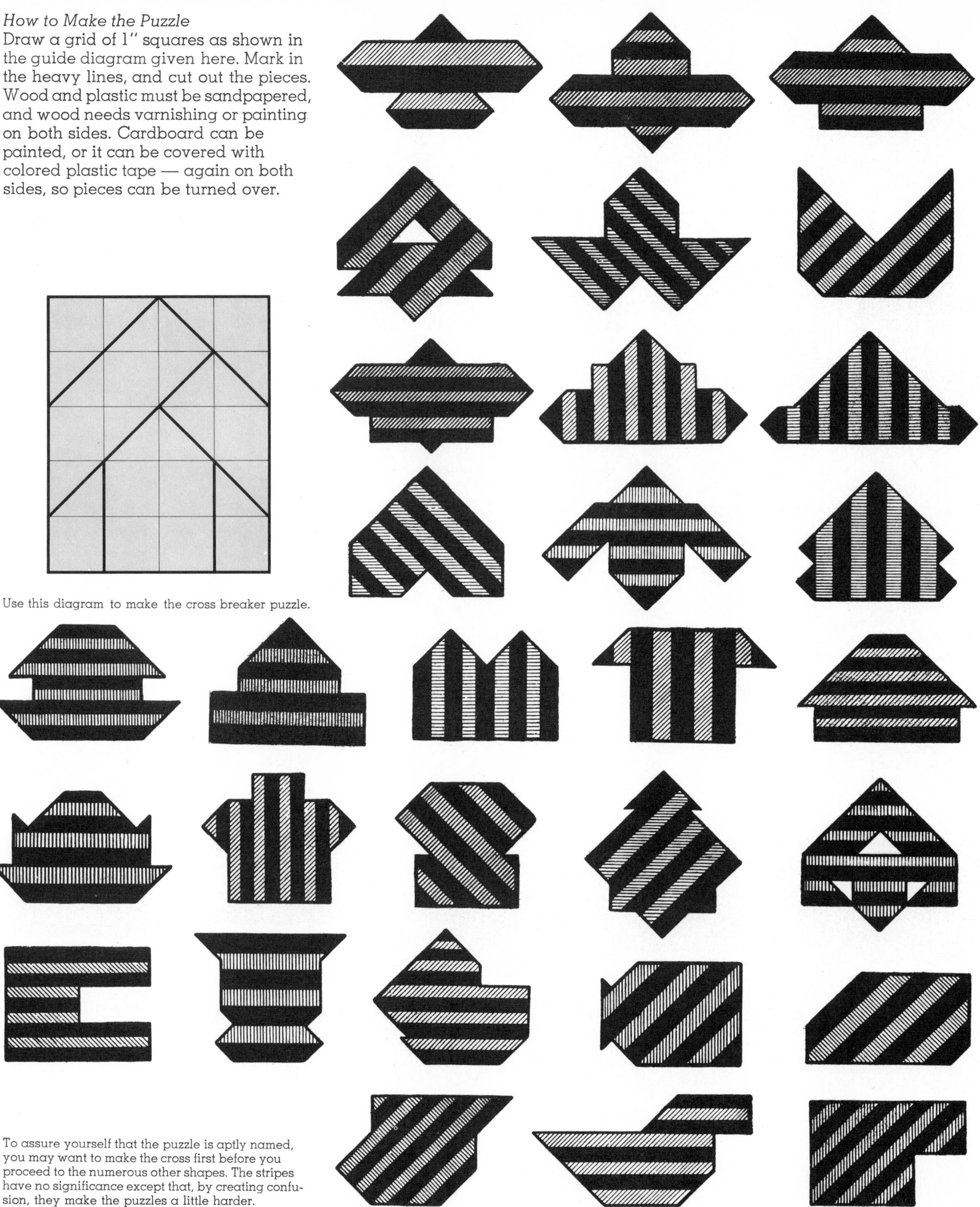

To assure yourself that the puzzle is aptly named, you may want to make the cross first before you proceed to the numerous other shapes. The stripes have no significance except that, by creating confusion, they make the puzzles a little harder.

(See solution page 184)

The Nine Puzzle

Two of the shapes in this puzzle are four-sided, while the rest are triangles of various sizes. Use the pieces to form the shapes on the right and others your fancy can devise. Use all of the pieces for each figure without letting any of the pieces overlap any of the others.

A puzzle booklet and set of pieces for the nine puzzle could be bought in the late 19th century.

Materials
A piece of plywood, cardboard, or acrylic, 6″ × 4″. Varnish (for wood).

Tools
Ruler and pencil; fretsaw and sandpaper; knife and straightedge.

How to Make the Puzzle
Copy the grid below. The vertical lines are 2″ apart, and the horizontals are 1¾″ apart. E and F are each equidistant from the ends of the rectangle. Mark lines AB and CD, then BE and CE, followed by FG, FH, KH, and IJ. Cut out the pieces. Wood and plastic need to be sandpapered; wood should be varnished or painted on both sides. Paint cardboard, or cover it with tape.

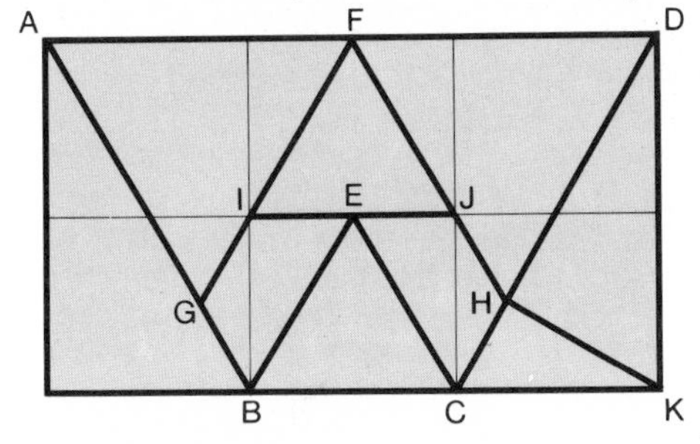

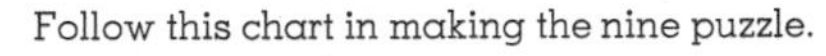

Follow this chart in making the nine puzzle.

The simplicity of these shapes is deceptive; copying them with the puzzle pieces can be difficult.

(See solution page 184)

Dissection Puzzles

Some of the most beautiful puzzles are those that cut a geometric shape into the smallest possible number of pieces that can be reassembled to form a new shape. The puzzle sets shown on the next few pages are partial solutions to such problems because the necessary cuts have already been made. You are left with the problem of reassembly. (Sometimes the pieces must be turned over in order to do this). On page 34 there are a number of puzzles in which you also have the job of working out the cuts. On pages 38 and 39 there are instructions for making all the puzzles.

The Patchwork Quilt

The ladies below have figured out how to get a square quilt from the curious shape shown. First they remove the Greek cross entirely. Then they cut the remainder into four identical parts along the heavy lines. Can you determine how they then sew these four pieces together to make a single square piece?

The man watching them poses another problem: can they remove a square and cut the remainder, along the stitching, into four identical pieces that can be sewn together to form a Greek cross?

Having run out of material, these women have decided to remove the cross. How will they sew the remaining pieces together to make a square?

(See solution page 184)

Greek Cross into Square

The Greek cross lends itself to many elegant dissection problems, especially those involving squares. The puzzle below shows only one of the many ways in which the cross can be cut into four pieces that can be put together to make a square. When the square is assembled, that ancient good-luck symbol, the swastika, appears at its center. This particular way of turning the cross into a square was not known until the middle of the 19th century — an indication of how elusive good solutions can be. One can never be certain that the best or simplest known solution of a dissection problem will never be improved upon.

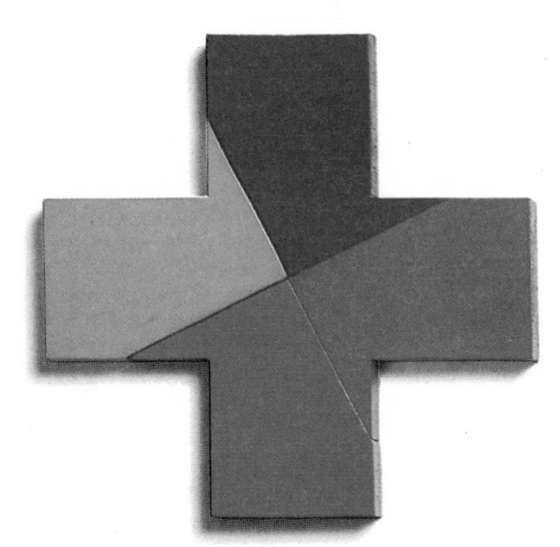

Transform this Greek cross into a square.

Five Problems

The figure below is a rhomboid. The problem you are presented with is to rearrange its five parts into five other geometric shapes in turn. These are a square, a Greek cross, a rectangle, a right-angled triangle, and a trapezium (a four-sided figure with no sides parallel). When you have made all of these shapes, you will probably have forgotten how the original rhomboid was made, so that is also one of the problems to solve. These challenging puzzles will doubtless keep you occupied for some time. Perhaps you will find even more pleasure in watching your friends as they try to solve them.

Five other shapes can be made from this rhomboid.

Greek Cross into Square

To most people the dissection of a Greek cross into four parts as shown below will perhaps not seem quite as elegant as that on the left. Yet the shape that the pieces can make is every bit as square. It is interesting to see whether the puzzle is made easier or harder by the fact that in this case the pieces are all quite different, each with its own characteristics. As with most questions concerning skills, you are likely to find that the answer varies with the person attempting to solve the puzzle. There is no clue to reassembly that can be offered this time, except that this is among the simpler dissection puzzles.

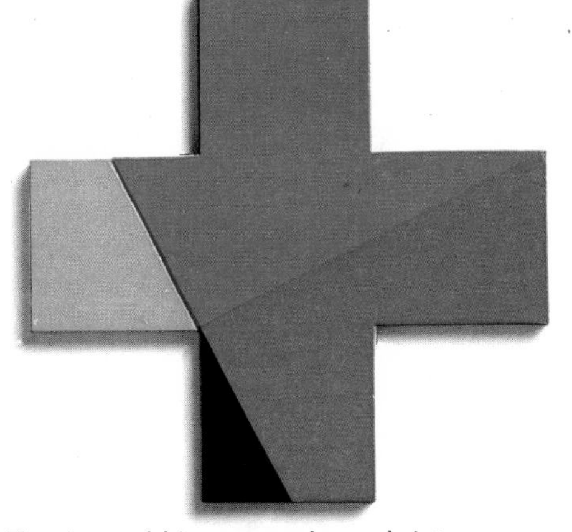

The pieces of this cross can be made into a square.

Star into Square

The six-pointed star below is known to mathematicians as a hexagram and to the world at large as the Star of David. The pattern of cuts gives little hint that the pieces can be regrouped into a square. Although this dissection was discovered independently by two mathematicians, you do not have to be a mathematician to solve the puzzle.

Make a square from the five pieces of this star.

Greek Cross into Square

The Greek cross below has a square-shaped hole in the center. There is a pleasing rightness, therefore, about the fact that its pieces can be rearranged to make a square that lacks a central Greek cross. There is, in addition, a way of arranging the pieces so that the result is a solid square that is rather smaller than the previous "hollow" one.

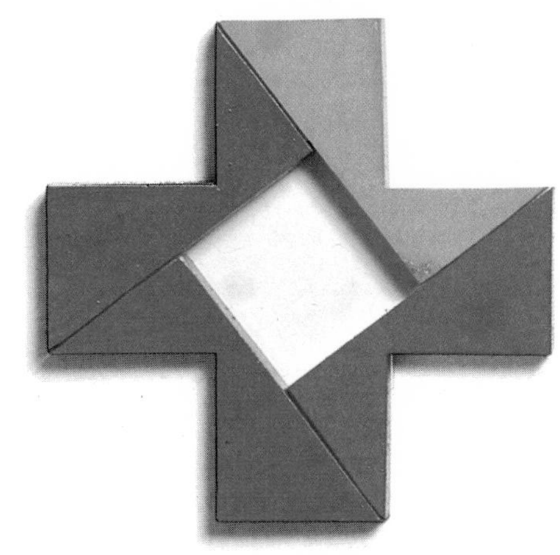

This cross can be made into a square in two ways.

Hexagram into Hexagon

Rearrange the pieces of the Star of David below to make a regular hexagon — that is , a figure with six equal sides (the cell of a honeycomb is a hexagon). This way of transforming a hexagram to a hexagon was discovered only in 1961. If you like really difficult puzzles, you could try doing the dissection with a smaller number of pieces.

A six-pointed star that becomes a six-sided figure.

(See solution page 184)

Decagon into Square

Mathematicians call the figure below a regular decagon — regular because its sides and angles are all equal; a decagon because it has ten sides. The angles, incidentally, are all equal to 144°. This model has been sliced up with seven cuts to make eight highly irregular pieces. However, they can be reassembled to make that familiar and highly regular figure, the square. When you have worked out the right way of doing this, try to reverse the procedure; take the square apart and reassemble it so that the decagon reappears.

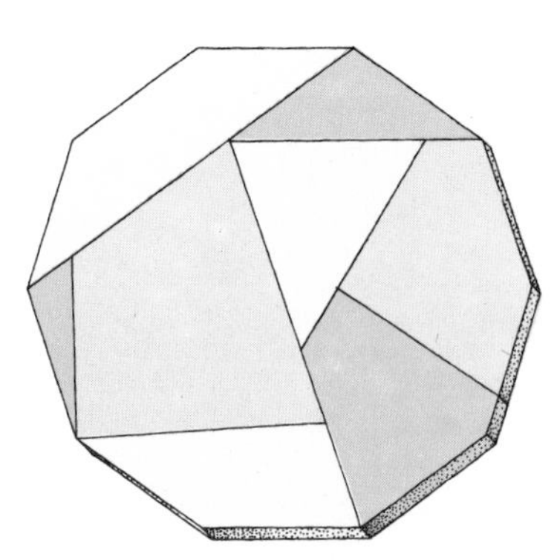

Square off this figure by a little rearranging.

Greek Cross into Pentagon

Once again we meet the Greek cross, which is amazingly versatile in its ability to be transformed into other figures with the aid of a little surgery. The cross gets its name from the fact that it is found in certain ancient Greek sculptures as a symbol on a cake. This is supposed to be the origin of the modern Easter hot cross bun. In this puzzle the cross has to be taken apart and reformed into a regular pentagon — a figure with five equal sides, like the one in the next puzzle. None of the pieces needs to be turned other side up.

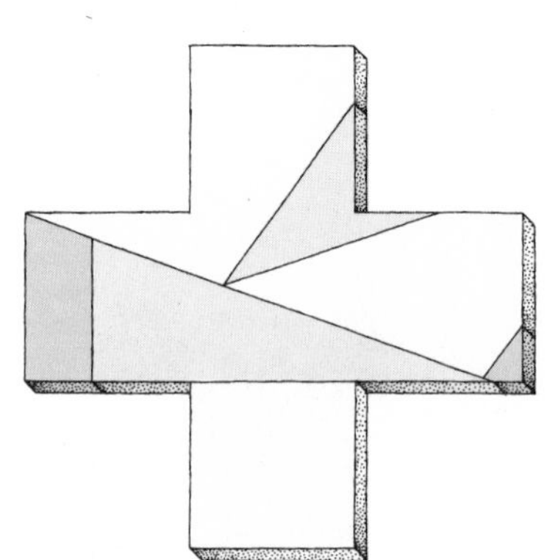

Make this Greek cross into a pentagon.

Pentagon into Square

The shape below is a pentagon, a figure bounded by five straight sides. When the sides are all equal, as they are in the figure below, the shape is called a regular pentagon, and it has angles of 108°. The pentagon here has to be taken apart and its pieces made into a square. Looking for right angles in the dissection shown here could be of some assistance in constructing the square. For that reason you might find the reverse problem more challenging, since there is only one angle of 108° in the dissected square to guide you.

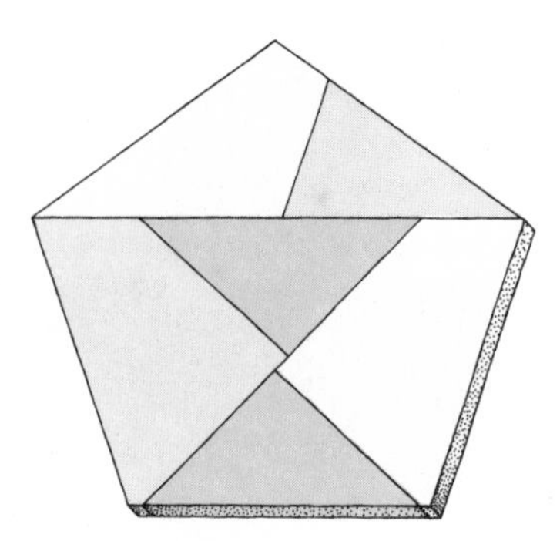

And make this pentagon into a square.

Greek Cross into Hexagram

Once again the Greek cross presents itself for remodeling. The shape that has to be constructed is a hexagram, which is more familiarly called the Star of David. This is a six-pointed star that can be regarded as consisting of two equilateral triangles superimposed. (The Star of David appears twice on the preceding page.) This eight-piece dissection is noteworthy for the intricacy of its shapes; it will test your skill as a carpenter if you decide to make it. This puzzle is likely to prove one of the most fascinating of those presented here.

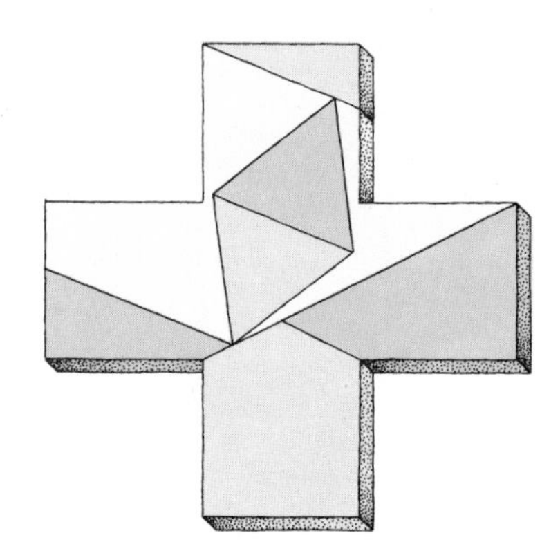

Regroup these pieces and a star is born.

Triangle into Hexagram

If you like to give your fancy a free rein, you might be able to see a delta-winged jet in the outline of the simple equilateral triangle below. The puzzle is to regroup its pieces to form a hexagram, a star with six points. As you might expect, the arrangement of the pieces in the star turns out to be as symmetrical as it is in the triangle. This puzzle is perhaps one of the easiest for the amateur craftsman to construct yet one of the most satisfying to solve by virtue of the simplicity and balance of the shapes that compose it.

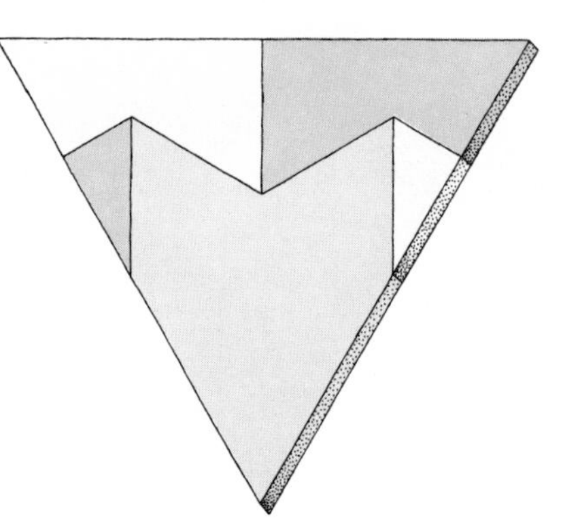

Rearrange this triangle to make a six-pointed star.

Greek Cross into Hexagon

Here is the Greek cross again, which crops up repeatedly throughout these dissection puzzles. This time the problem is to transform the cross into a hexagon. This geometrical figure is defined as having six equal sides and is familiar as the shape of the honeycomb cell. (It should not be confused with the hexagram, or six-pointed star.) There are two examples of hexagons on the opposite page. The angles between its sides are all equal to 120°, and three angles of this size appear in the dissection below; this may help you.

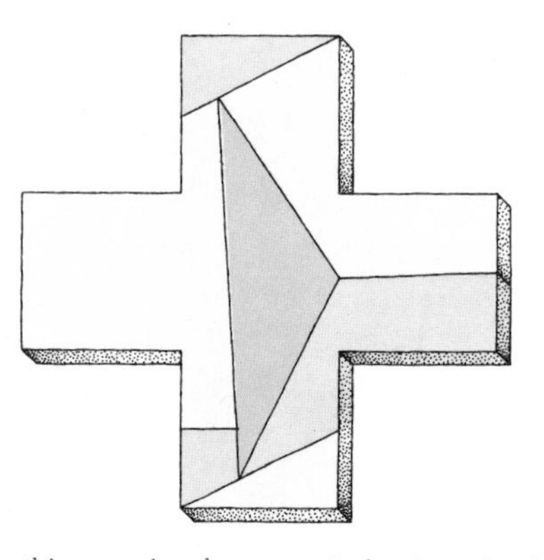

Inside this cross is a hexagon, trying to get out.

(See solution page 184)

Latin Cross into Triangle

The Latin cross is a change from the Greek cross, which appears so frequently in the preceding puzzles. Whereas the arms of the Greek cross are equal in length, the Latin cross differs in that its longest arm is twice the length of the other three. The Latin cross below has been dissected into five dissimilar pieces. The problem is to rearrange these pieces into an equilateral triangle — a triangle whose angles are equal to 60° and with equal sides.

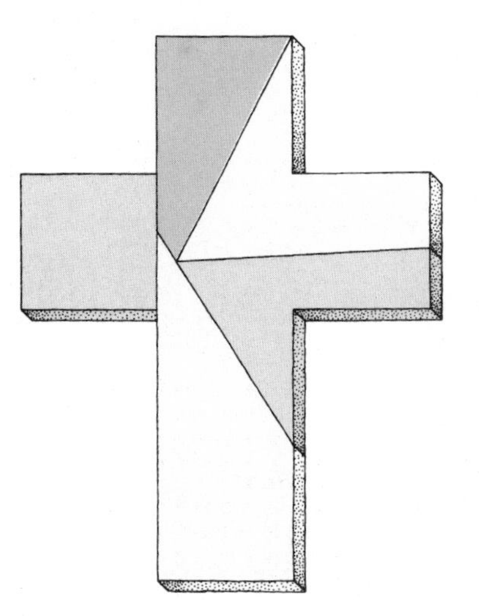

Find the rearrangement that will make a triangle.

Square into Latin Cross

All of the cuts in the square below meet at right angles; perhaps this is what gives the puzzle its pleasingly solid appearance. It is also one of the easier puzzles to construct at home with the necessary accuracy. The five pieces of the dissection have to be rearranged to make a Latin cross, having one arm longer than the other three. The Latin cross is the initial shape in the preceding and following puzzles, so consult them if you are unfamiliar with it.

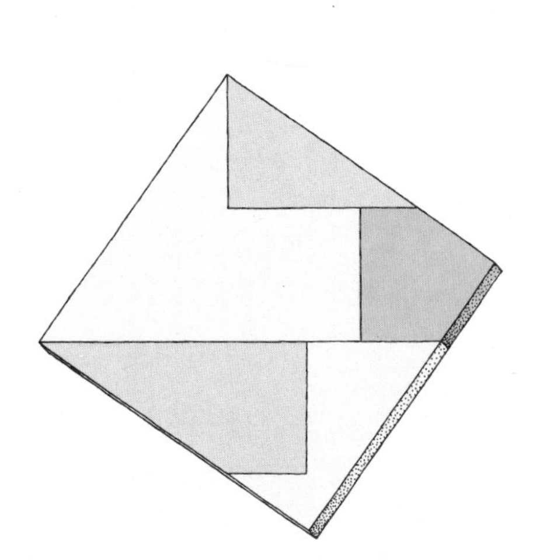

Break up this square to make a Latin cross.

Latin Cross into Hexagon

This is the last of our puzzles to employ the Latin cross, which is second only to the Greek cross as one of the puzzler's favorite figures. This time it has been dissected into six pieces and the task is to rearrange them to make a regular hexagon — that is, a figure bounded by six equal sides. The hexagon's angles are all 120°. Several 120° angles are evident in the figure below and are promising candidates for the final figure's corners. Try the reverse puzzle, too.

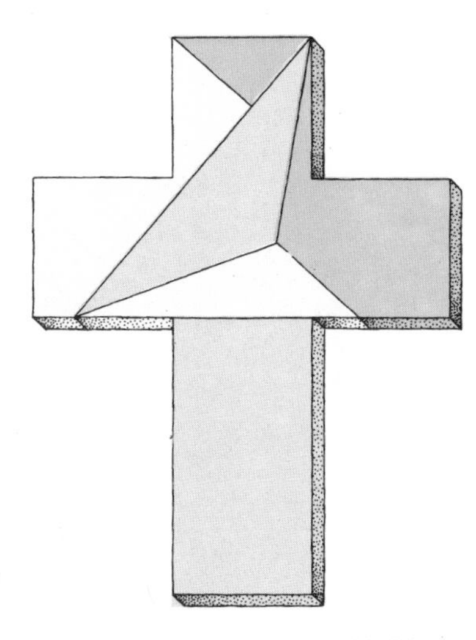

The six pieces here can form a six-sided figure.

Hexagon into Octagon

The hexagon, or six-sided figure, seen below has been divided into nine pieces in a complex way. The pieces can be arranged to form an octagon, the mathematician's name for a figure with eight straight sides. The transformation from one many-sided figure to another offers the puzzler a complex and stimulating problem. Because there are so many variously shaped pieces the puzzle is exceptionally attractive when painted. It is highly suitable as the kind of coffee table object that is guaranteed to provoke conversation among guests.

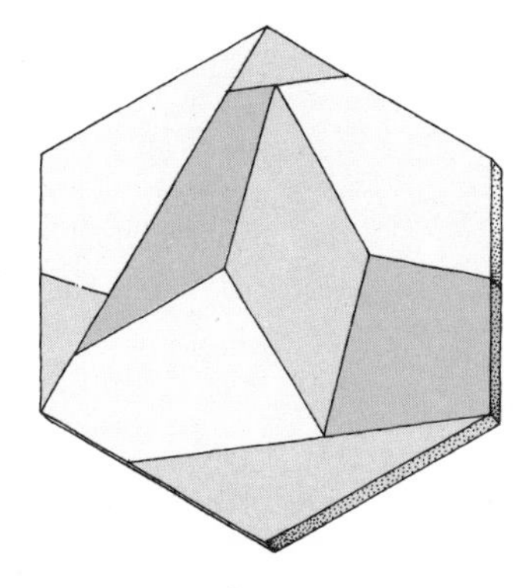

A little reorganization can add two sides.

Three More Squares

Mathematicians have not yet christened the odd-looking shape below, probably because they do not encounter it very often. It is the brainchild of the great dissection puzzle creator Harry Lindgren, who was interested in it solely because it could be turned into something else — that is, four squares. There are no prizes for finding the first square. You might have difficulty in challenging a friend to reconstruct the original shape from the four final squares — for how do you describe it to him? So keep this illustration handy.

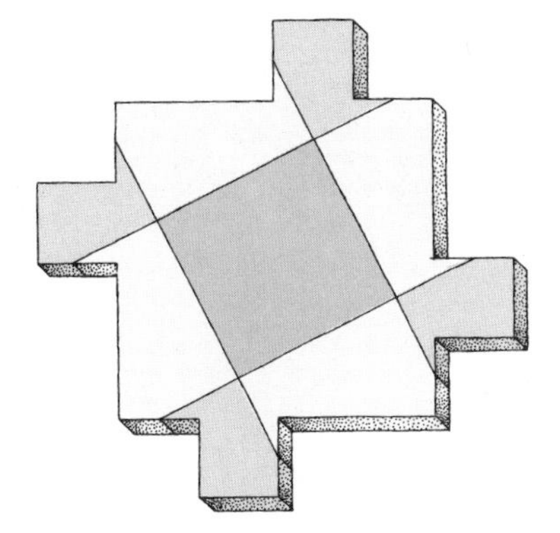

Tidy up this shape by making it into four squares.

Hexagon into Pentagon

This is the last dissection we shall come across of a single hexagon, or six-sided figure. Here it has been cut into seven pieces, and these have to be reassembled to make a pentagon, or five-sided figure. The pentagon's angles are 108°, and a few such angles are to be found in the dissection below. They are likely (though by no means certain) to be corner angles in the final assembly. Working in the opposite direction, reconstructing the hexagon from the pentagon is a problem of roughly the same degree of difficulty.

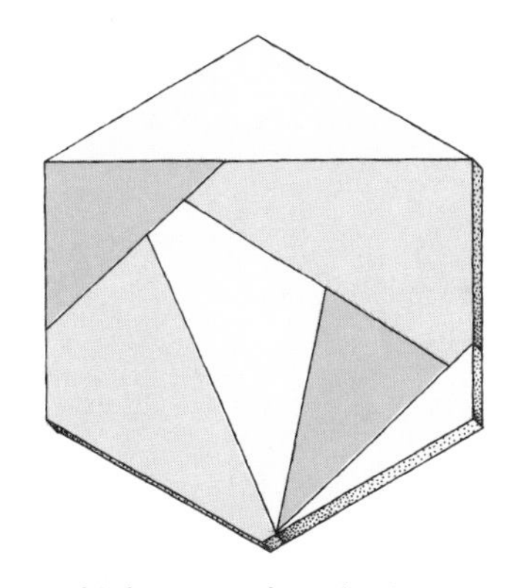

Rearrange this hexagon, demoting it to a pentagon.

(See solution page 184)

The Supernova

This celestial outburst, magnificent in its rainbow hues, is well worth the keen attention of the people surrounding it. At any moment it can break up and form three smaller stars, equal in size to each other and identical in shape to the parent star. With the same swiftness, they can recombine into this luminary.

Make three small replicas of this 12-pointed star by reshuffling its pieces; then recombine them to form the original.

(See solution page 185)

Octagram into Octagon

On this page is a series of puzzles calling for the dissection of stars. The eight-pointed star below is called an octagram. It has been dissected into six pieces. These can be reassembled to form a regular octagon, a figure with eight equal sides and angles. The cuts here are more symmetrical than might appear at first, and you could be guided in your reconstruction by the fact that the same symmetry will appear in the octagon that you finally assemble.

Make this star into an eight-sided figure.

Hexagram into Triangle

Once again we encounter the six-pointed Star of David, or hexagram. Here it has been dissected into five pieces. Perhaps they lack elegance, but they have been made in just this way because the dissection's creator was trying to cut the figure into the smallest number of pieces that could be reassembled to make a triangle. The final triangle is equilateral — its angles are all 60°. None of the 60° angles below belong to the triangle's corners.

Make an equilateral triangle from this star.

Dodecagram into Latin Cross

Although dodecagram only means 12-pointed star, it is one of those words that are so impressive that they must be used occasionally. The construction below is intricate enough to deserve a sonorous title. The seven pieces of the dissection can be arranged to make a Latin cross, an extremely elegant shape (two Latin crosses are shown on page 31). When you have made the cross, the reverse problem of forming the dodecagram from it is not difficult.

Change this 12-pointed star into a Latin cross.

Hexagram into Dodecagram

This six-pointed Star of David, or hexagram, has been dissected into ten pieces and can be rearranged into a dodecagram — that is, a star with 12 points or "rays." It is in fact possible to dissect the hexagram into nine pieces to achieve the same result, but it then is necessary to turn over three of the pieces in the course of reassembly. For that reason some puzzle buffs regard dissections like this one as "purer."

These ten pieces can make a 12-pointed star.

Decagram into Decagram

This remarkable stellar object is either a hollow star — a type at present unknown to astronomers — or else a more normal star that is just exploding, and is seen a moment before it breaks up into ten fragments. But new stars can be born from the remnants of old ones. Perhaps you can construct another ten-pointed star from the pieces of this one. When you have done that, try to turn it into a decagon, with ten equal sides.

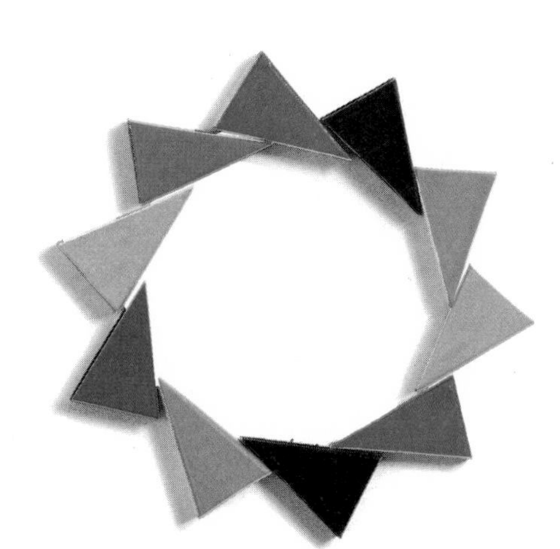

A star or a decagon can be made from this figure.

Dodecagram into Dodecagon

At first glance the 12-pointed star, or dodecagram, below seems to have a dangling tail, which is reminiscent of those gaudy rosettes sported by prize-winning cattle. However, the appearance of asymmetry is misleading; the star's outline is in fact perfectly regular, and it is the complicated internal cuts that make it seem unbalanced. The shape to be constructed is a dodecagon, having 12 equal sides and angles.

Reassemble this star to make a 12-sided figure.

(See solution page 185)

Self-Destruction of a Snake

Can you arrange the pieces of this snake to show it, tail in mouth making the disastrous mistake of swallowing itself?

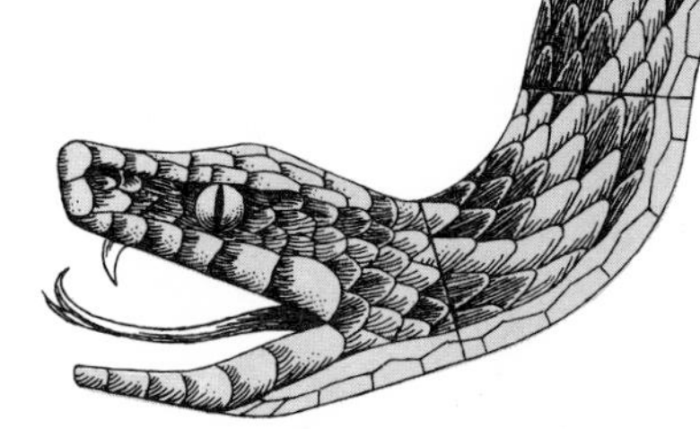

Arrange this snake into a loop so that it begins to swallow its own tail.

A Change of Suit

This puzzle differs from the preceding ones, for not only do you have to transform this ace of hearts, but you have to work out the needed cuts. Divide it into three to make the ace of spades.

Bring about a change of heart — into a spade.

The Broken Horseshoe

Since this horseshoe has lost its luck by being hung upside down, there is no harm in breaking it up for this puzzle. With two cuts, divide it into seven pieces, each containing one nail hole. Stack the pieces for the second cut.

Break the horseshoe into seven pieces, each with a nail hole.

The Cross and Crescent

Can you reassemble the seven pieces of the crescent to make the Greek cross? The cross is not drawn to scale.

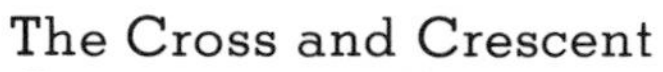

Construct the Greek cross from the crescent.

One Table from Two Stools

The two stool seats, with holes to make them easy to carry, can be made into a table in the form of a solid disk by first dividing them into eight pieces.

Make a single table from these two stool seats.

Merging the Hexagons

These hexagons can be combined to make a single larger hexagon with remarkably few cuts. It is only necessary to cut one of the hexagons into four pieces, leaving the other untouched.

Make one large hexagon in place of these two.

Getting Things Square

It's a beautiful piece of wood, but of what use is that shape? Perhaps if it were square . . . . In fact it can be made into a square with only two straight cuts, resulting in three pieces.

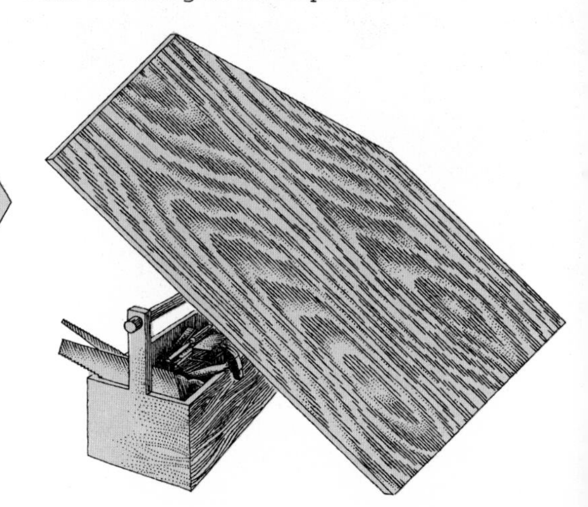

Create a square by making only two cuts.

(See solution page 185)

Disappearance Puzzles

Did you know that cutting up shapes and moving them around can cause mysterious disappearances or changes in size? On the right, for instance, are 17 tiles assembled into a square. At the far right they are rearranged to make a square of the same size, using only 16 pieces. The missing piece has vanished without leaving a hole in the square.

Below this puzzle is another in which the opposite happens. Two triangles and two trapezoids are assembled as a square with an area of 64 units. Then they are regrouped into two other shapes. If you count the units in these, you will find a peculiar change in size.

A warning about these moving-piece puzzles. You would find it hard to make them. They depend on the artist's sleight of hand.

The puzzle below is a Dutch specimen of Sam Loyd's great puzzle called "Get off the Earth." Thirteen Chinese warriors prance in a ring. They are momentarily dissected by a slight twist of the globe, and suddenly there are only 12.

If the square on the left can accommodate 17 tiles, how can a mere 16 make up the one on the right?

The same four pieces have been assembled into shapes containing respectively 64, 65, and 63 units.

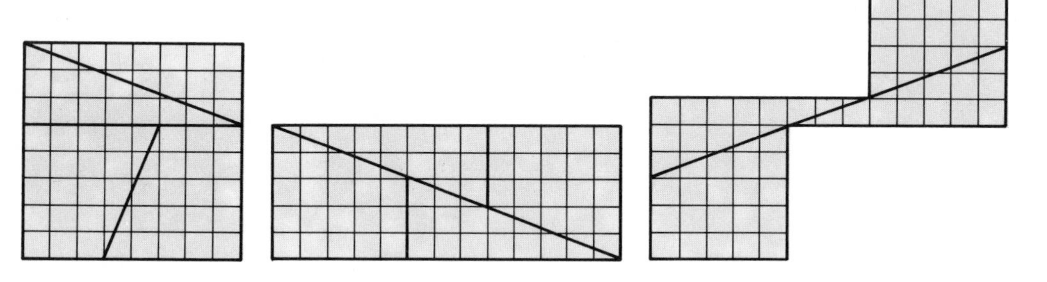

This famous puzzle was widely distributed in 1896. The globe of the world could be twisted, and the baffling effect was that one of the Chinese warriors would vanish. How can it be explained?

(Solution: keep in mind that parts of bodies drawn outside the globe do *not* move. Bodies are reassembled, as it were, by turning the globe, and at point N.O. and further down one warrior disappears.)

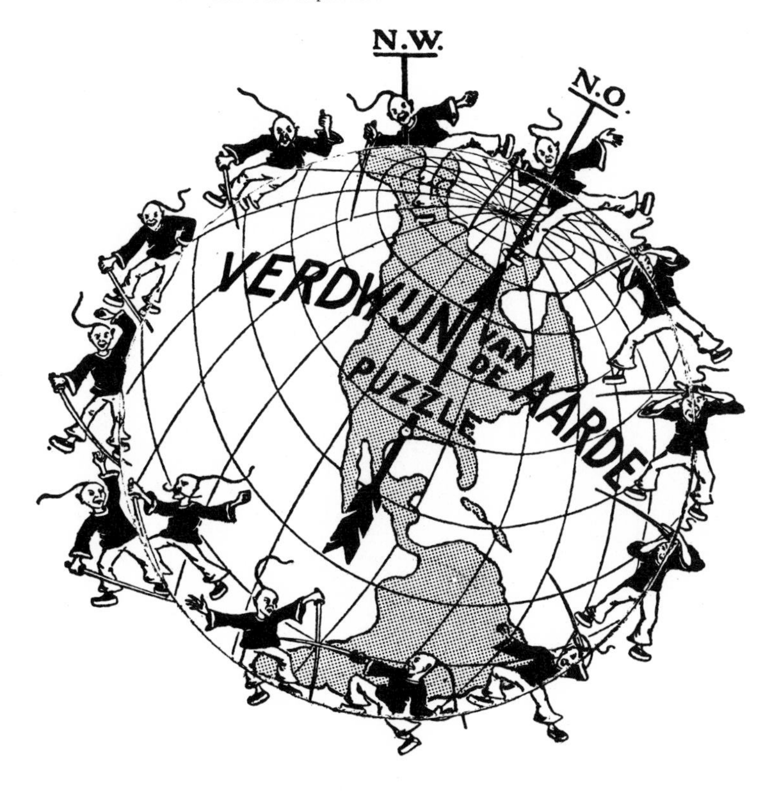

(See solution page 185)

Letter Dissections

There are no bounds to what the fanatical dissection puzzle enthusiast will try to dissect. After polygons, stars, and self-consuming snakes, why not letters of the alphabet? Cutting up the curved ones is a little too tricky, unless you use very distorted versions of the letters. But the straight-line letters below all look quite natural. Each of them can be rearranged to form a solid square.
It is necessary to settle on definite values for the proportions of the letters. In the cases shown, the vertical height of the letters is five times the thickness of a vertical or horizontal bar, and the latter equals the breadth of the sloping bars, measured along a horizontal line. These dimensions have become traditional among dissection puzzle makers.

The number of pieces that a dissection is composed of is an unreliable guide to the difficulty of its discovery. Harry Lindgren discovered all of these dissections except that of the letter E. He found that V and Y were hardest and that X and Z, which look equally complicated, were fairly easy.

When you amuse yourself with these puzzles, you will probably find that it is more challenging to make the letters from the square than the reverse. None of the puzzles, however, is difficult.

All of these letters of the alphabet are made up of straight lines only, and so are especially suitable for dissection puzzles. Each letter has to be taken apart and reassembled to make a square. In some cases it will prove necessary to turn an asymmetric piece over. If your initials happen to be among the letters here, you will perhaps want to construct them first. Carefully made and colored, these puzzles would be attractive in any home.

On the right is the triumphant completion of a monumental letter N — perhaps intended as a dissection puzzle for a giant. The seven pieces were hewn from a single original square. The workers can now take a rest — until they get the order to reassemble the pieces in their former square shape.

(See solution page 185)

Materials
Plywood, cardboard, or acrylic. You will also need varnish (for some woods) or paint (for some woods and for cardboard).

Tools
Ruler, pencil, compasses; fretsaw and sandpaper (for wood or plastic); knife and straightedge (for cardboard).

How to Make the Puzzles
All of the dissection puzzles shown on the preceding pages can easily be made at home (except the two trick puzzles at the top of page 35). Simply follow the guide diagrams at right. When copying the diagrams you will probably find it convenient to take each unit (that is, the side of a small square) as $1/4''$ or $1/5''$, whichever is more appropriate for a particular figure. It is not hard to draw the figures on the material, but it is even easier to copy the shapes on graph paper, cut them out, paste them down temporarily on your material, and cut around them. In tracing these figures, the more accurate you are, the better your pieces will fit together in both the initial and final assemblies. Notice in particular that even when several lines come together, they do not always meet at a point. For instance, in the pentagon at the left of the second row from the bottom, the two cuts that pass through the bottom side do not meet the corners.

Cutting cardboard should present no difficulties. If you are making your puzzle from wood or acrylic, use the thinnest blade and the finest teeth possible in the fretsaw to get the sharpest possible corners. You may get slightly more accurate pieces if you draw and cut each one separately, rather than in the assembled form as they are drawn here. The harder the wood, the better the edges will be. Teak is very hard, has a pronounced grain, and looks so attractive that it does not need to be varnished or painted, merely oiled a little. Mahogany is another fine wood suitable for making durable puzzle sets.

When you make wood or plastic pieces, smooth their edges with fine-grained sandpaper. Plywood or cardboard pieces can be painted. Alternatively cardboard can be covered with colored paper. In general the puzzle pieces should be colored on both sides.

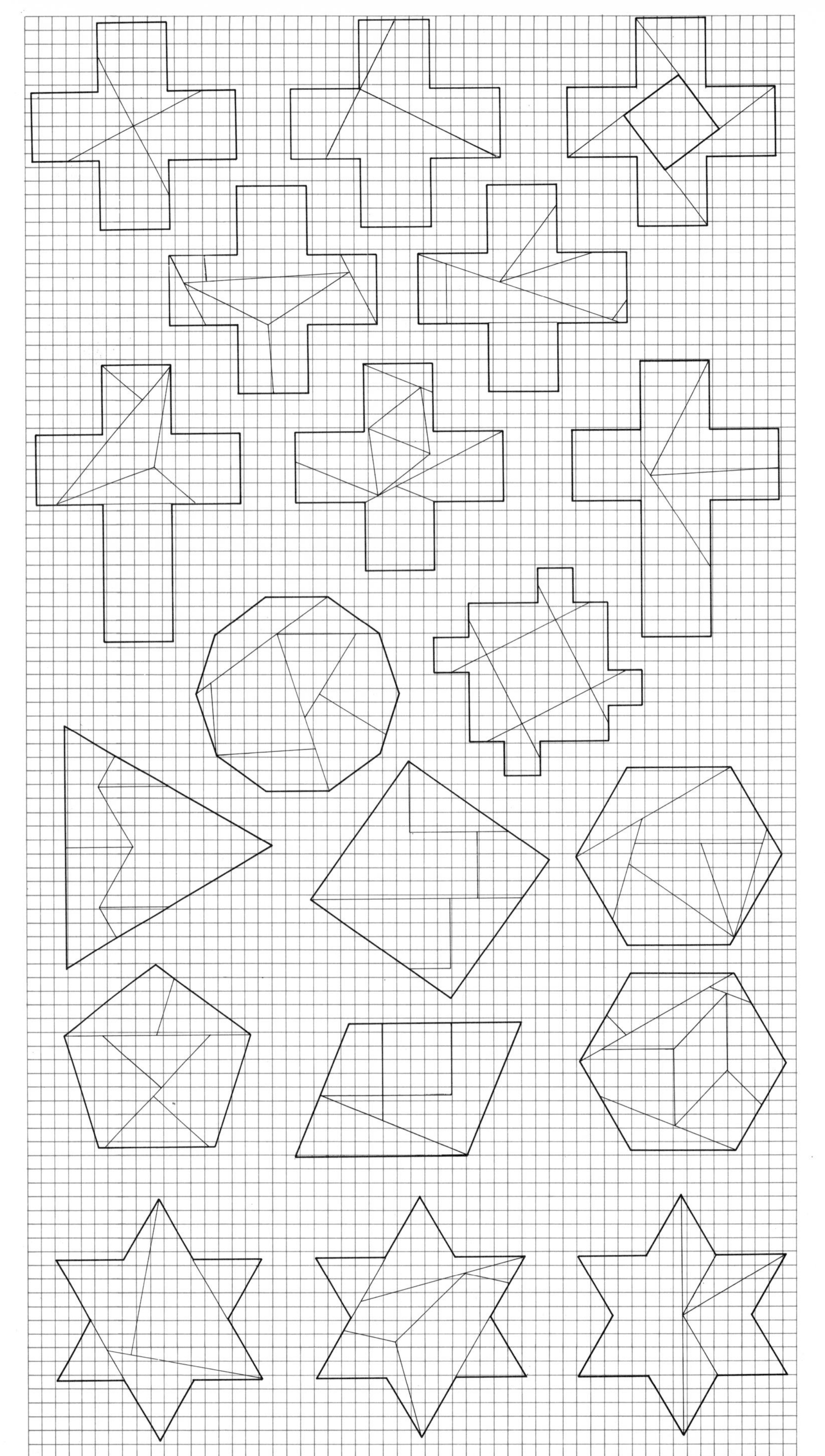

Following these diagrams it is easy to make puzzle sets that are pleasant to handle and to look at.

Polyforms

A rhombus formed from all 12 hexiamonds. Study of the 12 pieces shows that each is made up of six identical equilateral triangles. There are only 12 ways in which the triangles can be put together, and each shape is represented once in the elegant set of wooden pieces that make up this rhombus. The idea of assembling triangles in this way was first suggested by W. L. van der Poel. There are over 40 other known solutions to the problem of assembling a rhombus shape from the complete hexiamond set.

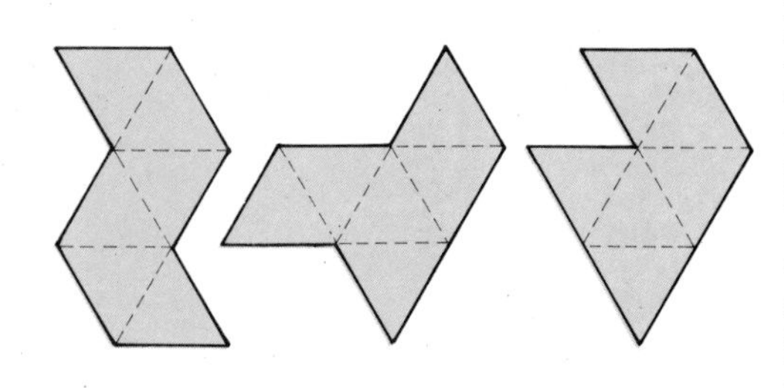

Three hexiamonds, showing how they are made up from six identical equilateral triangles joined together at their edges in varying arrangements.

Mathematically minded puzzle creators have given us many different kinds of puzzles with shapes that we can call *polyforms.* A polyform is obtained by joining groups of identical unit shapes in specific ways. For example, identical equilateral triangles can be joined edge to edge. Two of them make a diamond shape; thus a shape formed from three triangles can be called a *triamond,* one made from four triangles a *tetriamond,* and so forth. At the left is a solution to a puzzle utilizing *hexiamonds* — the shapes formed by joining six triangles.

Identical squares can also be connected at the edges to make interesting shapes. Two squares joined together make the shape of a domino. So when an unspecified number of squares is joined, the result is called a *polyomino,* a name first used by Solomon W. Golomb in a talk to the Harvard Mathematical Club in 1953. A *tromino* consists of three squares, joined either in a row or in a V-shape. Four squares joined together make a *tetromino*, of which there are five different types (the two shapes obtained when a non-symmetric shape is turned over are considered as only one). There are 12 possible *pentominoes*, each of which consists of five squares joined. They are illustrated opposite. There are 35 possible *hexominoes*, each consisting of six squares.

Some of the oldest polyform puzzles have to do with chessboards. For example, the puzzler Henry Dudeney tells how in the course of a disagreement between two chess players the board was broken over the head of one of them. By a remarkable chance, 12 of the pieces consisted of five squares joined together, all in different ways. There was one other piece, consisting of four squares that made a larger square. The pieces of the board were, in fact, the 12 pentominoes and the square tetromino, although these names had not been coined in Dudeney's day. The problem was to reassemble the board. There are many ways of doing this. In 59 solutions the tetromino (or a two-square by two-square hole) is at the center. The example shown opposite is only one of these solutions.

Puzzle connoisseurs encountering polyominoes for the first time usually find pentominoes the most interesting. The tetrominoes (five pieces) are too few to do much with, and the hexominoes (35 pieces) are too numerous — they make the game too complicated.

The most common type of polyomino problem is to cover a given silhouette — a square, a cross, or an irregular shape — with a specific set of polyominoes without overlapping the pieces. In another type the trick is to find a shape that can be made from various combinations of polyominoes — say, three different sets of four pentominoes.

Inevitably, the computer enthusiasts have turned their attention to polyominoes. They have discovered, for example, that a 6×10 unit rectangle can be assembled from the pentomino set in 2339 different ways (rotated and reflected arrangements are not regarded as different). People, however, do not rest content with finding solutions; they also want to gain an esthetic experience from them. Some devotees dislike arrangements in which there are crossroads — that is, four pieces meeting at a point. Also, they do not appreciate straight lines that cross a pattern from side to side.

Polyforms can be made from solid units as well as from the flat ones that have been considered so far. For example, solid polyominoes can be formed by making the thickness of the piece equal to the side of a unit square, as if a number of cubes had been joined to each other. It is then possible to devise other puzzles. Solid pentominoes, for example, can be assembled into rectangular solids. Cubes can be joined together in twisty, non-planar ways, as they are in Piet Hein's Soma cube.

The Soma cube consists of seven pieces, six of which are made up of four cubes joined together, and one that is made up of three cubes (see page 46). The cubes are obtained by dissecting a large cube into 27 smaller ones. One problem that can be attempted with the Soma pieces is to form them into the large cube. The pieces can also be arranged into a variety of other forms.

Having entered the third dimension, why stop there? Golomb and other inventors of puzzles have ventured into the fourth, fifth, and higher dimensions. Such exotic constructions can only be mathematically described, not modeled.

Pentominoes

The 12 pentominoes, each consisting of five squares, resemble various letters of the alphabet. I, L, P, T, U, V, W, X, Y, and Z are obvious. F looks as if it's had an accident, however, and N takes some imagination. The complete set of pieces shown here is used in a solution to our first pentomino puzzle: to make a square with eight unit squares on each side and with a 2 × 2 hole. There are many thousands of ways this can be done if the hole is placed anywhere in the large square. Apart from the example shown, there are 58 solutions with a central hole.

After finding a few solutions of your own, try this more difficult problem. Look at the solution below; it can be divided into two congruent parts — that is, two shapes that are identical. Divide the pattern into two parts along the joins that run from center top right to the center hole and from the hole to center bottom left. How many other solutions that can be divided into two congruent parts can you find? Some sample solutions are shown on page 185. After experimenting with this problem, try the puzzles on the next two pages. Pieces may be turned over.

This square is assembled from the complete set of pentominoes. Can you make squares in other ways?

The 12 pentominoes. Each is made of five squares joined edge to edge to form different shapes.

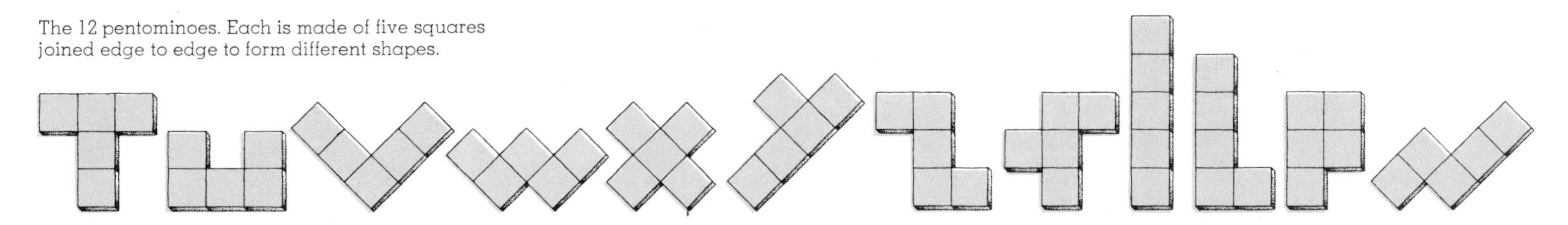

(See solution page 185)

The figures shown are to be covered with the 12 pentominoes, whose shapes are illustrated on the previous page. Since each piece is five unit squares, each figure contains 60 squares.

The first five puzzles are 8 × 8 so-called chessboards with holes of four single-unit squares in them. Following these are the four rectangles that can be constructed from 60 squares, with unit dimensions of 3 × 20, 4 × 15, 5 × 12, and 6 × 10. The first of these is the most difficult, and there are only two distinct solutions. A variety of figures follows; the cross is notably difficult.

The last two figures are divided into congruent halves by a heavy line. Each of these figures can be assembled from the pentominoes in such a way that it can be divided into the halves shown. It is not essential to divide the figures thus, and many more solutions can be found if the line is ignored.

There is practically no limit to the number of patterns you can devise that are to be covered with the pentominoes. Just bear in mind that they have to contain 60 unit squares.

Two solutions of a triplication problem appear at the top of the facing page. Select one pentomino, and try to make a model of it, using nine of the remaining pieces. The model will be three times as wide and high as the original. All 12 pentominoes can be modeled.

Many of the alternative solutions of pentomino puzzles are related; one can be generated from another by manipulating a few pieces. For example, at the top left of the V shown on the page opposite there is a rectangle composed of a T, a Y, and an L pentomino. This rectangular section of the V can be rotated or picked up and turned over without affecting the silhouette of the V. Each orientation of the rectangle counts as another solution. Combining rotations and inversions gives four different solutions of the puzzle. Whenever you can spot a group of pieces that has a symmetrical outline, like the rectangle, you can generate new solutions in the same way. Sometimes a set of two, three, or more pentominoes can be recombined without changing their overall outline, yielding further solutions. Occasionally two groups in a pattern may have identical outlines. Exchange the groups and you again have two solutions instead of one.

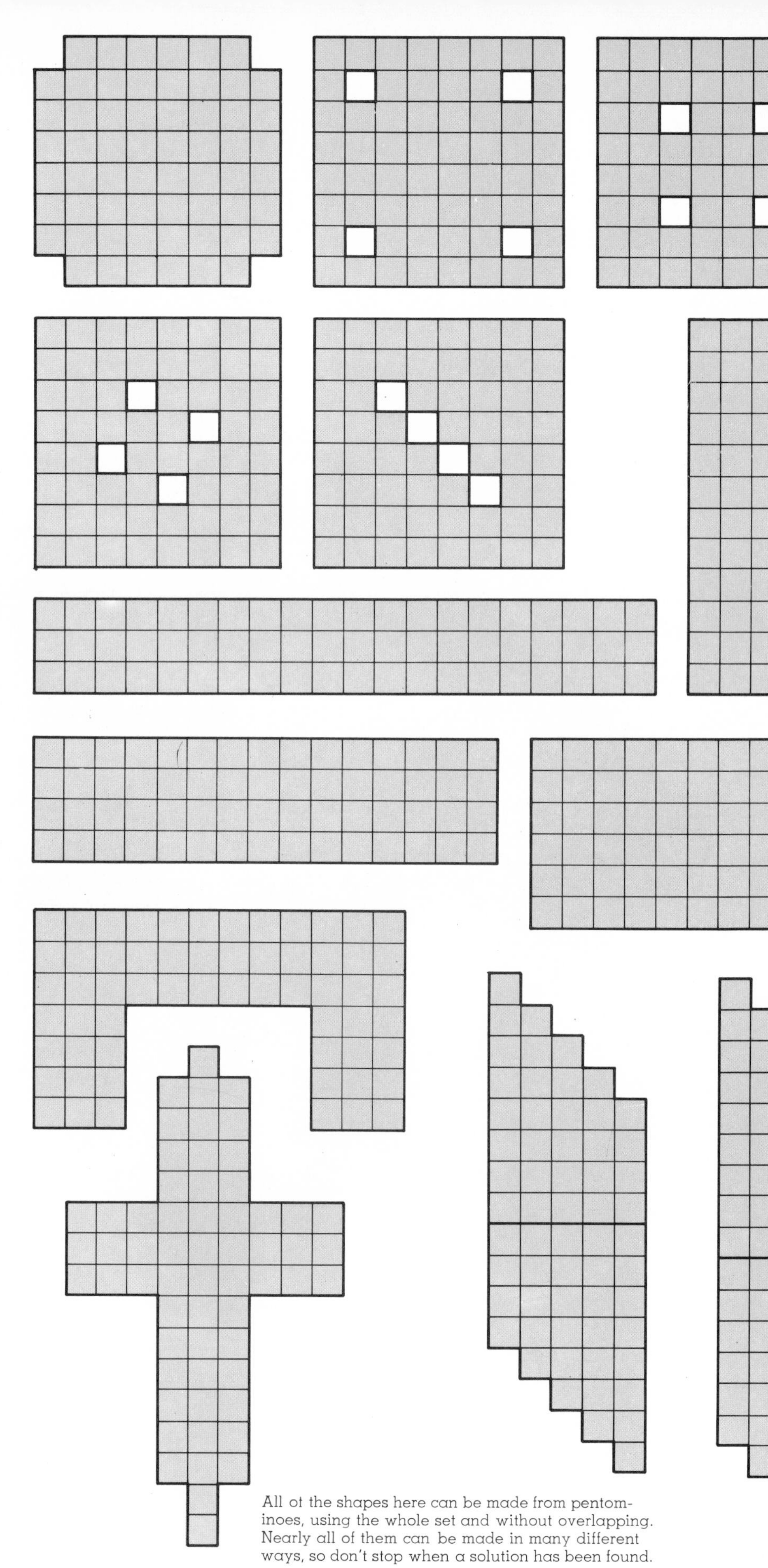

All of the shapes here can be made from pentominoes, using the whole set and without overlapping. Nearly all of them can be made in many different ways, so don't stop when a solution has been found.

(See solution pages 185-186)

Each pentomino can be modeled with nine of the others. Here are two examples, the V and the X.

This puzzle enthusiast has achieved success with a typical pentomino problem: making a 64-square triangle that includes a four-square hole. He can go on to invent other puzzles based on this. For example, he could try making a triangle of similar size with four-square holes of different shapes or with four separate one-square holes, and so forth. He may be setting himself problems that no one has ever tackled before, and will not know if a solution is possible until he finds it. This is one of the fascinations of polyominoes — the possibilities of discovery.

(See solution page 186)

Solid Pentominoes

The pentomino puzzles on the previous pages do not take into account the thickness of the pieces. If you make your pentominoes from wood whose thickness is equal to one side of the unit square, not only will you be able to try all of the previous puzzles, but also you can enter the world of three-dimensional forms. Here, for example, is a $3 \times 4 \times 5$ rectangular solid. This is only one of the 3940 ways of building it.

The solid pentominoes are called planar because each of them lies in one plane. Some of the so-called polycubes, which are non-planar, are described on the next page. We shall find that the solid pentominoes by themselves offer great scope to the puzzler.

The puzzle figures on the opposite page can all be constructed from the planar solid pentominoes. In the top row are three rectangular solids with dimensions $3 \times 4 \times 5$, $2 \times 5 \times 6$, and $2 \times 3 \times 10$.

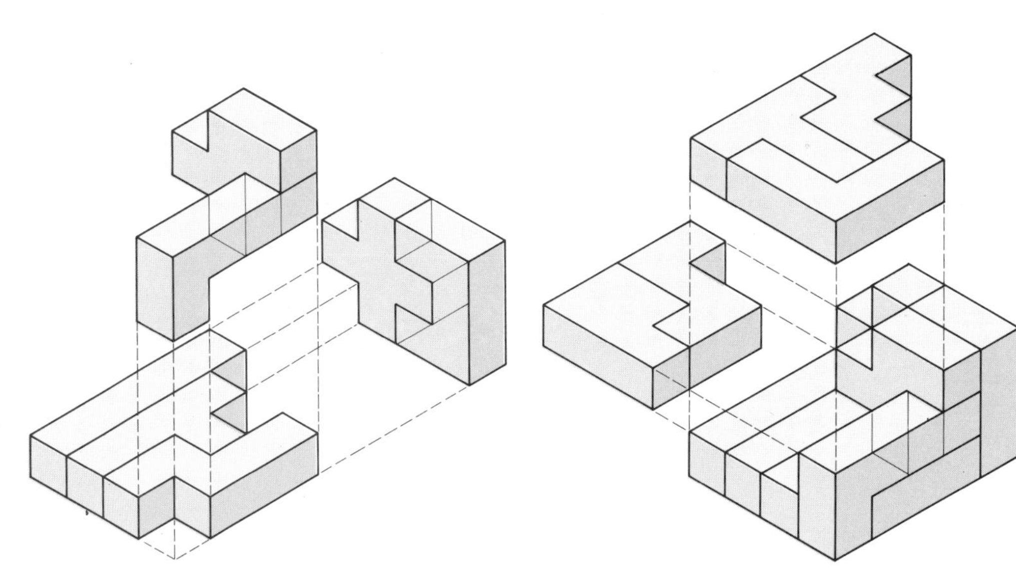

To get you started on solid pentomino puzzles, here's one way of making the $3 \times 4 \times 5$ rectangular block. There are many more. On the left, the first seven pieces are put together. Assemble each group of pieces, such as the one consisting of the X and the U pentominoes, before positioning it as the dotted lines indicate. In the second diagram this block of seven is visible, with the remaining five pentominoes linked together, ready to be slid into place. The assembled pieces can be seen in the picture below.

A tidy-minded way of storing the solid pentominoes when not in use: as a $3 \times 4 \times 5$ rectangular block.

(See solution page 186)

The solution of the middle top puzzle is very interesting. It consists of two 5 × 6 rectangles, which could also be laid side by side to make one 6 × 10 rectangle. This is therefore one particular solution of one of the flat — that is, two-dimensional — puzzles on page 42.

The first figure in the second row is a staircase. Then comes a nameless form, consisting of a wall one unit thick and three units high surrounding a 1 × 7 enclosure (your first puzzle can be to find a name for it). The pyramid at the end of the row is made from only 11 of the pieces; it is fairly difficult.

The three figures in the bottom row are models of three of the solid pentominoes. Each model uses all of the pieces, is twice as long and twice as broad as the piece modeled, and is three units deep. The model of the U pentomino will actually stand as an arch as shown.

Not all of the pentominoes can actually be modeled in this way. Two of them are known to be impossible (we leave it to you to find out which ones). It is now known that the F can be made in only one way. The T, U and Y shown here are certainly possible. Then you can try to construct your own initials.

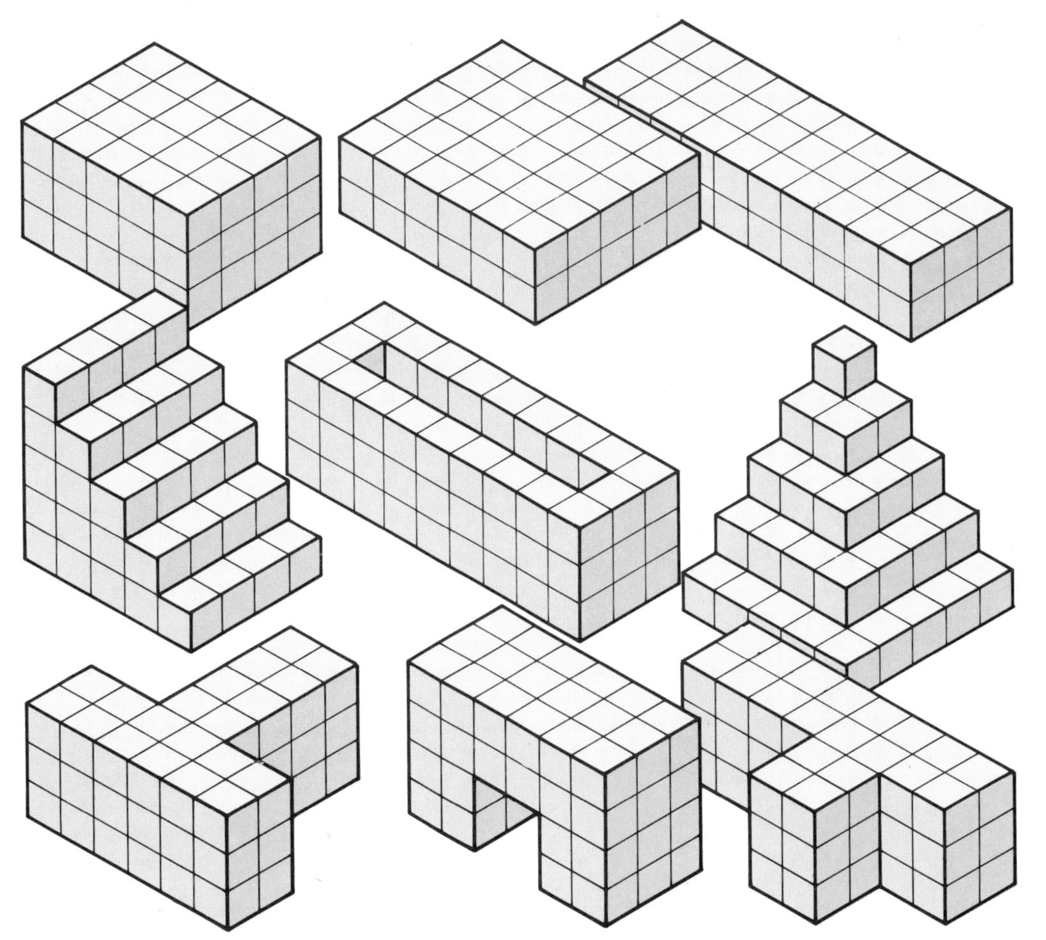

Above: If you think building blocks are kid's stuff, try making these shapes from solid pentominoes.

Materials
For ordinary polyominoes: plywood, acrylic, or cardboard about 1/4" thick. For solid polyominoes: wood about 1/2" thick. Varnish or primer and enamel paint (for wood); or colored paper or tape (for cardboard).

Tools
Ruler and pencil; fretsaw and sandpaper (for wood or plastic); knife and steel straightedge (for cardboard).

How to Make Polyominoes
You can draw on paper the shapes of the set of polyominoes that you wish to make, cut them out, paste them onto your material, and cut around them. Or you can draw the shapes directly onto the material. The total amount of material needed depends on the size you choose for a unit square; 1/2" on a side is usually convenient. If you have a checkerboard or chessboard, it is a good idea to base your polyominoes on the size of its squares. Then you can use the board for the many polyomino puzzles that can be devised to cover an 8 × 8 square. For solid polyominoes, however, the edge of the unit square is fixed by the thickness of the wood (which can be plywood or something harder and more attractive such as oak or mahogany).

Below: A set of solid pentominoes. You can make them by following the instructions given on this page.

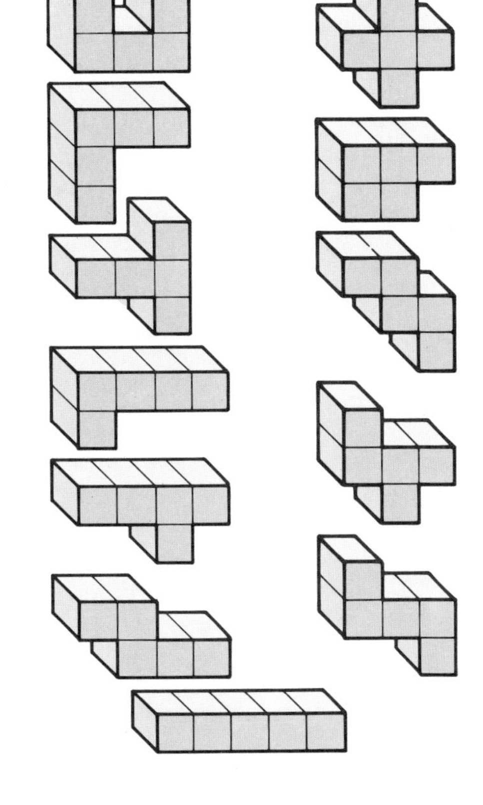

The shapes of the complete pentomino set appear here. If you want to make a complete set of tetrominoes, remember that there are five of them (assuming you make only one version of each asymmetric piece). There are 35 hexominoes (again counting each asymmetric piece only once).

When cutting out the pieces from wood or plastic, use a thin fretsaw blade with the finest teeth possible. Hard woods, like teak or mahogany, give the cleanest edges. Sand down the edges with fine-grained sandpaper. If you want a colored polyomino set, seal the wood by painting the pieces with a priming agent, and follow this with a coat of enamel paint.

Cardboard can be cut with a knife and straightedge and painted or covered with colored paper or plastic tape.

(See solution page 187)

The Soma Cube

The noted Danish inventor of puzzles Piet Hein was once doodling with pencil and paper while listening to an erudite mathematical lecture. In his imagination he began to play with the simplest solids that can be formed by joining equal cubes. Taking only those that have "bends" in them — those that are not simple rectangular solids — he found that there is only one shape that you can make from three cubes, and six that you can make from four cubes. Those seven shapes contain 27 cubes — the same number that is contained in a $3 \times 3 \times 3$ cubical array. Piet Hein then realized that his polycube shapes could actually be fitted together to make a larger cubical shape. That was when the idea of the Soma cube was born.

The seven Soma pieces are shown here. The smallest is one of the solid trominoes (an ordinary tromino consists of three unit squares, as discussed on page 40). Three of the four-unit pieces are solid tetrominoes; the other three are shapes new to us, because they are non-planar. Notice that the two pieces at the bottom are mirror images of each other. Turning these two pieces will not make one look like the other (any more than a left-hand glove can be made into a right-hand glove without turning it inside out). They are unlike an asymmetric solid tetromino, which can be turned into its mirror image just by being turned over.

The seven pieces that go into the Soma cube. They represent all the ways in which three or four cubes can be arranged other than in straight lines.

When Piet Hein christened the Soma cube, he might have been thinking of the fictitious drug soma in Aldous Huxley's *Brave New World,* which carried its user into an introspective dreamlike state. Like so many of the diversions offered in this book, the Soma cube can be equally absorbing.

We do not know exactly how many ways there are of constructing the large cube from the seven pieces; certainly there are hundreds. You will find several

The single piece removed from this Soma cube gives a hint about one way of putting it together. There are hundreds of other ways to make the cube.

in the solution section. If, like most people, you do not have the spatial imagination of a Piet Hein, you will need a set of Soma pieces to tackle the puzzles shown on this page. Yet Soma addicts claim that after gaining some familiarity with the pieces, they speed up their solving enormously, and even find solutions in their heads. So providing children with a set of Soma cube pieces is giving them more than an entertaining recreation — it is also an excellent way of nurturing their grasp of spatial relationships.

Many of the forms shown on this page are recognizable as familiar objects: for example, a chair, an aircraft carrier, a snake, a bed. Challenge your friends to see who can build a given shape most quickly. You can also devise many more 27-unit forms of your own.

Materials
A suitable length of wood, square in cross section, up to about 1" thick; wood glue; varnish or paint if desired.

Tools
Pencil and straightedge; set square; fretsaw; fine-grained sandpaper.

How to Make the Soma Cube
A perfectly feasible way of making the Soma cube pieces is to buy a set of children's building blocks and glue them together. However, an attractively grained wood, like the larch used in the set shown opposite, will make much more elegant-looking cubes. The suitable length referred to in the specifications is at least 27 times the thickness of the piece of wood that you select. Since it is not possible to make the grain consistent among the cubes that make up each piece, it is best to cut the wood into 27 individual cubes and make sure, when you glue them together, that they are all differently oriented within each piece. (This can be seen in the picture on page 46.) If, however, you wish to paint the pieces, you can save some trouble by cutting some two-unit and three-unit lengths when sawing the wood. In either case, be careful to mark off your wood accurately with the set square. Keep the blade of the fretsaw vertical when sawing to ensure square corners on the cubes. Sand the edges with fine-grained sandpaper, and glue the cubes into the shapes shown on the opposite page. The pieces can be varnished; alternatively seal the wood with a primer and paint it with enamel paint.

Arches, walls, plinths, memorials, towers, serpents, ships, and castles, created from the Soma cube.

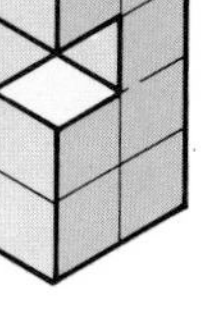

(See solution page 188)

The Balancing Soma Cube

You will probably ask why the Soma cube shown here is being used in a balancing act. Surely the mental difficulties of making the cube are great enough without adding the acrobatic difficulties of defying gravity?

When you've assembled the Soma cube in different ways, you will realize that the feat shown here is even more remarkable than it seems. This is because the majority of Soma cube constructions will not perch on a small base like this. The pieces do not support each other and the whole cube collapses. In fact, we know of only two ways of putting the cube together to perform this trick, although there may be others.

When you try it, remember that the cube must hold together by its own inherent stability, not because of the incidental roughness or stickiness of the pieces. The point of balance is in the center of the bottom face, and the cube will not hold together if turned so that another face is at the bottom; it certainly will not do so in the two solutions that we give.

"Step right up! See Amos the Strong Man as he balances a Soma cube on one hand, without benefit of string or tape to hold the cube together!" For Amos, who has brains as well as muscles, has found out how to put the cube together so that it will balance on a point without falling apart. Can you equal his feat? There are at least two ways of assembling the cube so that it will hold together.

(See solution page 188)

Matchstick Puzzles

Spare-time hobbyists and long-term convicts sometimes pass their time enjoyably by building ornate miniature replicas of Chartres Cathedral or Sing Sing prison from thousands of used matches, glue, and shellac. As matchbox collectors have already discovered, there is more to matches than just lighting stoves or cigarettes.

However, you don't have to set aside a few years of your life to achieve some feat of matchstick architecture, and although guaranteed isolation and quiet may be of some help, it isn't necessary to become a hermit. A corner at home is usually sufficient. In some cases, less reclusive locations may be employed as building sites. Modest but impressive structures such as the box below may be attempted while you sit in a café and enjoy a drink. This kind of project can be helped or hindered by the company of encouraging friends. Your success will probably be threatened less by a lack of building skill than by the breathing or coughing of inconsiderate onlookers. If, after several attempts, you decide the conditions you are working under are not favorable, you may want to go on to the purely mental delights of the matchstick puzzles on the following pages. The selection includes a few trick questions certain to fool all but the craftiest of the friends on whom you inflict them.

Nothing holds the 114 matchsticks of this structure together except the skill of its design. If you have determination and time to spare, give it a try. The first phase of building is log-cabin technique — one four-match square piled on top of another.

1. The design below is made of nine matches. Move four of them to form a pattern of five triangles (they're not necessarily identical, and one triangle might be part of another).

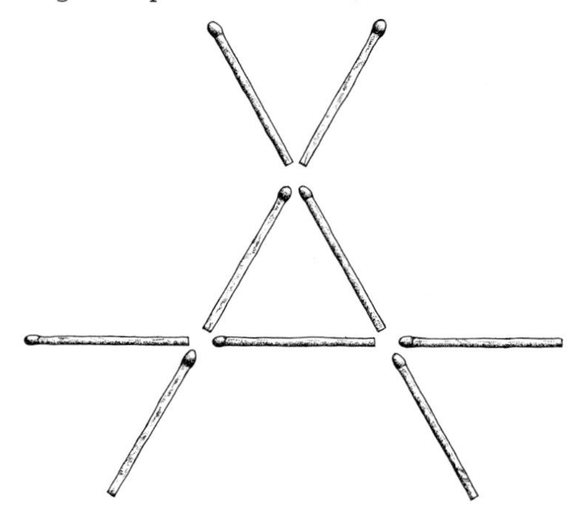

2. Make the design below, which requires 12 matches. Then alter it by moving just three of them to produce a final result that consists of three identical squares touching each other.

3. There are seven identical triangles in the pattern below. (There is also an eighth triangle with sides two matches long.) Move six matches to form six identical rhombuses (diamond shapes).

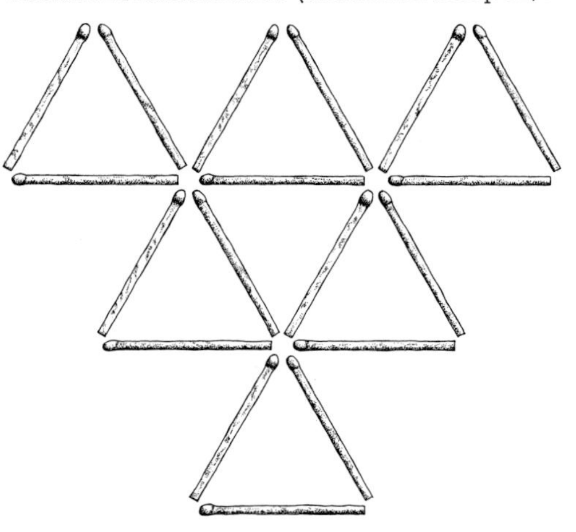

4. Make three identical squares from the pattern of 15 matches below by:
a) removing three and moving two;
b) removing three and moving three;
c) removing three and moving four.

5. In these, you may cross matches:
a) move three, make three squares;
b) move four, make three squares;
c) move two, make seven squares;
d) remove two, leave two squares.

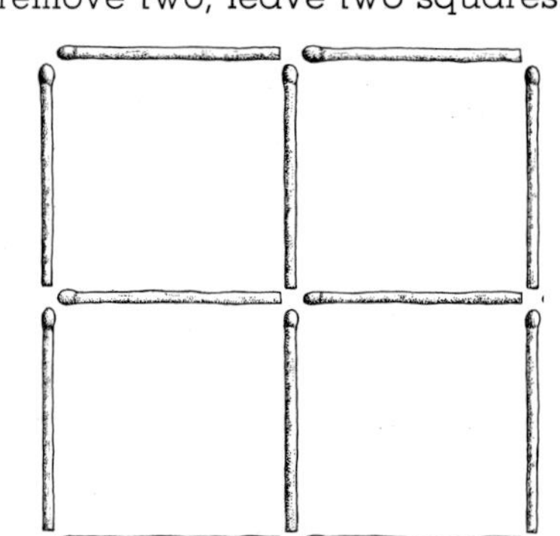

6. Sixteen matches are required to make the pattern below consisting of five equal squares. Move three of the matches to form a new pattern consisting of four identical squares in contact.

7. This elegant figure consists of 48 matches. Move just four of them to form a perfectly symmetrical figure made up of 17 identical squares.

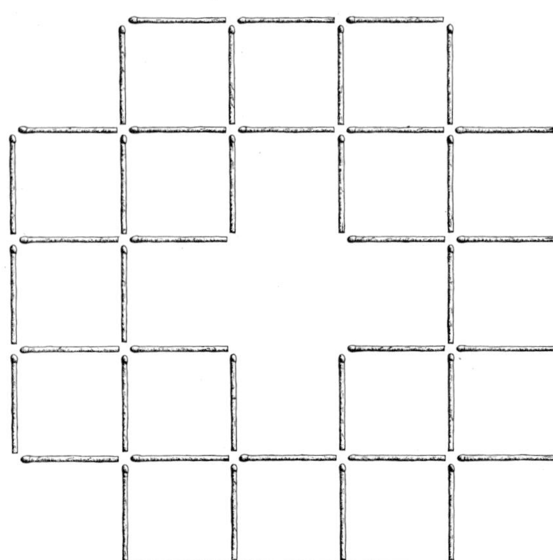

8. From this pattern: a) remove eight matches to form six non-identical squares; b) remove four matches to form eight identical squares.

(See solution page 189)

9. This Star of David, made from 18 matchsticks, contains six identical triangles and two larger ones. By moving two matches, change the figure so that it contains only six triangles.

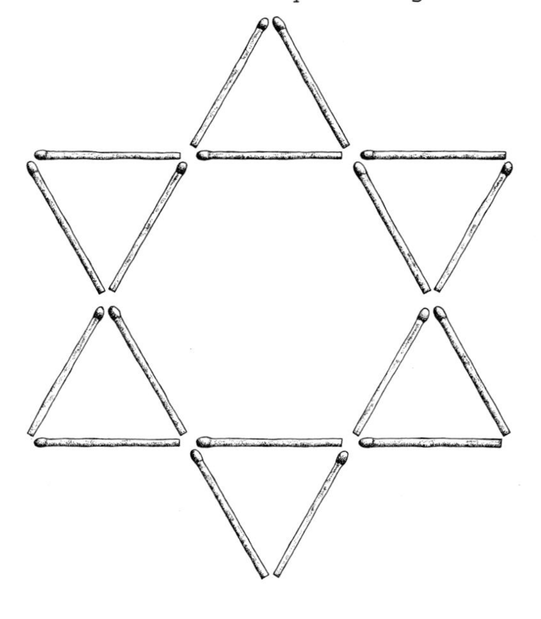

10. Sixteen matches go into the making of these five identical squares. By moving only two matches, turn it into an array of four identical squares.

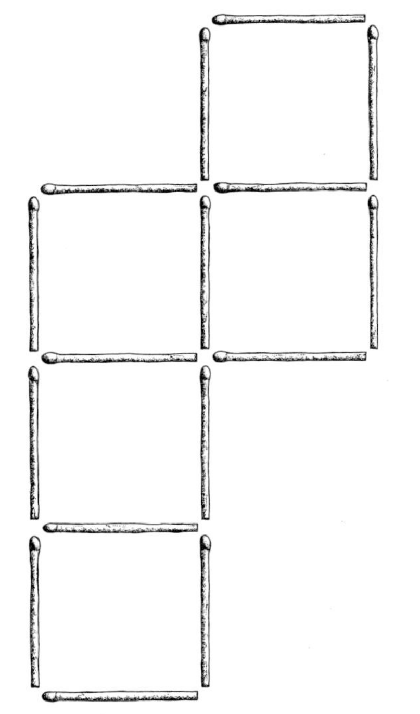

11. Transform this pattern as follows: a) remove four matches, leave five identical squares; b) remove six matches, leave five identical squares; c) remove six matches, leave three squares; d) remove eight matches, leave four identical squares; e) remove eight matches, leave three squares.

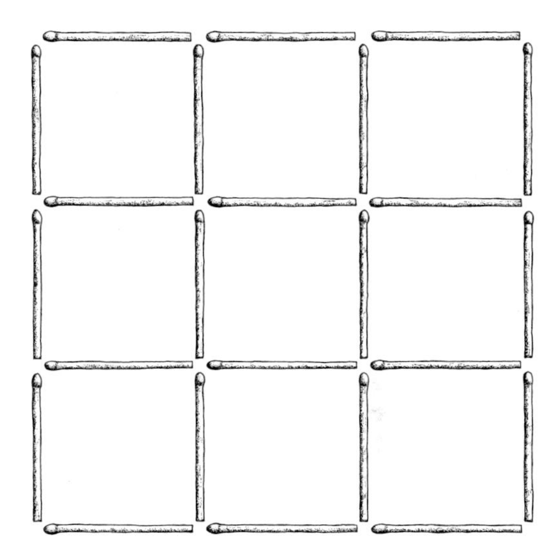

12. Use 13 matches to make this pattern of six identical triangles. Then remove three matches to leave three triangles.

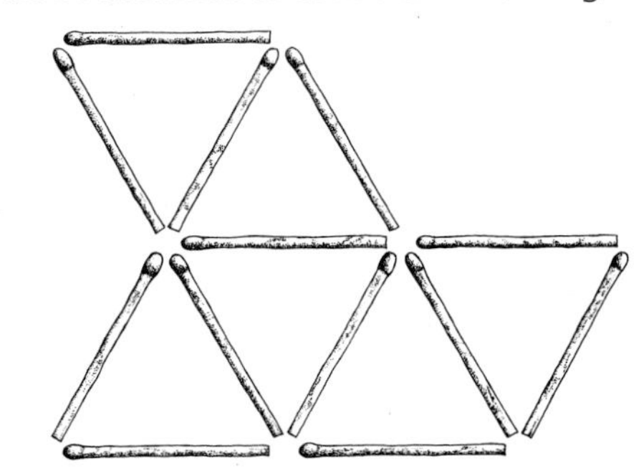

13. a) Move four matches to make three equilateral triangles; b) move four matches, make four identical diamonds.

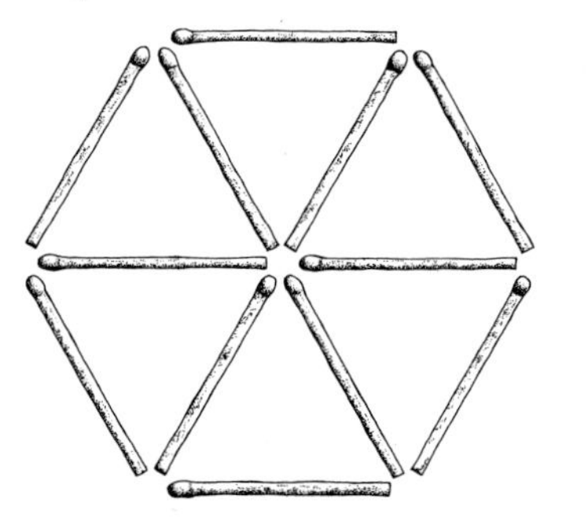

14. Remove four of the matchsticks in the pattern below so that just four identical triangles remain.

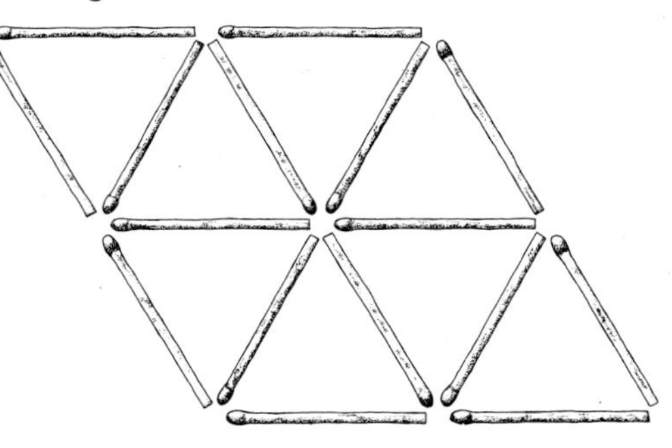

15. a) Remove five matches to leave five identical triangles; b) move six matches to form six identical diamonds making up a symmetrical star shape.

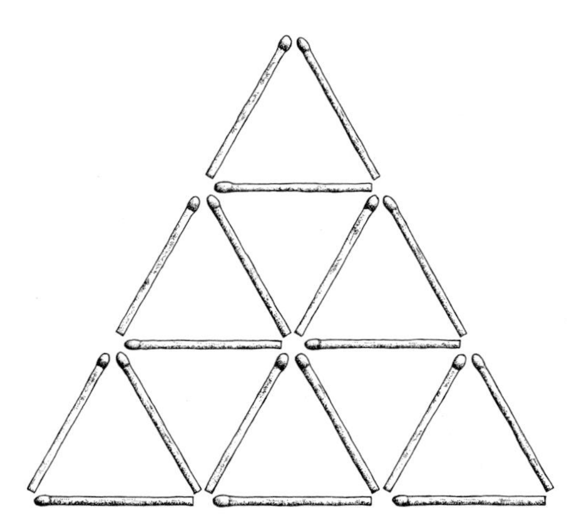

16. Take 15 matches and make this figure. Then move two matches to form an array of five identical squares.

17. Eighteen matches make up the pattern below. Remove six of them so as to leave three identical squares.

(See solution page 189)

18. In the figure below, 24 matches make up nine identical squares (but you can find 14 squares of various sizes). Some of these puzzles can be solved only by crossing matches. Using all 24 matches, make: a) three squares; b) four squares; c) five squares; d) six squares; e) seven squares; f) nine squares; g) 20 squares; h) 42 squares; i) 110 squares.

19. You will need 12 matches to construct the pattern of two nested squares below. Now attempt these two problems: a) remove two of the matches and reposition six of the others in such a way that you are left with three identical squares; b) remove two matches and reposition four of the others so as to achieve the same result, namely three identical squares.

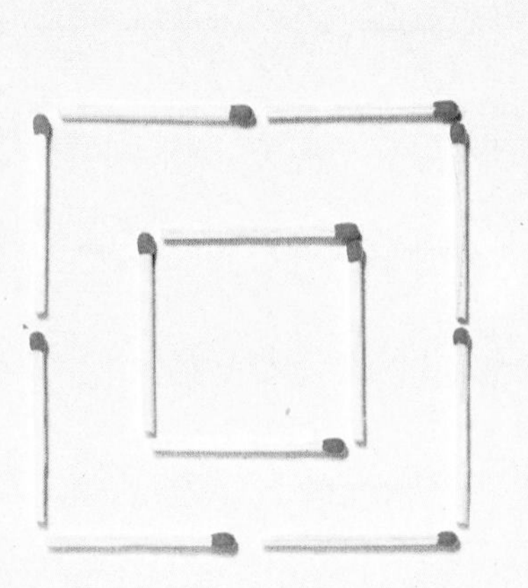

20. Make four equilateral triangles from just six matches. It can be done, without breaking any matches.

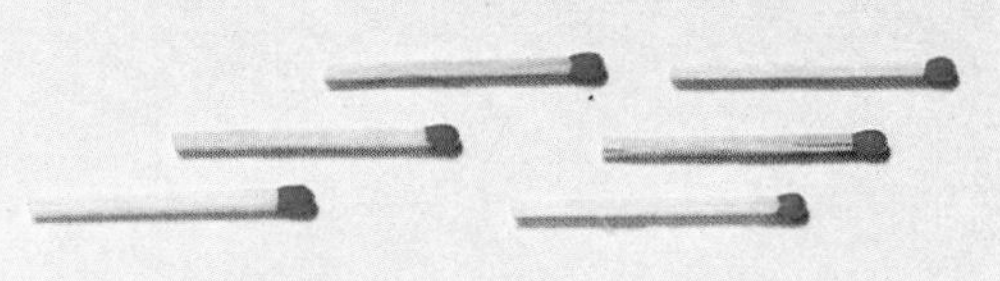

21. Move two matches below to form seven identical squares.

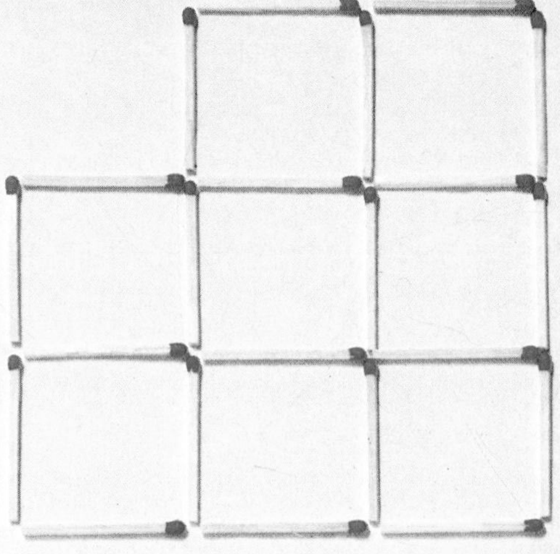

22. Place 36 matches in six rows of six. Remove eight so that each row and column has either four or six matches.

23. With eight matches, make a pattern containing two squares of different sizes and four identical triangles.

24. Surprisingly enough, it is possible to create three squares of equal size from a mere six matchsticks. How?

25. The design below is made from 12 matchsticks. Move five of them so as to create a pattern consisting of three squares that are identical.

26. Use 24 matches to make the pleasing pattern based on a six-pointed star below. Then move six of the matches to make a new pattern that includes twelve identical parallelograms in a symmetrical arrangement.

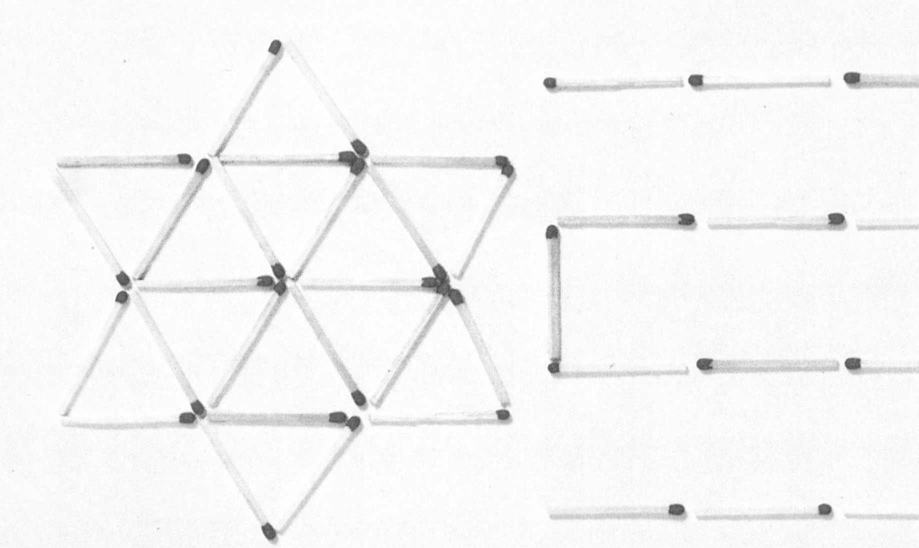

27. You will require 15 matches to make this snakelike pattern. See if you can transform it into two squares by: a) moving four matches; b) moving five matches. The squares you are aiming for are not identical.

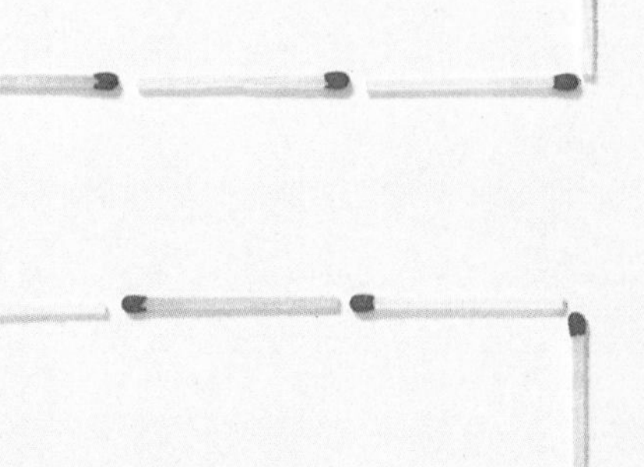

(See solution page 189)

28. Use five matches to form a square with one match on each side and one forming a diagonal. Now remove the diagonal. Can you reposition the other four matches to make a figure identical with the original one?

29. Take 12 matches and lay them out in three rows of four. (That's the easy bit. If you have trouble doing this, do not attempt the next part.) Now move three matches so that you have four in every row and column.

30. You need four matches and a coin for this puzzle. Arrange the matchsticks so that they provide a support for the coin, and so that neither the coin nor the heads of the matches are touching the table on which they are all resting.

31. The ten matches below make up a pattern of three squares. Remove one of the matches and change the positions of three others to form one square and two parallelograms.

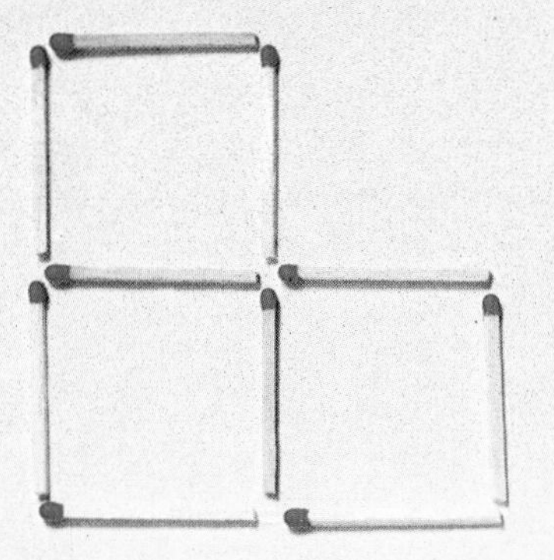

32. As the figure shows, ten matches are sufficient to make a charming, if drafty, house. Here we see it from the northwest. Move two matches so that we view it from the northeast.

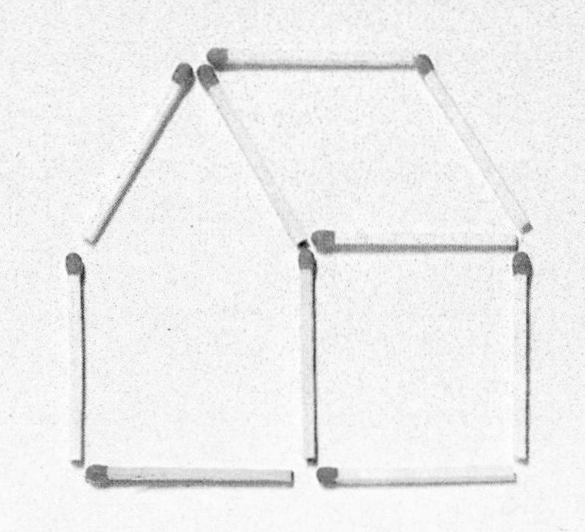

33. This pleasantly balanced pattern is made up of nine matches. See whether, by moving three of them, you can create an equally symmetrical pattern of three rhombuses (diamonds).

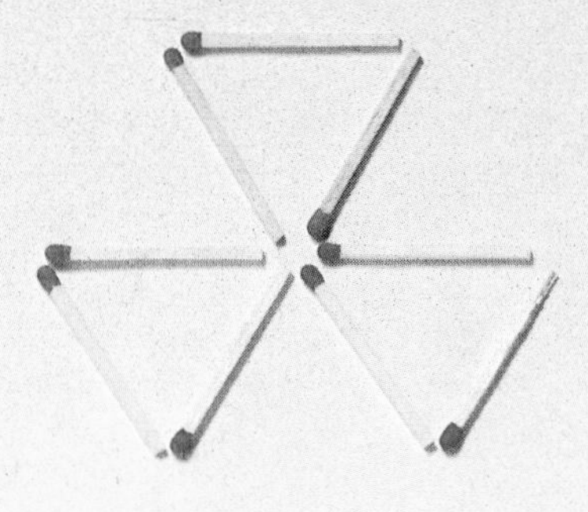

34. Here 36 matches make nine identical squares. See if you can reposition 14 matches in such a way that you get an array of 14 identical squares.

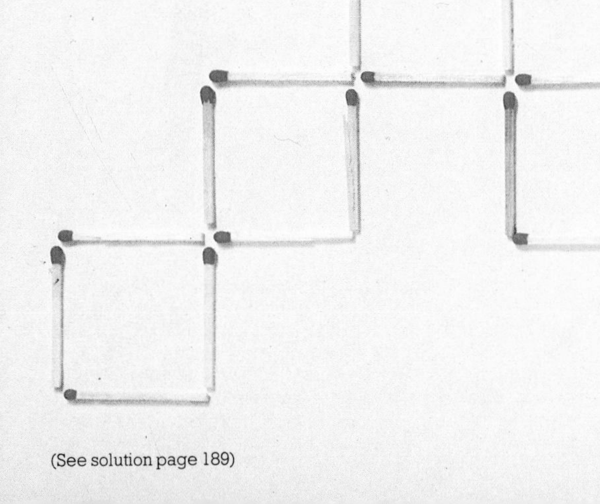

35. For this puzzle you will need five matches and a cavalier attitude toward the laws of arithmetic. Put three matches side by side on the table. Now add two more matches to make eight. (No breaking of matches is allowed. Miracles are really not essential.)

36. Remove seven matches from the array below in such a way that it becomes four identical squares.

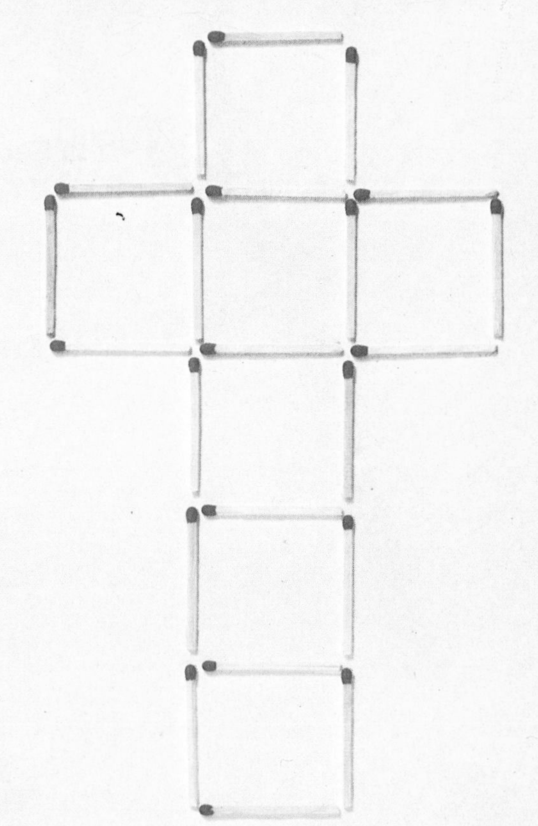

(See solution page 189)

37. This spiral pattern can be turned into three squares (unequal in size) by moving four matches. How?

38. Take 26 matches and make this fencelike structure. Then move 12 of them to make just three squares.

39. Make the shape below and then add eight matches to divide it into four parts of the same shape and size.

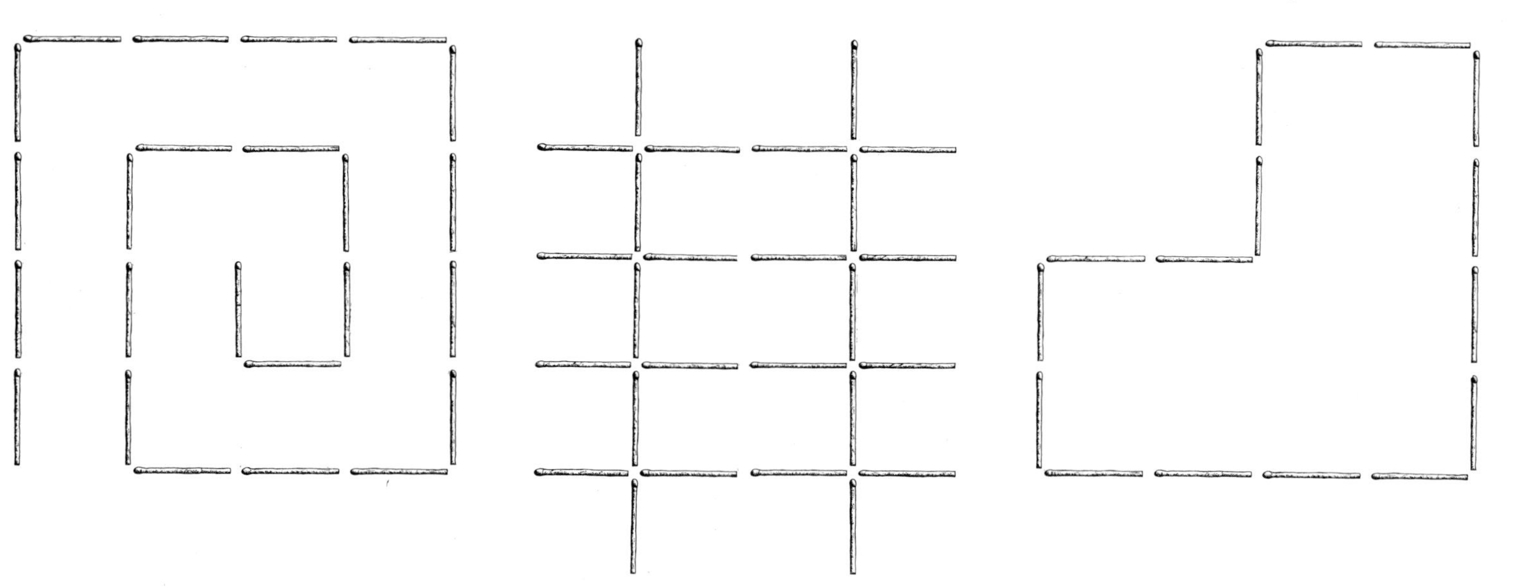

40. Kitchen matches, large and preferably brightly colored, are best for building this elaborate bridge. Once again this is a job for steady hands and a sober mind. The bridge will stay up, once erected; but the problem to which you have to address yourself is just what systematic procedure to use in building it.

(See solution pages 189-190)

41. What is the minimum number of matches you can remove to leave a pattern containing no squares?

42. Remove ten of the matches from this pattern to leave behind four identical squares with unit sides.

43. This pattern contains six "unit" squares and two larger ones. Move six matches to make six squares.

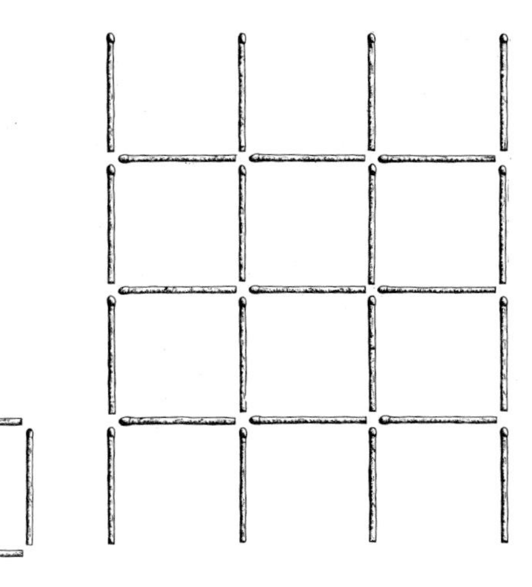

44. Move four matches in the pattern below in order to create a new one consisting of five squares.

45. Here there are ten matches, but not a square in sight. Move four matches to form two squares.

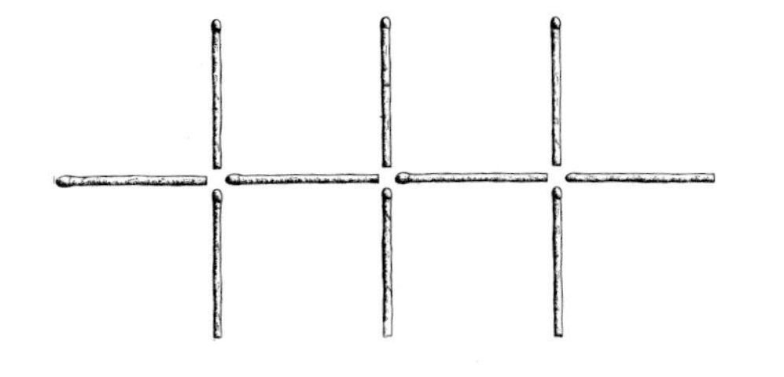

46. These 18 matches form six small squares and a large one. Move four matches, make three squares.

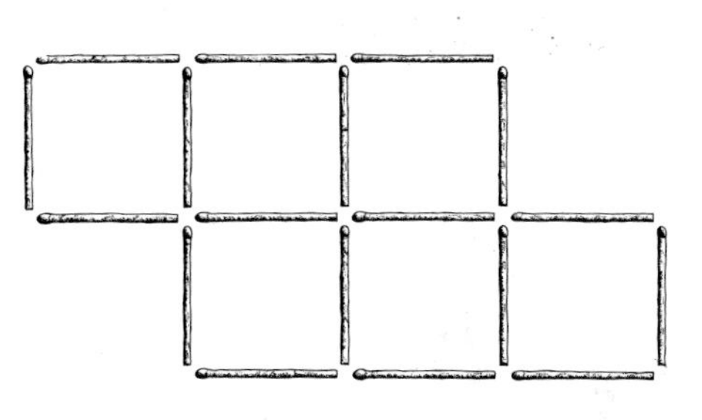

47. Invest in a second box of matches to make this figure, with its 52 matchsticks. Then remove 22 matches to make four identical squares.

48. Nineteen matches go into the making of this cross. See whether, by moving just nine of them, you can make a pattern consisting of four squares.

49. The larger square below is the somewhat unimaginative ground plan of one of England's stateliest homes. The duke wishes to continue occupying the castle, represented by the smaller square. But, prompted by family affection and a desire to reduce his tax bill, he divides his grounds among his five nieces. He avoids quarrels by dividing the grounds into five areas of the same size and shape. Can you do it with ten matches?

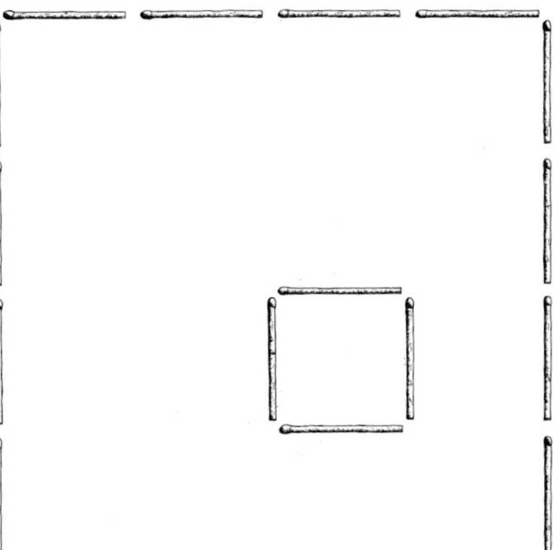

(See solution page 190)

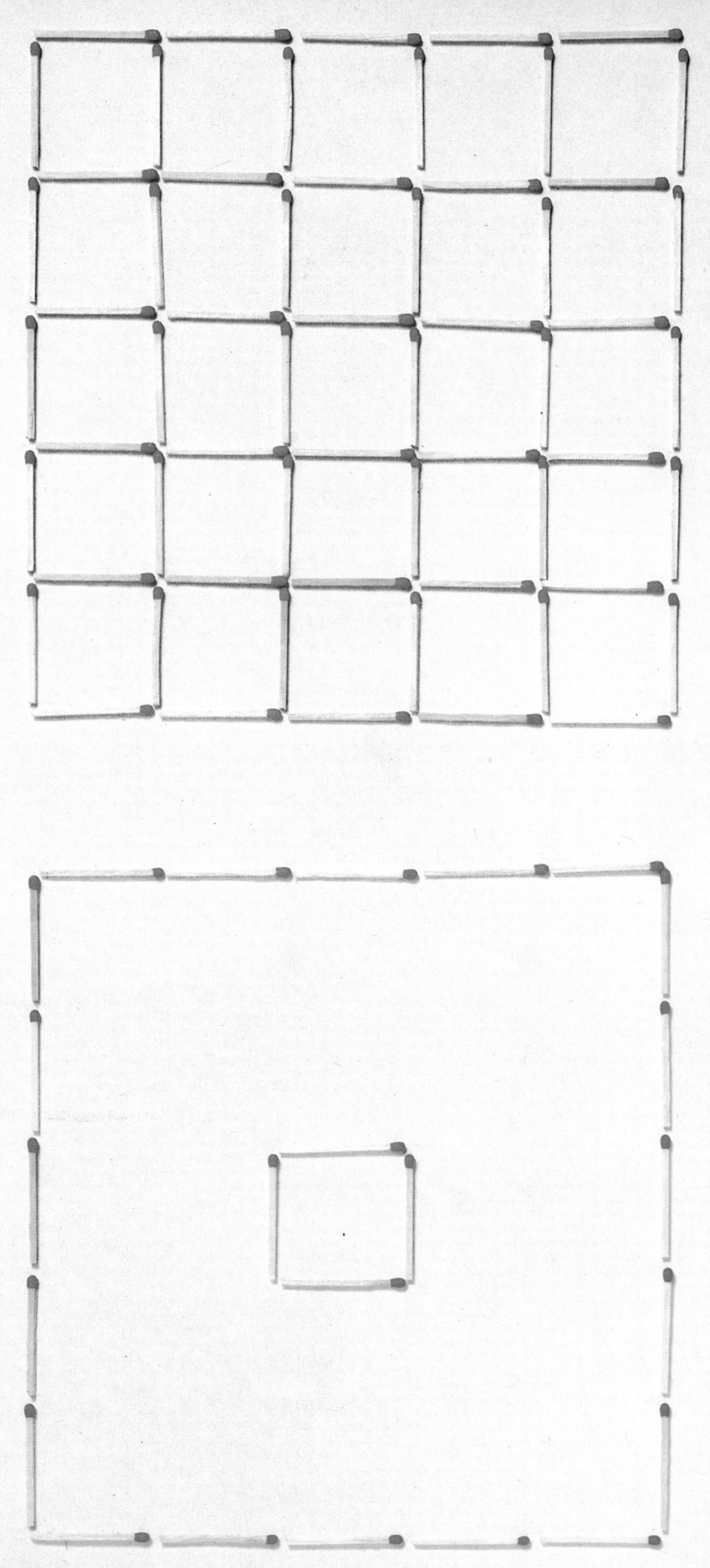

50. There are 60 matches at the left. They make 25 "unit" squares, 16 squares with two matches on a side, nine with three on a side, and so on. a) Remove 20 matches to leave a pattern of ten squares; b) remove 24 matches to leave nine identical squares in a symmetrical pattern; c) move 12 and add a further eight matches to create 25 identical squares in a symmetrical pattern; d) remove 16 matches to leave 13 identical squares in a regular pattern; e) remove 24 matches to leave five squares in a regular pattern; f) remove 24 matches and leave three squares.

51. Can you find a way to arrange nine matchsticks so that they form three squares of equal size, and also two equilateral triangles?

52. The farmer seen below has prospered modestly after years of hard work, and the map of his extensive grounds, with the farmhouse, now requires a full 24 matches. His tribe, too, has increased and he now has eight sons. He wishes to share the land among them by dividing it into eight pieces of equal size and identical shape. Can you show him how to do it, using only another 20 matches?

(See solution page 190)

Domino Puzzles

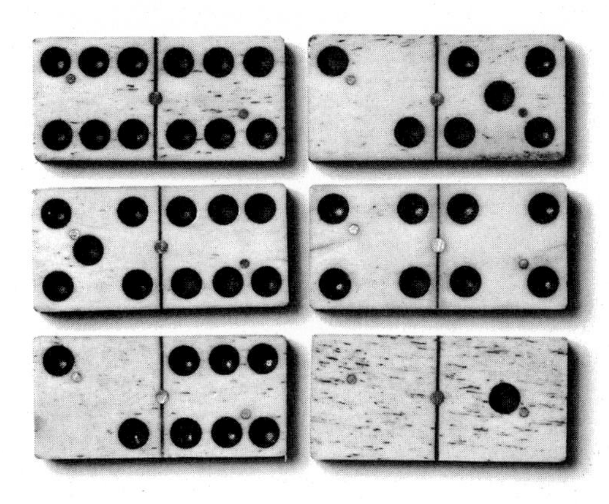

Made at the height of the domino craze in Europe, this late 19th-century double-6 set has the traditional ivory upper layer and ebony wood base.

China is the source of the few ancient records that mention dominoes, but fact and legend are confused in these records and the exact origins of dominoes remain unknown. In some accounts a soldier is credited with their invention around A.D. 200, while other reports favor a court official of Emperor Hui Tsung in the early 12th century. Domino games were known by the end of the 12th century, but domino puzzles were not invented for another 600 years. Originally dominoes were small and made from an ivory or white bone layer on a black bone or ebony base. The extensive use of bone led to the adoption of the term *bone* for a single domino piece, but now *tile* is the more common term. The upper surface of each tile is divided into two squares, or half-tiles, each of which may be blank or marked with a number of pips. The name of a set of dominoes is taken from the tile of the highest value (the highest number of pips), commonly double-6.

The game of dominoes appeared in Italy early in the 18th century. It spread to France, where it rapidly gained popularity, and soon domino games were common in cafés and bars. At least two competitors would be involved in the game, taking turns at placing tiles on the table so that the numbers on touching half-tiles matched. The winner was the first one to be rid of his dominoes. Within a few years dominoes spread to England with French prisoners of war, and from there were taken to America. It was in France, in the mid-18th century, that the craze for dominoes first developed into an interest in domino puzzles. Two types of puzzles evolved. In one a pattern had to be made in which the numbers on touching half-tiles matched each other. In the other type of puzzle a pattern had to be made in which rows or columns of numbers added up to the same total or in some other way used the arithmetical properties of the numbers.

Judging by the look on the face of the loser in Honoré Daumier's *Domino*, there may have been some money wagered on the result of this café game.

Two Equal Lines

This is an interesting beginning to domino puzzles. Using the six pieces of a double-2 set, make two lines, each of three tiles, so that the number of pips in each row is the same. Where the tiles meet, the pips must be equal in number.

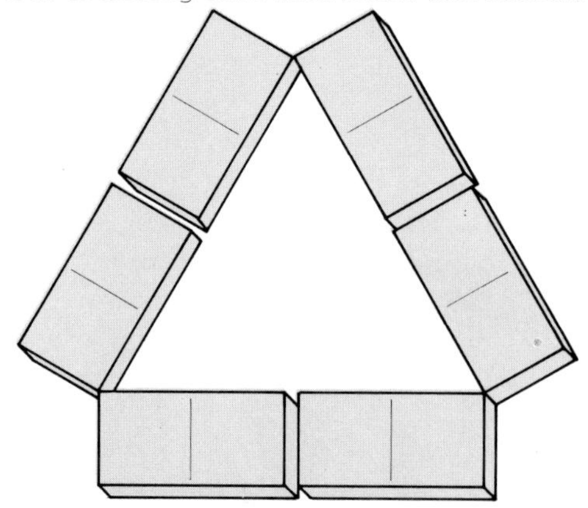

Six-Tile Square

Again take the six tiles of the double-2 set, and arrange them to form a square, as shown below. The four sides of the square must all have the same number of pips, but where the tiles meet, numbers of the half-tiles need not match.

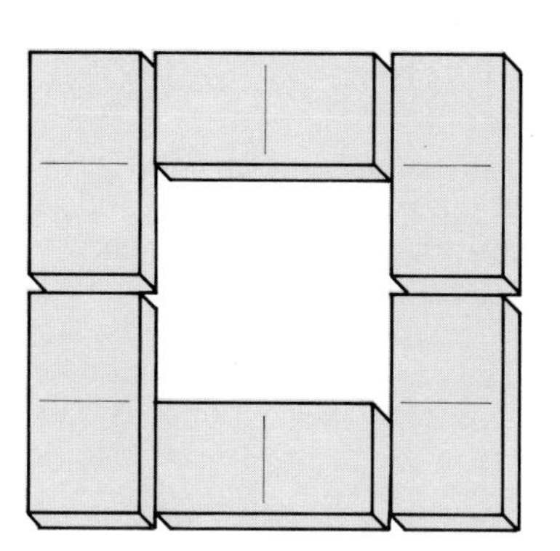

Double-2 Rectangle

Make a rectangular frame, five half-tiles long and three half-tiles deep. The frame uses all the tiles from a double-2 set. As with the square in the preceding puzzle, the numbers of pips on each side must add up to the same total.

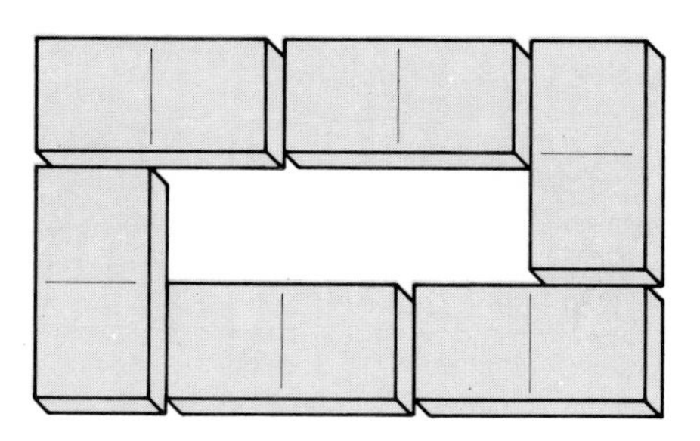

A Triangle with Equal Sides

Make the triangle below using the six tiles of the double-2 set. Each of the sides must have the same number of pips, but touching half-tiles need not match.

Magic Rows

Ten dominoes of the double-3 set are laid out in a line so that both rows of half-tiles contain the same number of pips. In addition, the two half-tiles in each column add to equal numbers of pips, but this sum is not the same as the sum of the ten half-tiles in each row. Individual tiles can be laid vertically or horizontally, as the diagram shows.

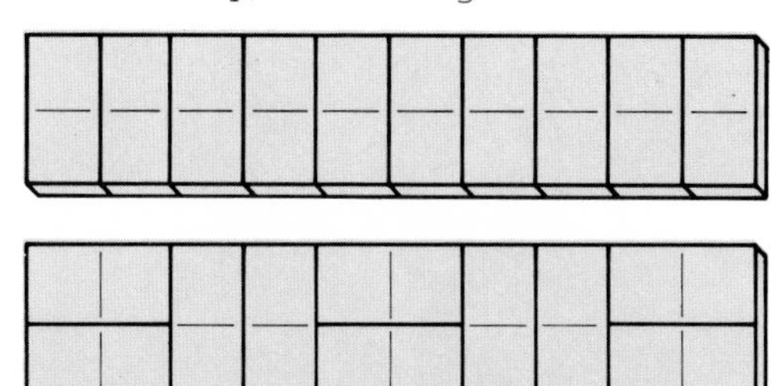

Magic Rectangle

Try to arrange the pieces of the double-3 set into this shape. It does not matter whether individual tiles are placed vertically or horizontally. The number of pips in each column must be equal; the rows may differ from each other.

Twin Rectangles

Two five-tile rectangles like this one can be made from the ten pieces of a double-3 set. Here the problem is to arrange the rectangles so that the pips on all eight of the sides add up to the same total number.

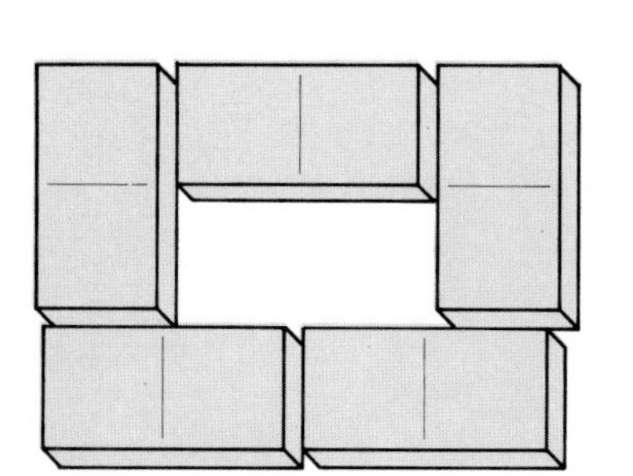

The Square in the Rectangle

Arrange the double-4 set so that there are only blanks in the right-hand column. Make the rows, columns, and diagonals of the remaining square add up to the same total.

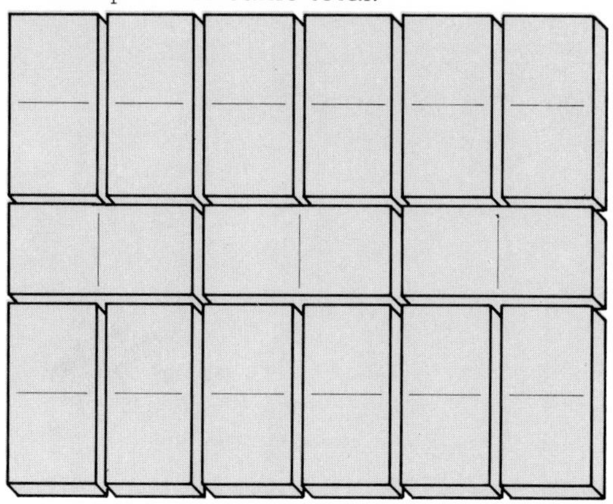

Three of a Kind

Take the 15 pieces of the double-4 set, and make three rectangles, following the pattern below. Where any two tiles meet, each half-tile must carry the same number of pips, but it is not necessary for the sides to add up to the same sum.

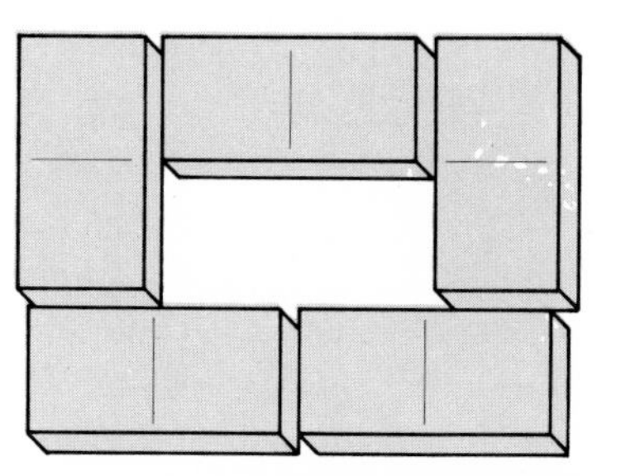

(See solution page 190)

Three in a Row

There are 21 tiles in the double-5 domino set. It is not difficult to lay these out in seven rows, each of three tiles, with the touching half-tiles matching in the numbers of pips. The puzzle here is not only to arrange them in this way but also to place them so that the number of pips in each line is the same.

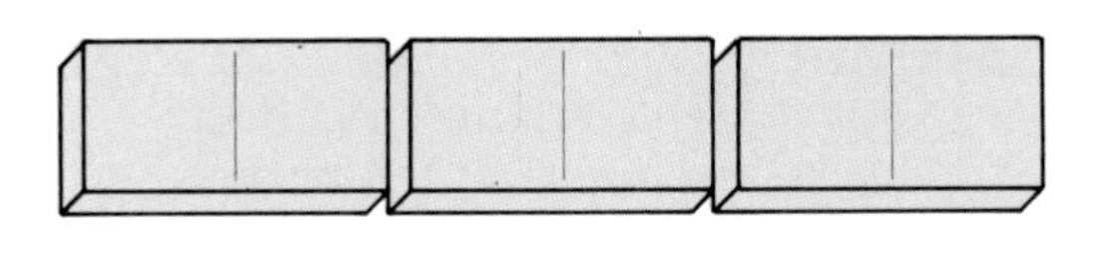

A Trio of Rectangles·

Arrange the 21 tiles of the double-5 set to form three rectangles, each of seven tiles. The puzzle is to so arrange them that the 12 sides have equal numbers of pips. In this puzzle the joining half-tiles need not match.

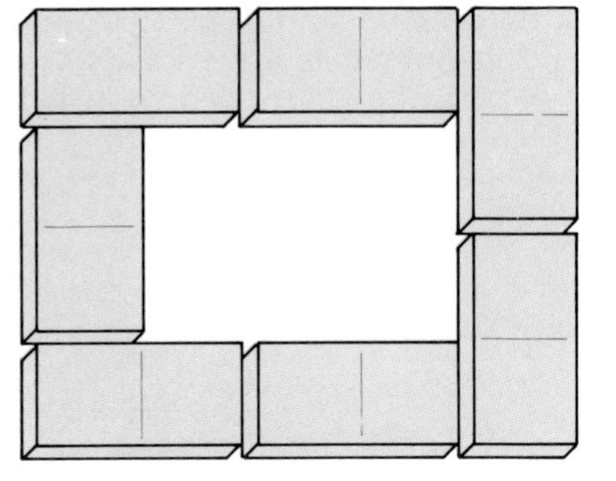

Domino Sums

It is possible to make mathematical puzzles with the numbers on dominoes. The three tiles have been arranged to form a correct addition (41 + 13 = 54). Make seven other additions with the tiles of the double-5 set. No blanks are allowed in the left-hand column of any of the domino sums in this problem.

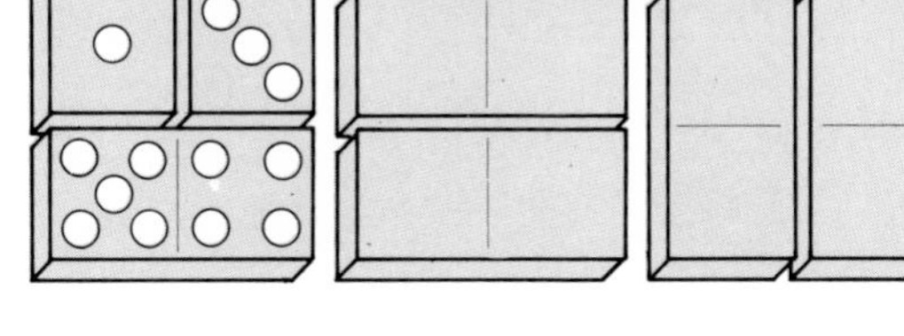

Domino Lattices

The patterns below are just some examples of the complex designs you can make using all 28 pieces of the double-6 set. Where the dominoes meet, the half-tiles carry the same number of pips. Try making some of these designs. Then experiment to see how many other symmetrical patterns, knots, and mazes you can originate yourself.

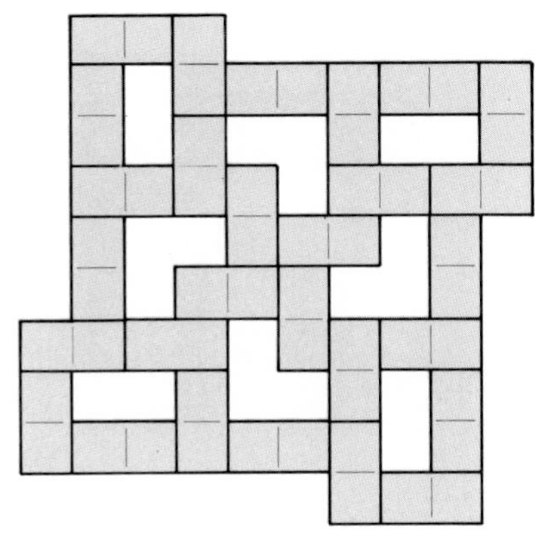

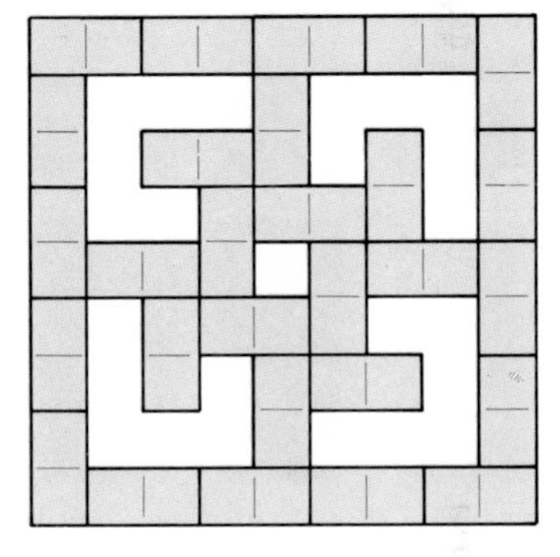

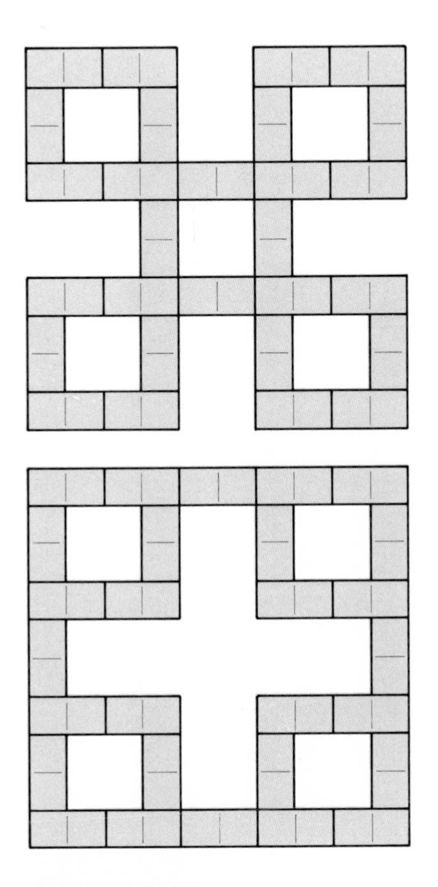

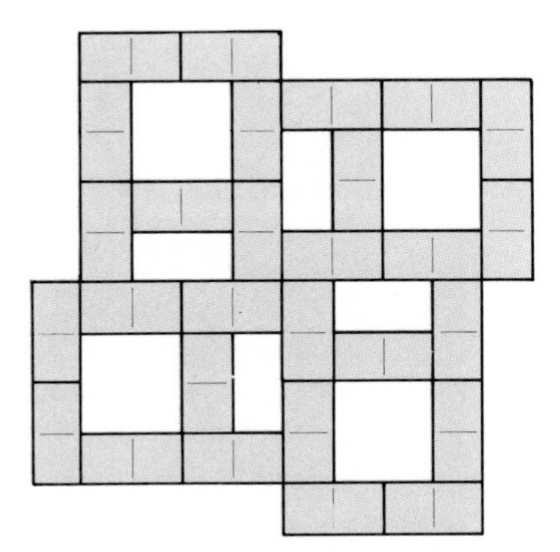

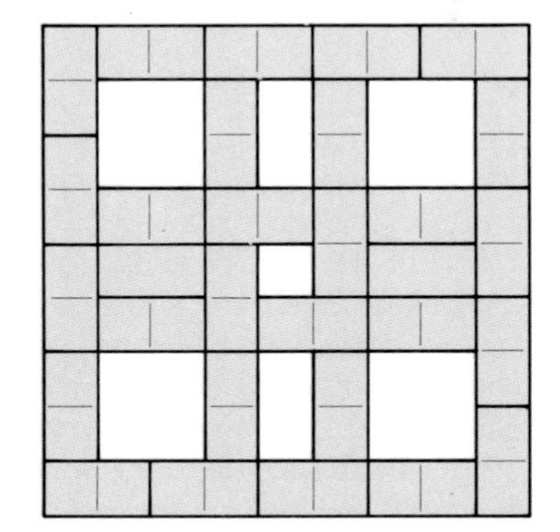

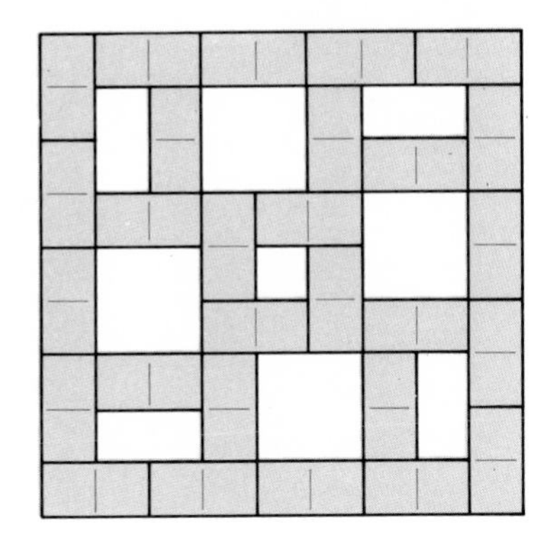

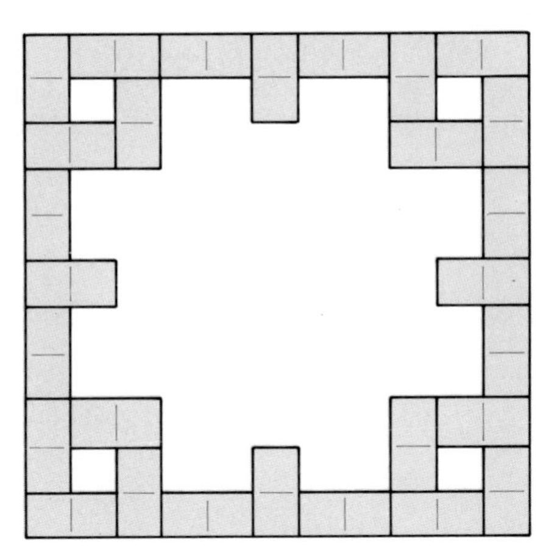

(See solution pages 190-191)

Magic Squares

The nine dominoes below, arranged in three rows of three, make a magic square with a constant of 12 — that is, there are 12 pips in each row, column, and diagonal. The number of pips on the tiles range from 0 to 8. Try: a) making a nine-tile magic square with a constant of 15, using only the tiles with totals of 1 through 9 pips; b) a nine-tile magic square of tiles with totals of 3 through 11 pips and a constant of 21.

The Window

In this puzzle four dominoes have been arranged to form a square frame with sides each three half-tiles long, around a central space. To begin this puzzle, select the four dominoes of the values shown below from the 28 pieces of the double-6 set. Make this window and note the results of the construction: each side of the window has the same number of pips. Now make another seven four-tile windows with all 28 pieces of the double-6 set so that for each square, the total number of pips is the same on every side. The half-tiles that are in contact need not match in the number of pips that they carry.

The Frame

This domino frame uses more tiles than the window on the left and is more difficult to assemble. The frame is made from tiles of the double-6 set, with each side adding up to 15. From your double-6 set take out the double-3, double-4, double-5, and double-6 tiles, and arrange the remaining 24 tiles to form three frames. It is possible to make the frames so that all 12 sides carry the same number of pips. Touching half-tiles need not match. A useful first step is to calculate how many pips will appear on each side of the frames.

The Latin Square

Select any 18 dominoes you wish from the double-6 set, and arrange them into a square with six half-tiles on each side. The aim in this puzzle is to use 18 tiles to make a square so that no number is repeated in any row or column. In the square shown on the right, this arrangement is far from perfect, for there are two 4s and two blanks in the top row, two 5s and two 6s in the third row, and two 3s in the fourth row. Try to correct this, or start anew to make a perfect Latin square.

The regular, serial arrangement of the pips on domino tiles makes them highly attractive to the mathematically inclined puzzler. Many of the possibilities are based on the addition of the pips, as in the examples above. When the square of dominoes on the right has been altered so that no numerical value is repeated in any row or column, it is known as a Latin square. Quadrilles (opposite page) are another fascinating diversion.

(See solution page 191)

Quadrilles

Edouard Lucas (1842-91), a French mathematician, gave the name *quadrille* to a domino figure consisting of blocks of four half-tiles, all the half-tiles in a block carrying the same number of pips. The simplest quadrille is that made with the double-2 set, shown in the top figure. This is the only quadrille that can be made from the double-2 set. It is made up of blocks of half-tiles bearing two pips, one pip, and no pips respectively. An example of a large quadrille is shown below.

It is important to remember that it is only possible to make a quadrille from domino sets in which each number appears four times or a multiple of four times. In the full double-6 set each number appears eight times, and a total of 14 squares, each made up of four equal half-tiles, can be created. Using the whole set, try to make the patterns shown on the left. Each square represents a block of four equal half-tiles; individual dominoes are not indicated. The two figures in the center are examples of symmetrical quadrilles — they can be cut along one axis to produce two halves that are mirror images of one another. In the left-hand figure the axis runs from top to bottom, while in the right-hand figure it is horizontal.

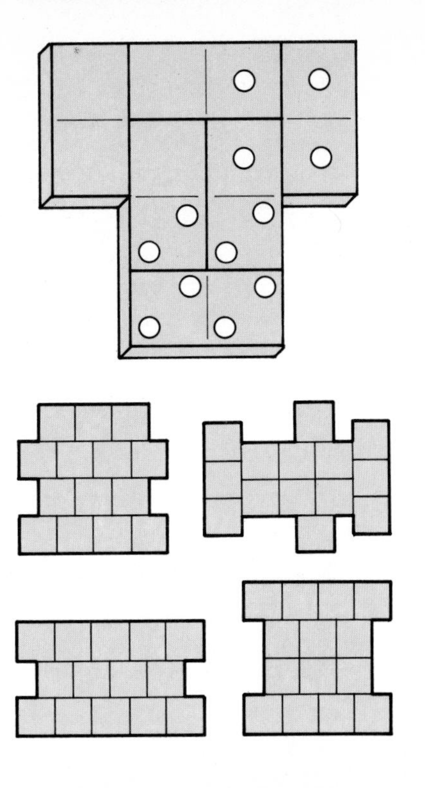

The two lower figures at the left can be filled with the 28 tiles of the double-6 set to make quadrilles that can be divided into four matching parts by both a horizontal and a vertical axis. Such quadrilles are called doubly symmetrical. The picture below shows a completed doubly symmetrical quadrille. Note that tiles may be horizontal or vertical. To experiment with still larger quadrilles, you will need a double-10 set, with which you can make a number of patterns containing 33 squares.

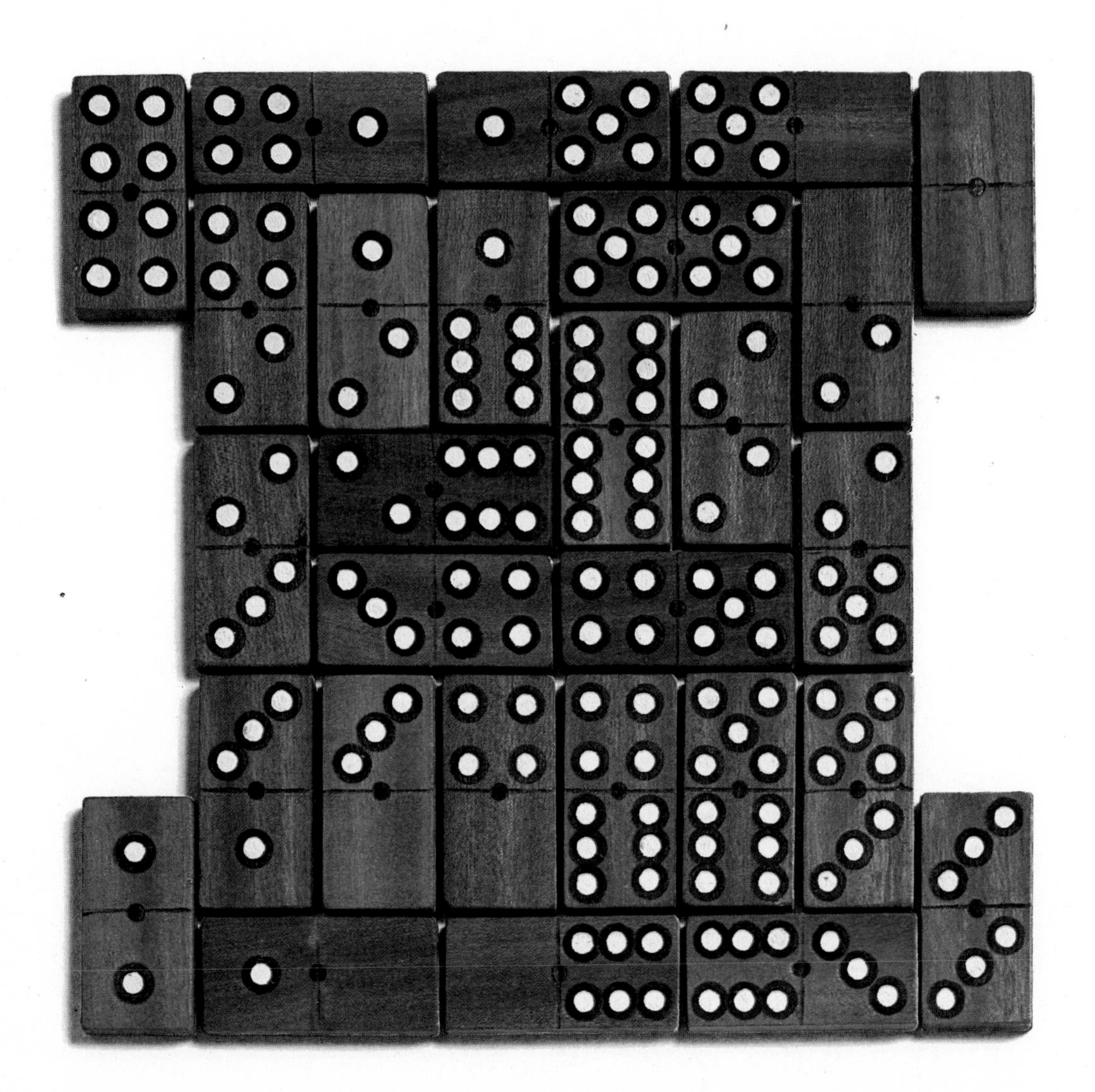

(See solution page 192)

The Empty Square

The square below comprises a double puzzle. Not only must the sides have the same number of pips, but touching half-tiles must match. You need all 28 pieces of the double-6 set.

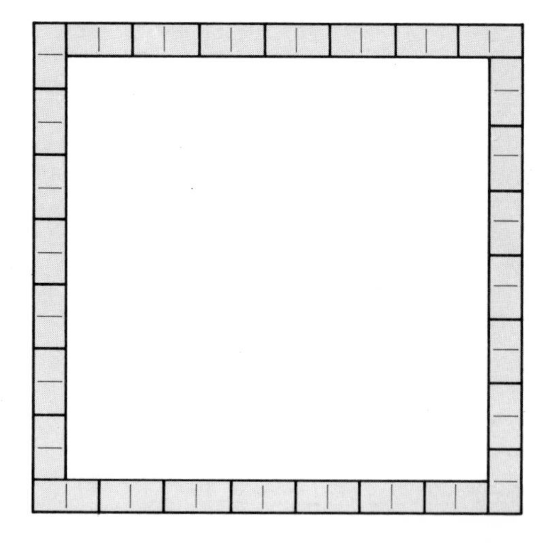

Rectangle Sums

Pit your wits against all 28 tiles of the double-6 set in this puzzle. Lay the dominoes in a rectangle, eight half-tiles across and seven half-tiles down. The tiles can be placed either horizontally or both horizontally and vertically to make the rectangle. Each column must contain the same number of pips. The rows must also contain equal numbers of pips, but this number will be different from the number of pips in the columns.

The Cartwheel

The seven spokes are made with the double-6 set and have the same sums. The innermost half-tiles read 0 through 6, in sequence; the outermost may be out of sequence. Joins must match.

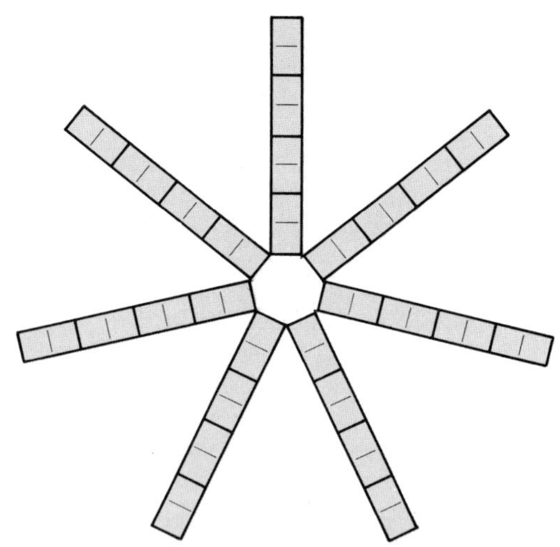

This engraving, *Les Jouers de domino*, shows the enthusiasm with which dominoes, a recent introduction, were received in Paris in 1800.

(See solution page 192)

The Hole in the Middle

A magic square can be made from 24 of the 28 tiles of the double-6 set, provided that a half-tile hole is left in the middle. The square's rows, columns, and diagonals add up to the same number. The tiles can be laid down vertically or horizontally. Choose any 24 pieces to make a square, each side of which is made up of seven half-tiles.

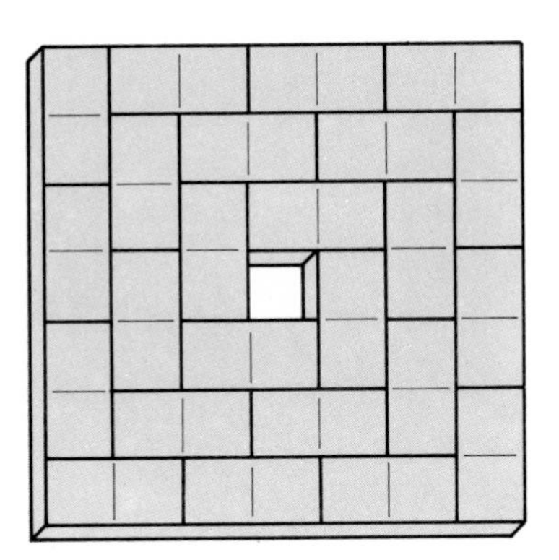

Square within a Square

Arrange the 28 tiles of the double-6 set, as shown below, to make two squares. All eight sides must have an equal number of pips; joins need not match.

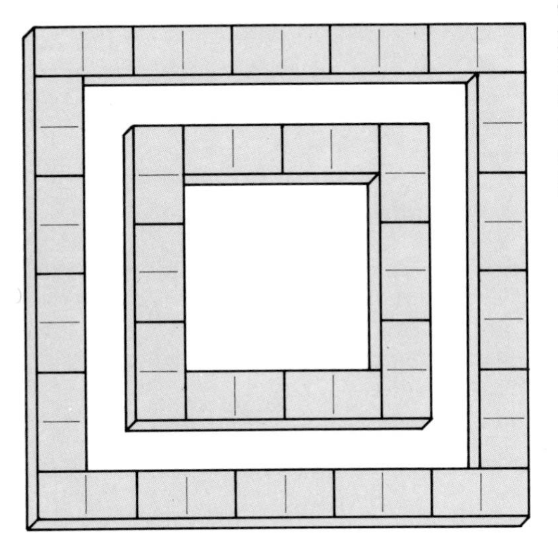

A Quartet of Rectangles

The 28 pieces of the double-6 set of dominoes can be divided into four groups, each with seven tiles. The tiles in each group can be arranged to form a rectangle, as shown below. In this puzzle the individual sides of the rectangles need not be equal, but the total number of pips in each rectangle must be the same. In addition, where the domino tiles meet, the half-tiles must have the same number of pips.

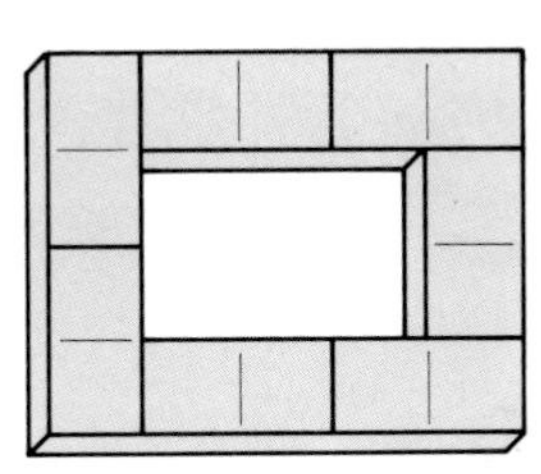

Unequal Squares

The 28 tiles of a double-6 set can make four different-size squares, with respective sides of 3, 4, 5, and 6 half-tiles. Make the squares so each of the 16 sides has an equal number of pips.

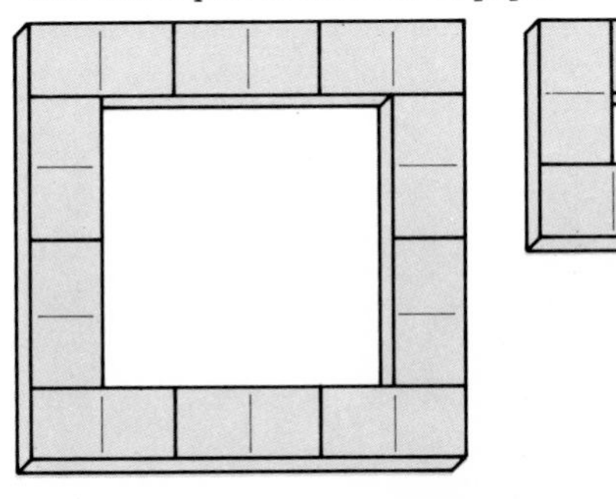

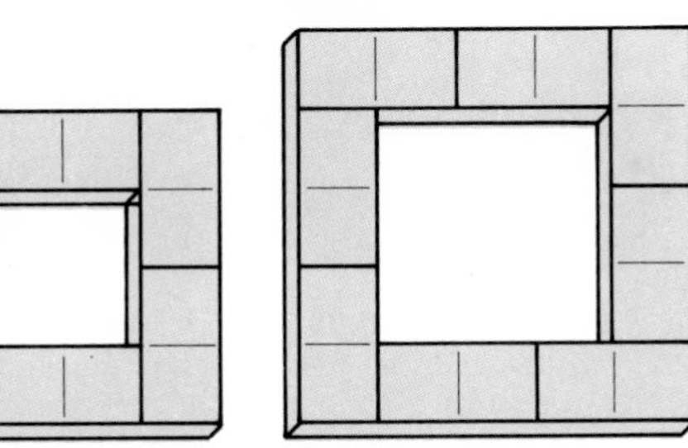

Multiplying Dominoes

The pattern below can be read as a multiplication sum, $24 \times 5 = 120$. Leaving out the double-blank, use the double-6 set to make more multiplication sums. No blanks are allowed on the left side.

Domino Waves

The double-6 set can be arranged to form seven "waves" or Z shapes, with joins matching and with the sum of the pips on the diagonal equal to the sum of the pips on the two remaining tiles.

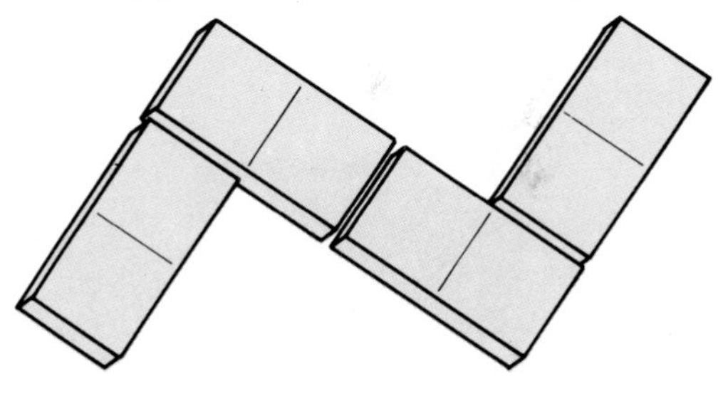

Double-Crossing Dominoes

This pair of Greek crosses uses all 28 tiles of the double-6 set. Placing the tiles either vertically or horizontally as shown, try to make the two crosses. The aim of the puzzle is to make the sum of the pips equal in each of the four bars — that is, the two horizontal bars and the two vertical bars. Each bar is taken to have eight dominoes — the two central pairs of tiles are thus counted twice.

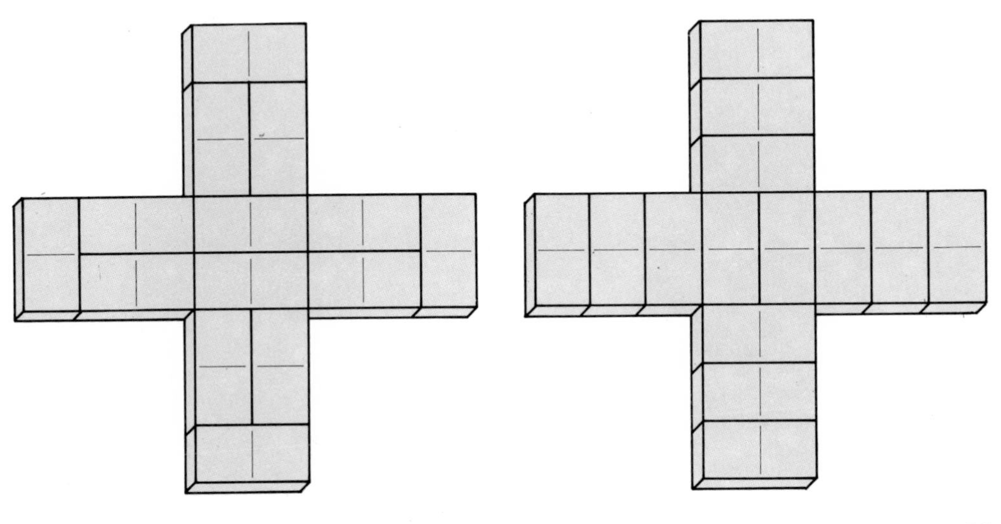

(See solution pages 192-193)

More Multiplications

Using only four tiles, try to make multiplication sums in which a three-figure number is multiplied by 2, 3, 4, 5, or 6 to give a four-figure product. The example below shows 551 × 4 = 2204. It is possible to make seven correct products with all 28 tiles of the double-6 set. Blanks may not be put on the far left.

Rectangular Quartet

The 28 dominoes of the double-6 set can be divided into four groups, each with seven tiles. By careful selection it is possible to make four seven-tile rectangles — as in the examples on the right — so that all 16 sides have the same number of pips. The maximum number of pips possible is 22 on each side of a rectangle, as in the upper example. In the bottom rectangle each of the four sides adds up to the lowest possible number — 4. Each of the 16 sides must equal a number between 4 and 22. Calculating this number would help in constructing the four rectangles, but it is not essential. As the examples show, the numbers on the half-tiles in contact need not match.

Double-5 Addition

In this puzzle you are required to use the 21 pieces of the double-5 set to form three additions. The example below, which shows a columnar addition using tiles selected from the double-6 set, shows 25 + 65 + 35 + 34 + 22 + 55 + 53. (The total, 289, is not shown.) Make three sums, all with the same total (not 289). Use five tiles in each sum. Place the tiles either vertically or horizontally to make two-figure numbers with no blanks in the left-hand column.

Domino Addition

The pattern of seven domino tiles below is to be read as an addition: 63 + 60 + 60 + 20 + 50 + 13 + 23. The sum, 289, does not appear. Try to make four additions from the double-6 set, each containing seven tiles, and all adding up to the same total (which is not shown in the calculation itself). The total need not be 289. You may place tiles either vertically or horizontally, as in the example shown. Blanks must not appear in the left-hand column of numbers.

Another Addition

The design below is another addition: 2112 + 4034 = 6146. The six dominoes of the double-2 set have the lowest number of pips that any group of six tiles can have, but they can add up to high numbers when arranged in a pattern like that below. Try to arrange the tiles of the double-2 set to make the largest possible total for the addition sum. A blank must not be placed at the left of any four-figure number.

Many puzzles can be created in which the numbers on dominoes are used for calculations. This page shows some examples of problems in addition and multiplication of domino pips.

Toward the end of the 18th century dominoes were so popular in France that the tiles were often lavishly decorated or incorporated into illustrated cards. These cards could be comic, bawdy or, like those opposite, grotesque. In this set the dominoes must be arranged so that the half-tiles that touch match in number in order to illustrate the story.

(See solution page 193)

Construction Puzzles and Packing Problems

The contrasting colors of several different woods define the faces of this puzzle. Designed by Stewart T. Coffin, this rhombic dodecahedron is just one of his polyhedral construction puzzles.

A child trying to fit toy bricks into a box is encountering construction puzzles for the first time, for his problem is just one of these three-dimensional puzzles.

Some of the easiest construction puzzles are the cluster or burr puzzles. At first the difficulty of these puzzles appears awe-inspiring; the same principle was once utilized in locks on Japanese trunks. These puzzles are based on the construction of a cross-shaped block from a number of bars into which notches have been cut. The bars interlock to fill the center of the block. Built into each puzzle is a lock, and once this lock is discovered, there is little problem in dismantling or reassembling the puzzle. These solid, so-called ideal, puzzles have become increasingly more complex, particularly in Western societies where computers have been used to devise a great many new designs and solutions. Around 1920 a number of experts in the puzzle world patented new puzzles on themes developed from the original burr puzzles. Some of these differ from the earlier puzzles only in having spaces in the center of the block, but this makes the puzzle far more difficult to solve. Often several pieces must be shifted in order to free one piece. What are known as magic boxes developed from these puzzles; these boxes are securely locked by an internal system of moving blocks. In some construction puzzles the key to the solution lies in rotating one part, while in others two halves of the puzzle are slid apart. More recently packing problems — extensions of the child's problems with his building bricks — have received a great deal of attention. In the modern industrial world, full of complex storage problems, such puzzles are part of everyday life.

Three examples of construction puzzles, all dating from the 19th century. The cube and the ball in the cage puzzle are simply made, and the wood has been left untreated. In the barrel puzzle the highly polished bars, made from fruit woods, create an elegant effect. Many such puzzles can be bought today, ranging from simple ones made in egg, ball, and cube shapes to sophisticated acrylic and polished-wood coffee table puzzles.

The Wooden Knot

However you approach this puzzle, there seems to be no way of penetrating the wooden knot and separating the individual pieces. While at first the knot appears to consist of three identical parts, only two of them are actually the same. It is the third piece that locks the puzzle, which therefore provides the key to its solution. It is a double puzzle, which challenges you to separate the parts as well as to reassemble the knot.

Materials

A block of hardwood, 9" × 4" × 1"
Varnish or wood oil

Tools

Fretsaw; a drill with a small bit; brush; pencil; ruler; sandpaper.

How to Make the Puzzle

Saw the block of wood into three equal rectangles, each 4" × 3". Prepare two of the blocks following the lower diagram below, to make two C shapes. Draw the pattern onto the blocks, and cut along the heavy lines, discarding the central T shape. On the remaining block draw the off-center rectangle as in the upper diagram. Drill a small hole inside this rectangle, insert the blade of the fretsaw, and cut along the heavy lines. Discard the inner rectangle. Sandpaper the wood along all cut edges, then apply varnish or wood oil. To assemble the wooden knot, follow the solution diagram and instructions.

Mahogany, an attractive and suitably hard wood, was cut and then lightly oiled to make the interlocking elements of this wooden knot puzzle.

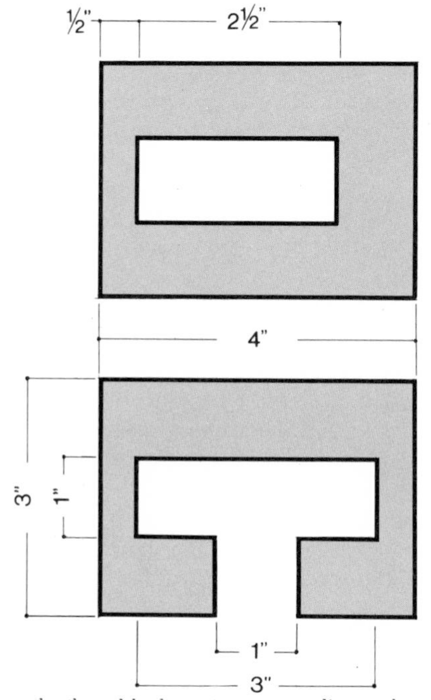

From the three blocks, cut one according to the top diagram, and two corresponding to the C shape.

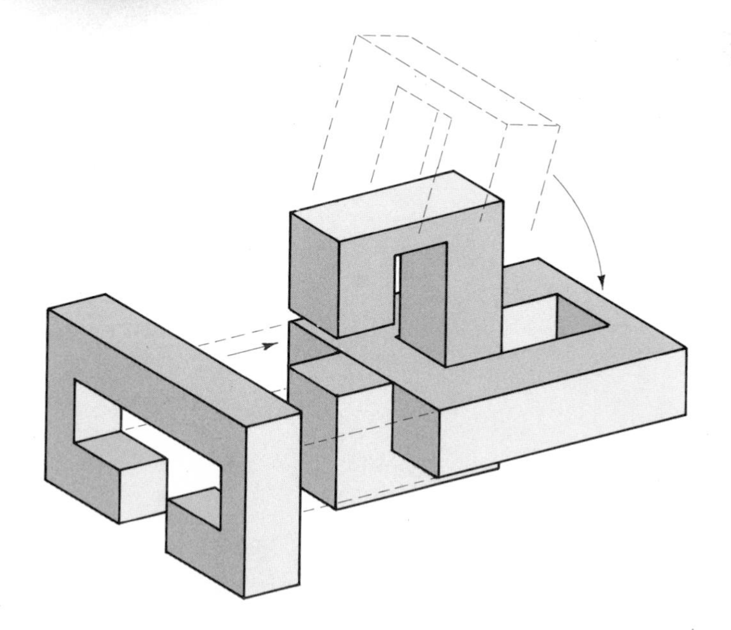

To assemble the puzzle, hold the O vertically, with its narrow end uppermost. Slot one of the C pieces onto it so that the long side of the C runs through the central hole in the O. Lay the O flat, so that its wide end drops into one arm of the T-shaped gap in the C. Take the second C and place it so that the gap in its side faces downward. Lift the first two components and slip the long side of the C through the gap in the first C and over the wide end of the O. Lift the O and push its wide end through the gap in the first C.

To separate the three elements of the wooden knot, hold the puzzle so that the O-shaped piece is vertical, with its narrow end uppermost. Push the horizontal C which encircles the O downward. With the gap in this C facing you, push the second C, which is slotted through the hole in the O, away from you. Slip the horizontal C through the gap in the vertical C. Turn the vertical C through 180° toward you so that the wide end of the vertical O can slip through the gap in the C part of the puzzle.

Rattle Puzzles

Rattle puzzles, though rarely seen today, were very popular in the Western world in the early 19th century. Often made of willow, these hollow construction puzzles contained lead pellets, or even a hard candy, which moved freely inside them. When shaken, the pellets would rattle against the wooden sides of the puzzle. At that time of high unemployment, people enterprising and skillful enough to make and sell the puzzles at a moderate price could make a reasonable living. Joseph Thake and his son, pictured opposite in an 1815 etching by J. T. Smits, hawked their puzzles around the bustling streets of London, shaking them at passersby to attract their attention.

When assembling the large rattle puzzle or either of the smaller ball puzzles, the last slat to be placed in position is one of those with a V-shaped notch in it. Therefore, to dismantle the puzzle, first find the diamond shape that lies over the notch. Push this through the notch and release the notched slat. The remaining slats can then be removed, one by one.

Two rattle puzzle sellers at work, in an etching from *Remarkable Beggars and Itinerant Tradesmen.*

Materials

A piece of wood, 52 1/2" × 1 1/2" × 1/8"
A piece of wood, 13" × 1" × 1"
A handle
Wood screw, 1/16" thick and 1" long
Wood glue
Marbles, pellets, or stones

Tools

Backsaw with a fine-toothed blade; a drill with a 1/16" bit; pincers; pencil; ruler; protractor; sandpaper.

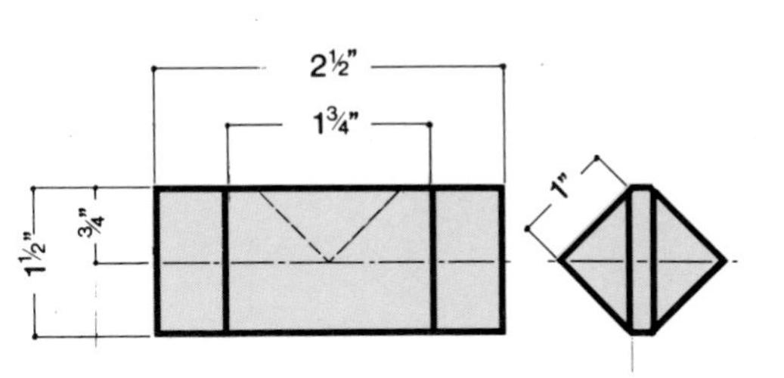

Cut out the V shape from two of the short slats. Glue two triangles at each end of every slat so that the end view appears as in the diagram on the right.

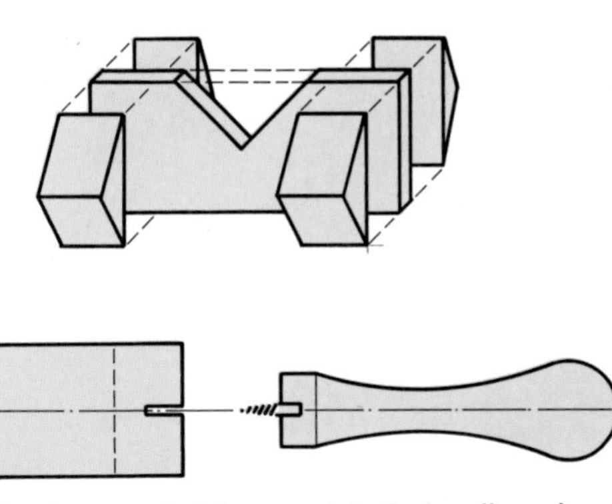

Glue the cut end of the screw into the handle and screw its point into a hole in one end of a short slat.

How to Make the Puzzle

From the 1/8" thick strip of wood, saw off a 15" piece. Cut the 15" piece of wood in half, making two slats, each 7 1/2" × 1 1/2". Mark off and cut the remaining wood into 15 equal slats, each 2 1/2" long. Take two of these shorter slats and draw a line along each, 3/4" from either long edge. Draw another line, at right angles to the first one, 1 1/4" from each short edge. Centering the protractor where each pair of lines crosses, mark two points on the top long edge, each at 45° from the cross points. Connect these two points at the center of the long line, making a V shape (top diagram at the left). Carefully cut out the V with the backsaw. On another short slat mark the midpoint of one sawed face, 3/4" from either long edge. Drill a hole 1/16" wide and 1/4" deep into the sawed face for inserting a wood screw. Take the piece of wood 13" × 1" square and saw off 34 equal pieces, each 3/8" deep. Draw a diagonal on each of these pieces of wood, and cut along the diagonal to make 68 triangles. Glue the long sides of two triangles on one of the flat planes of each of the 17 slats of wood so that they are flush with the short edges of the slat. In this way the inner surfaces of the two triangles will be 1 3/4" apart (top left diagram). Turn the slat over and glue two more triangles in similar positions on this side (center diagram). When the glue is dry, sandpaper all of the pieces. Drill a 1/16" hole into the wooden handle. With the pincers cut the top off a wood screw and push it, head first, into the hole. Screw the handle into the hole already drilled in one of the small slats. Glue both ends of the screw securely. Assemble all of the pieces to make a large rattle, or use the small slats to make two ball puzzles.

The Magic Disk

Three identical wooden disks are used to make up the magic disk. Each disk has been cut into pieces and the parts glued together in a special pattern. Once the disks are slotted together, no amount of pulling or tugging can get them apart. But force can be used in a certain way to separate the three components. Can you see how to do it? Can you then put the puzzle back together again?

Materials
Plywood, 20" × 7" × 1/4"
Wood glue
Paint or varnish

Tools
Fretsaw; drill with a 5/8" bit; pencil; compasses; ruler; sandpaper.

How to Make the Puzzle
Draw three 6" diameter circles on the plywood. Keeping a radius of 3", place the point of the compasses on each circle and mark off two additional points on the circumference, each a radius distance away. From each of these points draw a diameter through the center of the circle. Of the six resulting radii mark alternate ones heavily in pencil to indicate the cutting lines, as in the bottom diagram. Draw a diameter at right angles to each of the heavily marked radii. In this way each third of the disk is divided into four equal parts (bottom diagram). Drill a 5/8" hole through the center of the disk. Cut the disk into three parts by sawing along the heavy lines. Then reassemble the pieces into a disk shape and move one piece clockwise, passing it over the adjacent piece. A quarter of the first piece should overlap a quarter of the second piece. Glue the two parts together. Move these joined pieces clockwise until they overlap one quarter of the remaining piece. Glue this last piece in place, making sure that the overlapping curved edges of the pieces are flush with each other on the outside edge. Thus the central hole is retained. Repeat this procedure for the remaining two disks. When all three components have been prepared, sandpaper them well so that they can slip smoothly over one another. After painting and varnishing the puzzle, it is ready to be assembled. The inner surfaces of the puzzle may need extra sanding to keep them from sticking when working the puzzle.

This magic disk is made of three parts, each of which was made by cutting up one disk and reassembling it in a certain way. To solve the puzzle, separate the parts and then remake the disk.

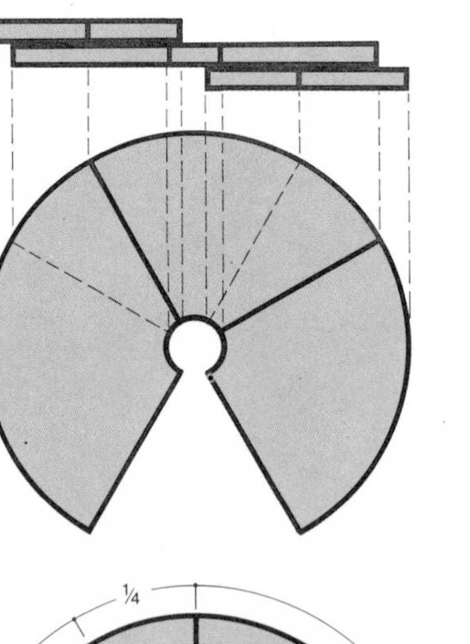

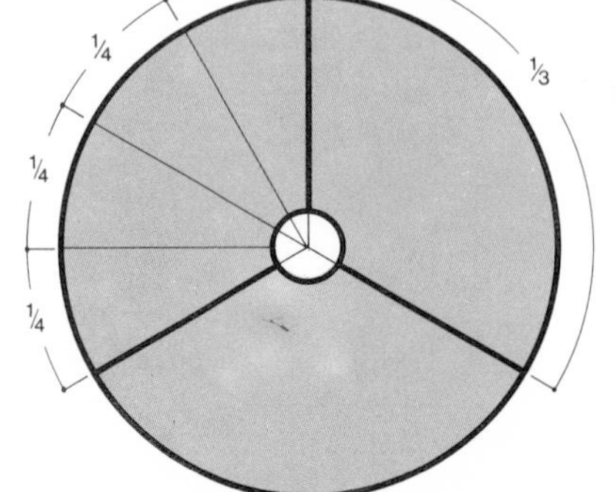

Mark the quarters of each third of the disk, as in the lower diagram. Cut along the heavy lines and reassemble the parts, following the top figure.

To separate the magic disk into three identical parts, centrifugal force rather than brute strength is needed. Place the disk on a flat surface and put a pencil into the central hole to serve as an axle. Holding the pencil steady with one hand, spin the disk around with the other, as fast as possible. The three components will be thrown outward by centrifugal force. Then you can gently pull the puzzle apart. Reassembling the puzzle takes more dexterity. Lay the puzzle out, as in the diagram above, so that each corner of one part lies at the center of the central hole of a neighboring part, leaving a triangular space in the center of the puzzle. Hold all three parts in position and push gently inward, following the arrows. The three components will slot together.

Van der Poel's Puzzle

This puzzle, named after its creator, is one of the most difficult of all construction puzzles. W. L. van der Poel, a leading Dutch computer scientist, for many years has made a hobby of designing and creating puzzles. When he designed this puzzle, his aim was to make as many pieces as possible mutually interlocking. The result was this 18-piece puzzle, which is made up of three sets of six bars. Each set of bars is at right angles to the other two sets. Inside the puzzle the bars interlock by means of cutouts whose depths equal half the width of a bar. The internal six bars, shaded in the diagrams below and right, interlock to make a shape similar to that of the burr puzzles (see page 72). Built around these six bars is a cagelike structure of 12 pieces. Van der Poel reasoned that in theory the cage could be built from 12 similar bars. However, this could never be achieved in practice, because the last piece could not be inserted into the puzzle. Therefore he built a lock into the design, which is made up of three pieces from the outer cage. Two of the pieces in the lock differ from the other ten outer bars.

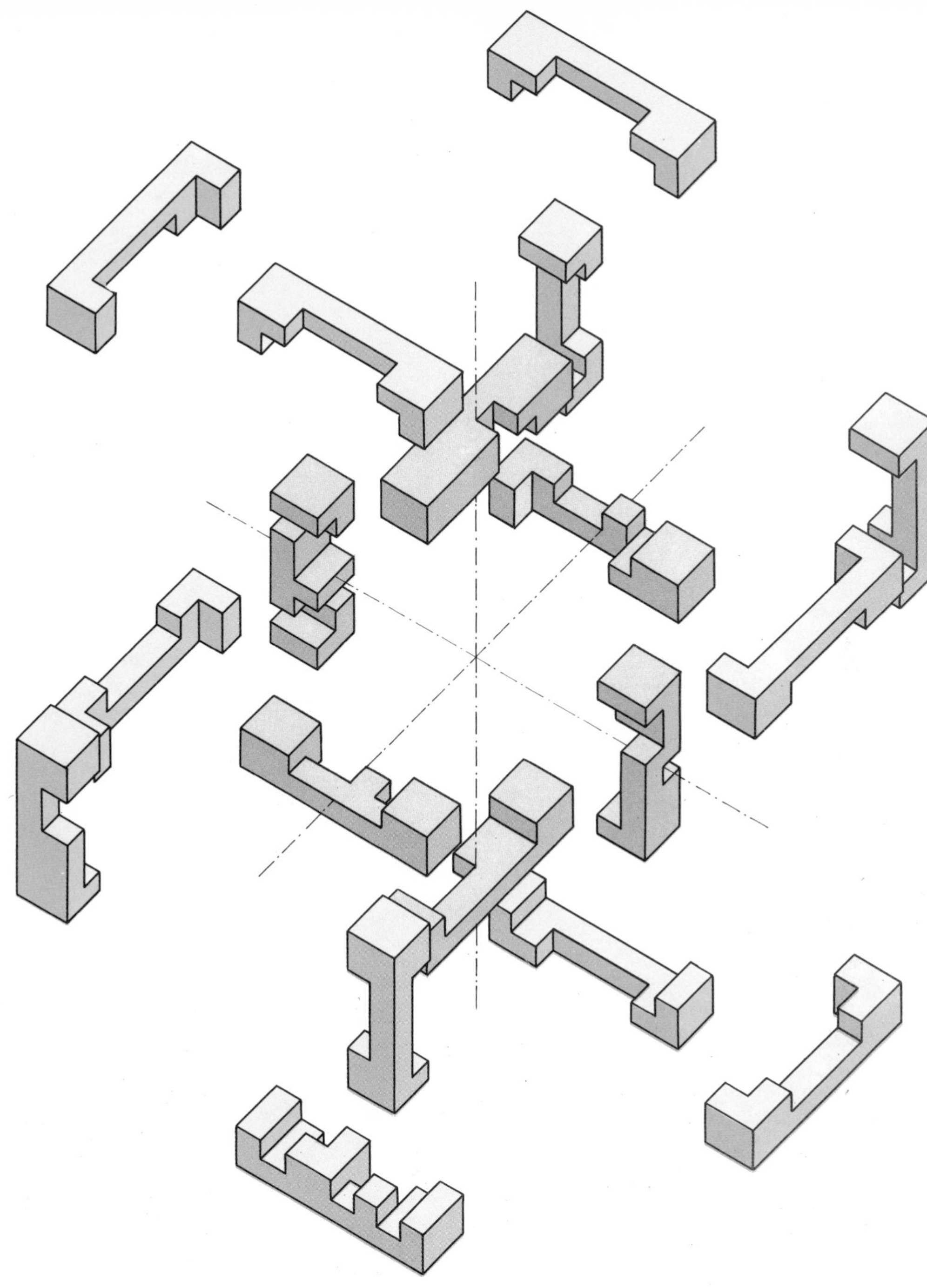

Copy the patterns for the bars directly from the exploded view. After you have cut out the pieces, arrange the six inner bars (shaded) and the outer bars as above in order to interlock the pieces.

In many burr puzzles the center is completely filled, so that no spaces remain between the bars. These so-called ideal puzzles are comparatively easy to solve, since in all of them one piece or set of pieces can be removed first in order to release the other pieces. However, Van der Poel's puzzle is not ideal, for there are spaces in the interior of the puzzle. It is these spaces that make the puzzle extremely difficult to solve. In a non-ideal puzzle the solver cannot simply remove one piece in order to begin taking the puzzle apart. He must first move one or more other pieces. To take out the first piece in Van der Poel's puzzle, another piece must first be moved, and this can be done only by shifting yet another piece. Several series of such moves are necessary in the solution of this complex puzzle. The puzzle consists of 18 bars of wood or metal, each 8 × 2 × 2 units. Unit cubes are cut from the bars to make the interlocking shapes. Ten of the outer bars are identical in shape, but the six inner bars and two of the lock bars (bottom and bottom left in the exploded view) differ. The sections are cut away with a backsaw or fretsaw and a chisel following the instructions on page 79. If hard wood or metal is used, a milling machine is essential. Assemble the pieces as in the diagram above.

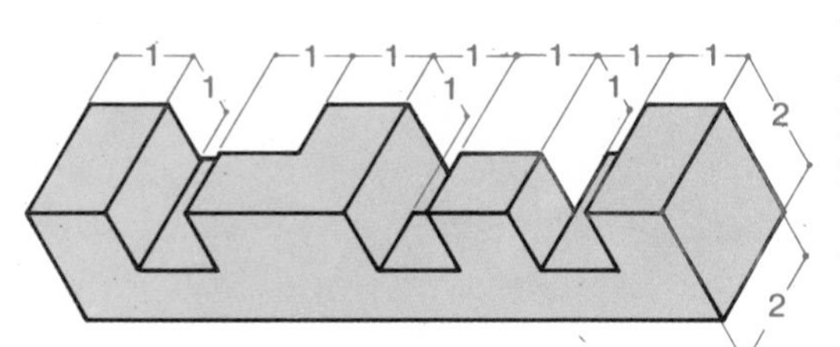

Unit cubes cut out from the 8 × 2 × 2 blocks create the pieces for Van der Poel's puzzle. The example shown here is the design for one of the three lock bars that secure the puzzle.

Burr Puzzles

Burr puzzles, also called Chinese cross puzzles and notched-stick puzzles, are probably the construction puzzles that are most well known to enthusiasts. They consist of a symmetrical crosslike structure made up of three pairs of interlocking wooden bars. Each pair of bars is at right angles to the other two pairs, and they are arranged so that there is no empty space in the center of the puzzle. The bars, which originally are blocks of equal length with a square cross section, have a number of cutouts which are made by removing cube-shaped volumes of wood, each with sides equal to half the width of the bar.

Cutouts can be made in the bars by using a milling machine or a chisel. If a milling machine is used, only simple saw cuts can be made, those with no more than two interior faces meeting at any point. If a chisel is also used, notches with inside corners can be cut in the wood. In these notches three faces meet at right angles, just as the walls and floor meet at a corner of a room. Some puzzle enthusiasts, such as T. H. O'Beirne, use only bars that have been cut with a milling machine or saw; others use bars cut by both methods.

The Dutch mathematician J. H. de Boer has made a detailed study of all these puzzles and has made his own set of bars using both a milling machine and a chisel. In determining the patterns of the bars, he first drew all the possible shapes on paper — two pages from his original notebook are shown on the right. Then he cut out the bars as well as their mirror images. He then grouped the bars according to the quantity of wood that had been cut from them. He gave each bar a three-figure number, the first figure of which referred to the group to which the bar belonged. Thus all the bars whose numbers started with 3 contained the same amount of wood, which was less than the wood in bars having a number starting with 4. De Boer arranged his bars into six groups. He then sorted them within the group according to the positions of the notches, each number representing a different placement of one unit notch. In addition, 424 would be the mirror image of bar 442. The simplest of all bars, with the least wood in it, has the code number 000, while six bars of exceptional shape were given numbers starting with 7 or 8.

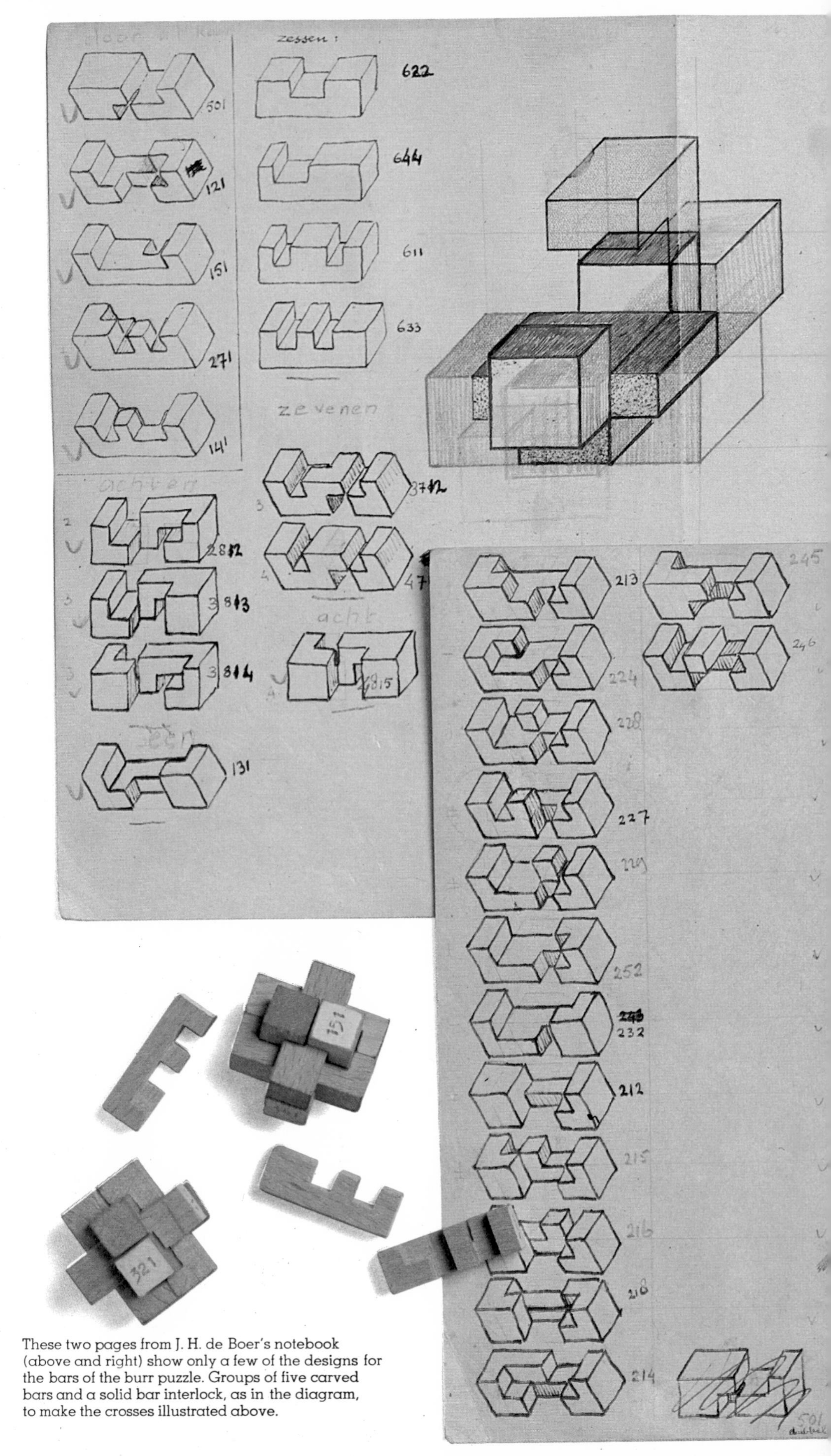

These two pages from J. H. de Boer's notebook (above and right) show only a few of the designs for the bars of the burr puzzle. Groups of five carved bars and a solid bar interlock, as in the diagram, to make the crosses illustrated above.

De Boer then arranged all of the bars in special boxes for easy reference (right). As with most construction puzzles a lock bar is needed to secure the interlocking bars of the cross. The lock in this burr puzzle consists of the solid, uncut bar. Of the six bars which make up any one cross, one of them must be such an uncut bar.

Having made the bars to his designs, De Boer then set about determining the number of possible combinations of bars that could make up a burr. With astonishing perseverance during his spare time over ten years, he finally established all possible combinations — a total of 2906, excluding mirror images. In just 11 of these six-bar burrs, the five bars, apart from the lock, were of equal weight, belonging to the same group.

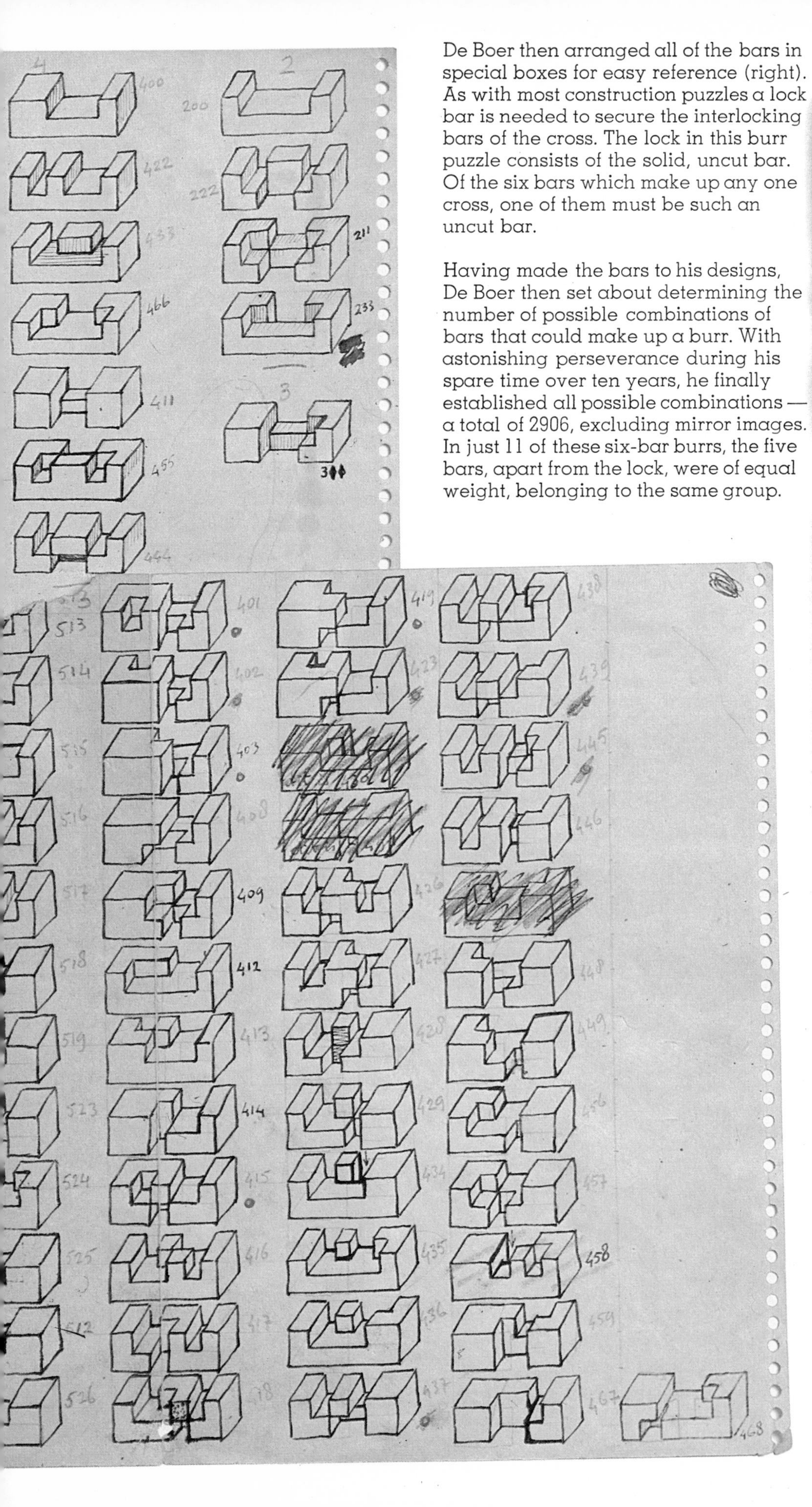

The numbers on each of these bars from De Boer's burr puzzle give an indication of the shape of each piece. The lightest piece, with the most wood carved away, is numbered 000 (top left), while bars with most wood remaining are numbered 500 and above. The bars marked 526 and 562 (bottom right) are mirror images of one another. In the lowest row of the central box are the solid lock pieces, one of which is present in each cross.

To make all of the pieces of the burr puzzle would take considerable time and patience, but it is not necessary to have all of the bars to tackle the problem of making the burrs. Each burr consists of five carved bars and the lock bar, interlinked to make the cross-shaped figure (opposite). Given the selection of 26 carved bars below and right, plus the uncut lock bar, there are no fewer than 69 various combinations of six bars to make the burr. This selection includes bars from five of the original groups made by J. H. de Boer. They have been renumbered, however, and are no longer within distinct groups. For example, bar 9 below corresponds to the original bar 200.

Each bar starts as a 6 × 2 × 2 unit bar of wood, and the lock bar is left as such. The remaining bars are carved by removing cubical pieces, the sides of which are half the width of the bars. Complicated cuts can be carved with a chisel, while simple cuts, as in bar 9, can be made with a scroll saw or backsaw if a milling machine is not available. Follow the diagrams and dimensions below, and the general instructions on page 79 in order to make your.

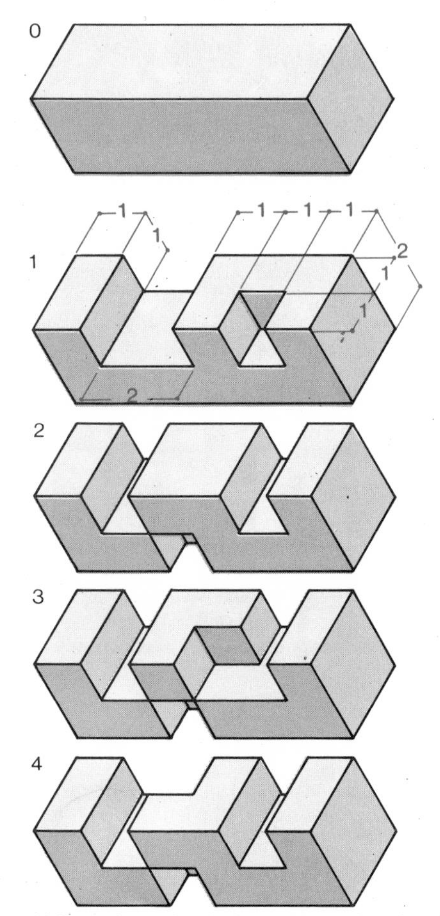

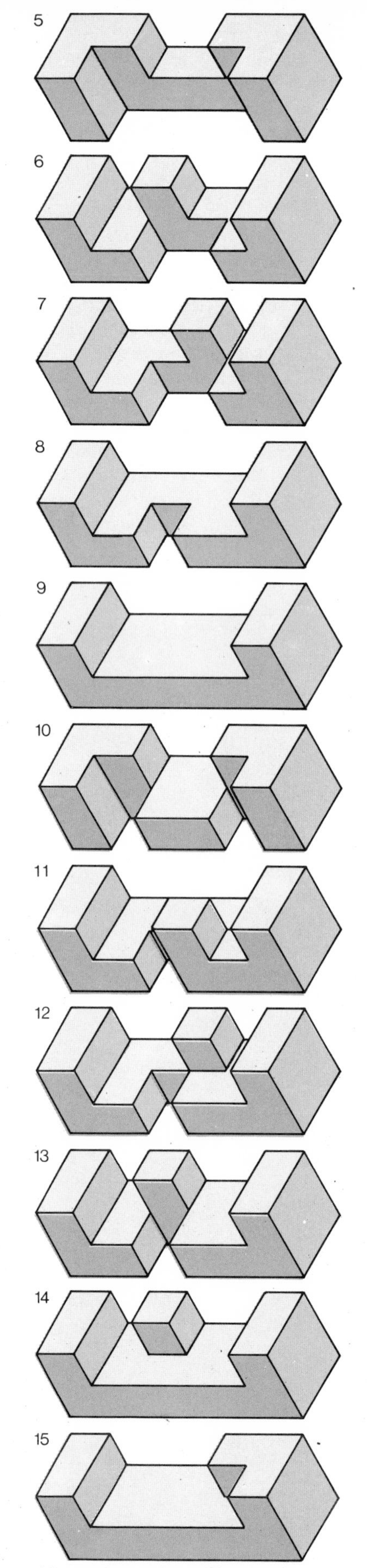

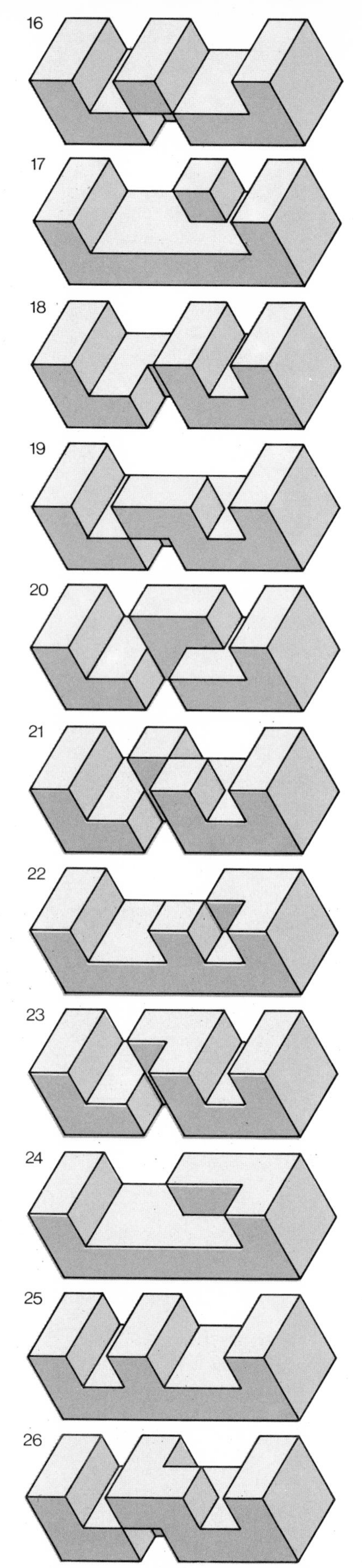

Carve 26 bars of wood with dimensions of 6 × 2 × 2 units to the shapes shown above. These, with one uncut lock bar, can be used to make 69 burr puzzles.

own burr puzzle. The 69 versions of the burr puzzle that use six of the 27 bars opposite are specified in the lattices here. In each case only five of the bars are numbered. The sixth bar is always the lock, bar 0, which takes up the left-hand position of the vertical pair of bars. Its pair is given in the center square of the lattice — for example, bar 8 in the

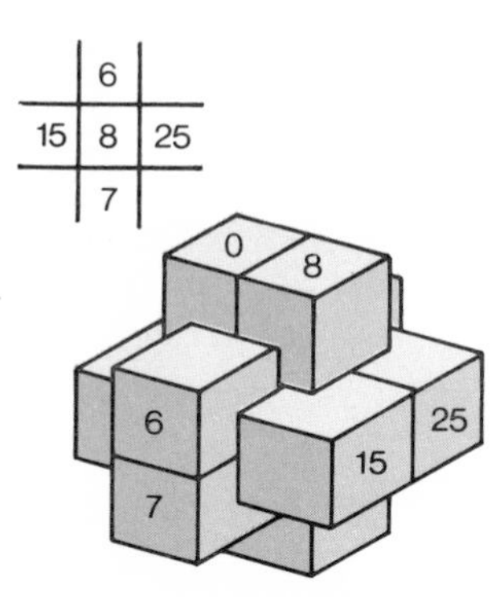

example above. The bars indicated on the left and right of the central number (bars 15 and 25 in the example above) refer to the horizontal pieces which run side by side across the burr. The remaining two bars, written above and below the central square, lie at right angles to the first two pairs. The top bar marked in the lattice lies on the bottom bar to make this last pair. In the example above, bar 6 lies on top of bar 7. When assembling the burr, arrange the bars with their notched faces toward the center of the puzzle before attempting to slot the pieces together. For six of the solutions the order in which the bars should be interlocked is given by the numerals marked on the pieces in the diagrams on the right. This order varies, but the lock bar, 0, is always last.

Top	Left	Center	Right	Bottom
9	10	11	7	15
9	10	8	7	22
9	10	12	6	15
9	10	18	5	15
9	10	12	5	22
17	10	8	6	15
17	10	11	5	15
17	10	8	5	22
9	6	19	7	15
9	6	4	5	15
17	6	19	5	15
9	6	8	10	24
9	6	11	7	24
9	6	12	6	24
9	6	18	5	24
9	6	12	5	1
17	6	8	6	24
17	6	11	5	24
17	6	8	5	1
9	7	13	10	15
9	7	21	7	15
9	7	13	7	22
9	7	23	5	15
9	7	20	5	22
17	7	13	6	15
17	7	21	5	15
17	7	13	5	22
9	5	16	10	15
9	5	26	7	15
9	5	16	7	22
9	5	3	6	15
9	5	3	5	22
14	5	16	6	15
17	5	26	5	15
17	5	16	5	22
9	5	13	10	24
9	5	21	7	24
9	5	13	7	1
9	5	20	6	24
9	5	23	5	24
17	5	13	6	24
17	5	21	5	24
17	5	13	5	1
14	7	8	10	15
14	7	11	7	15
14	7	8	7	22
14	7	12	6	15
14	7	18	5	15
14	7	12	5	22
25	7	11	5	15
25	7	8	5	22
14	5	19	7	15
14	5	4	5	15
25	5	19	5	15
14	5	8	10	24
14	5	11	7	24
14	5	8	7	1
14	5	12	6	24
14	5	18	5	24
14	5	12	5	1
25	5	8	6	24
25	5	11	5	24
25	5	8	5	1

Each of these 63 combinations makes a burr.

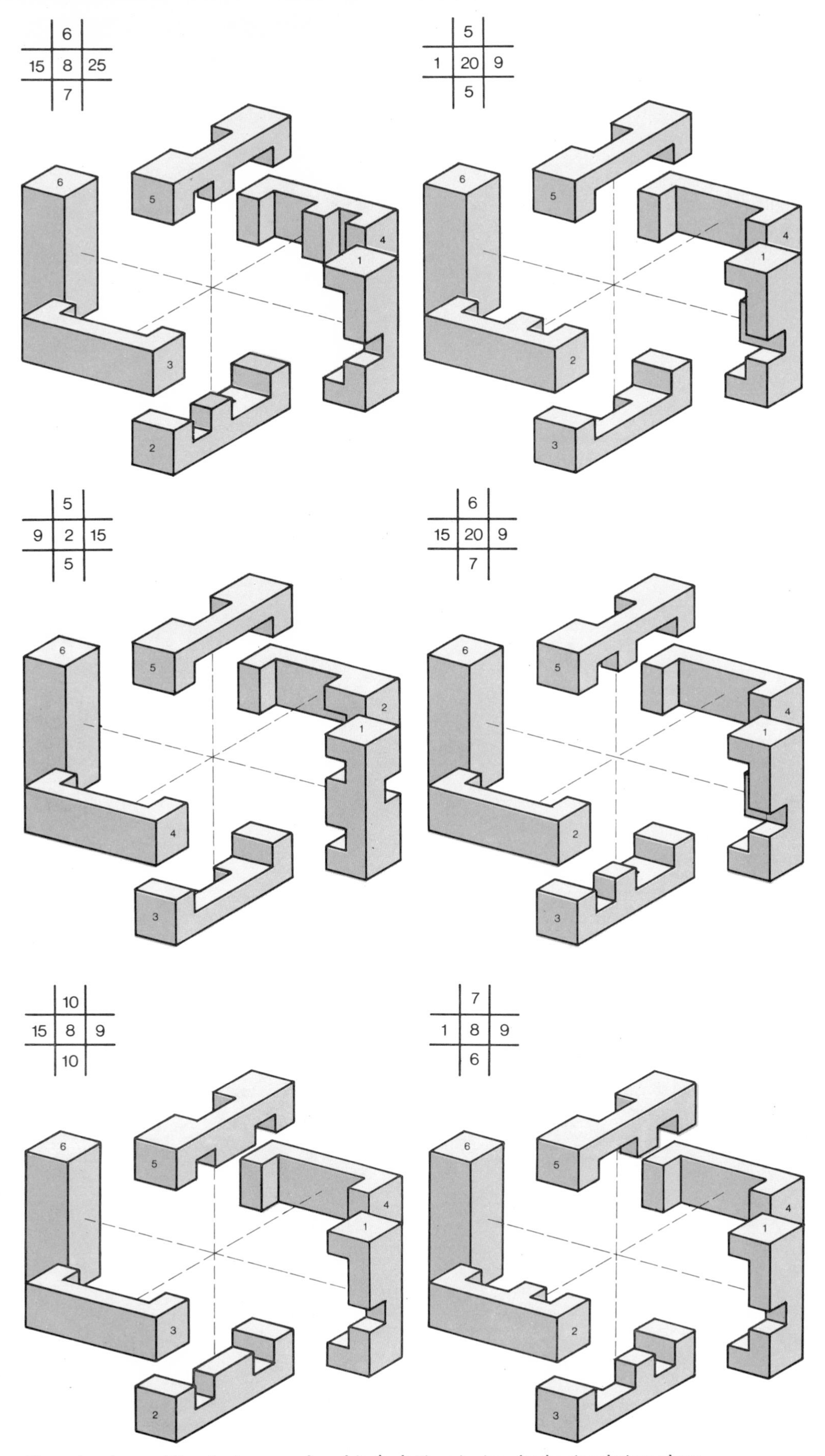

The order of assembling the bars, numbered in the lattices, is given for the six solutions above.

The Ball in the Cage

Twelve bars, of equal length, make up the cage which firmly imprisons the small ball in this puzzle. On initial inspection there seems no way of releasing the ball short of sawing through some of the interlocking bars. But you need not resort to this drastic and destructive solution. The shapes of the bars are given below, and general instructions on how to prepare and cut the pieces are given on page 79. In making and assembling the puzzle, you may discover how to solve it.

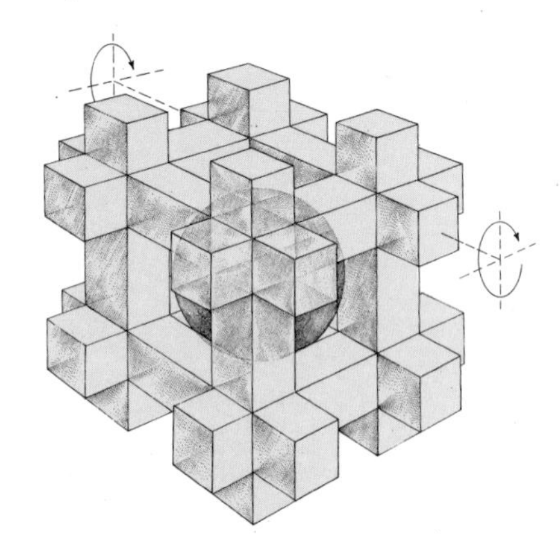

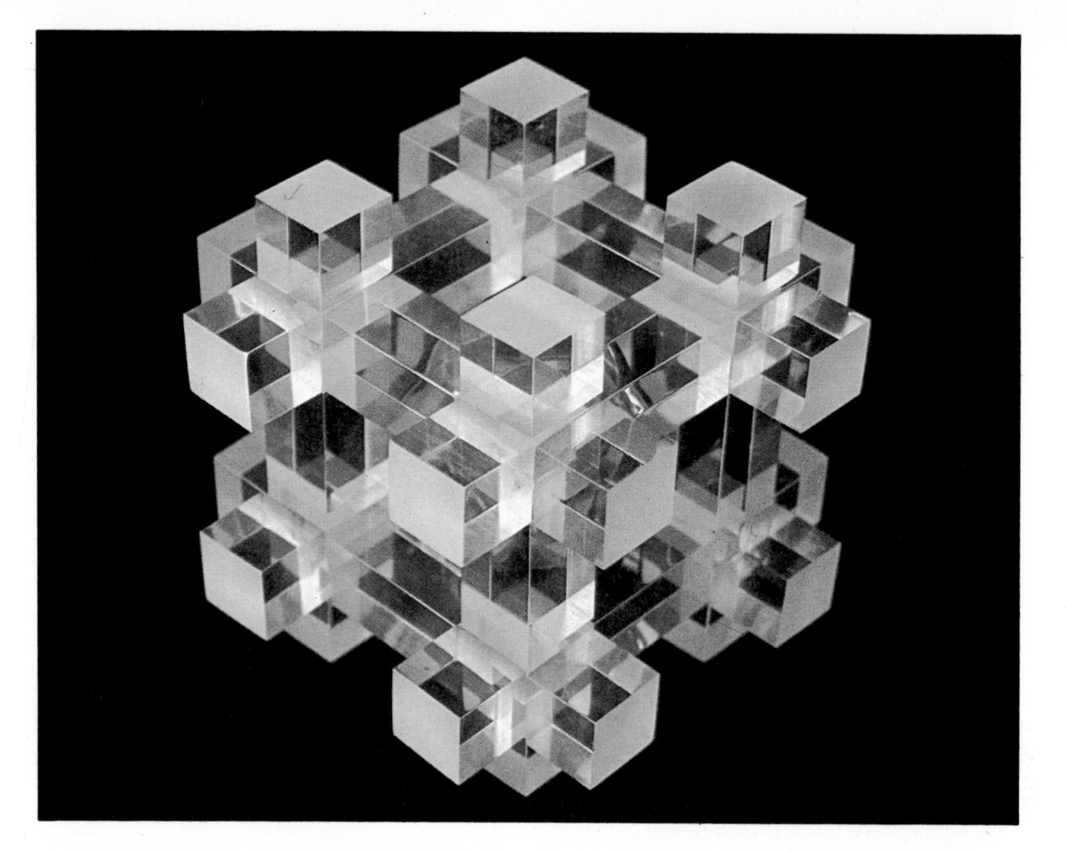

The secret of solving this intricate puzzle lies in twisting some of the bars in order to free the others. Find out which ones by trial and error.

Above the bar the proportions; inside it the quantity needed. The exploded diagram shows the exact position of the bars.

To release the ball, first find which pair of upper horizontal bars will move. Twist this pair until it is possible to release and remove a second pair of bars at right angles to the first. Remove the first pair of bars, and then the ball. Then, dismantle the puzzle completely, by twisting the vertical bars, and thus freeing the lower ones.

To reassemble the puzzle, lay out the lower four horizontal bars as in the diagram below. Stand the vertical bars at the corners and slot the pieces together, twisting the vertical bars to lock them in place. Place the ball inside the vertical bars, and then arrange the upper horizontal bars, twisting the last pair to secure the puzzle.

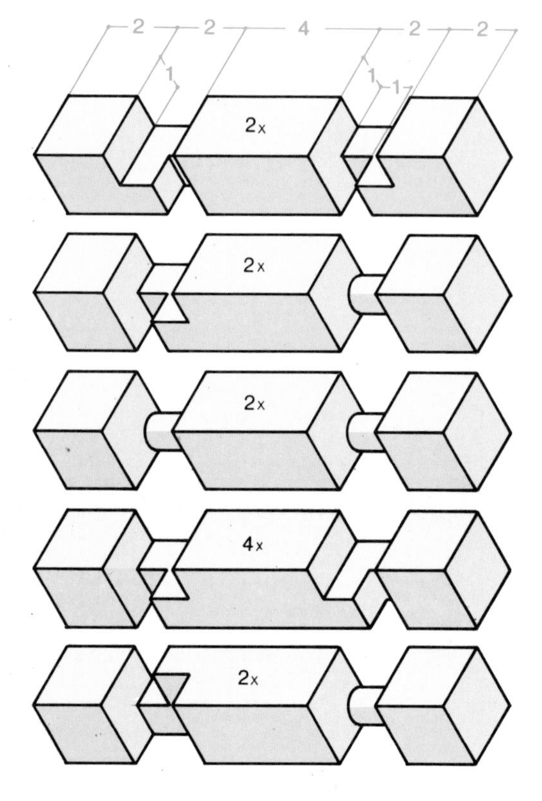

Cut these 12 bars to make the cage.

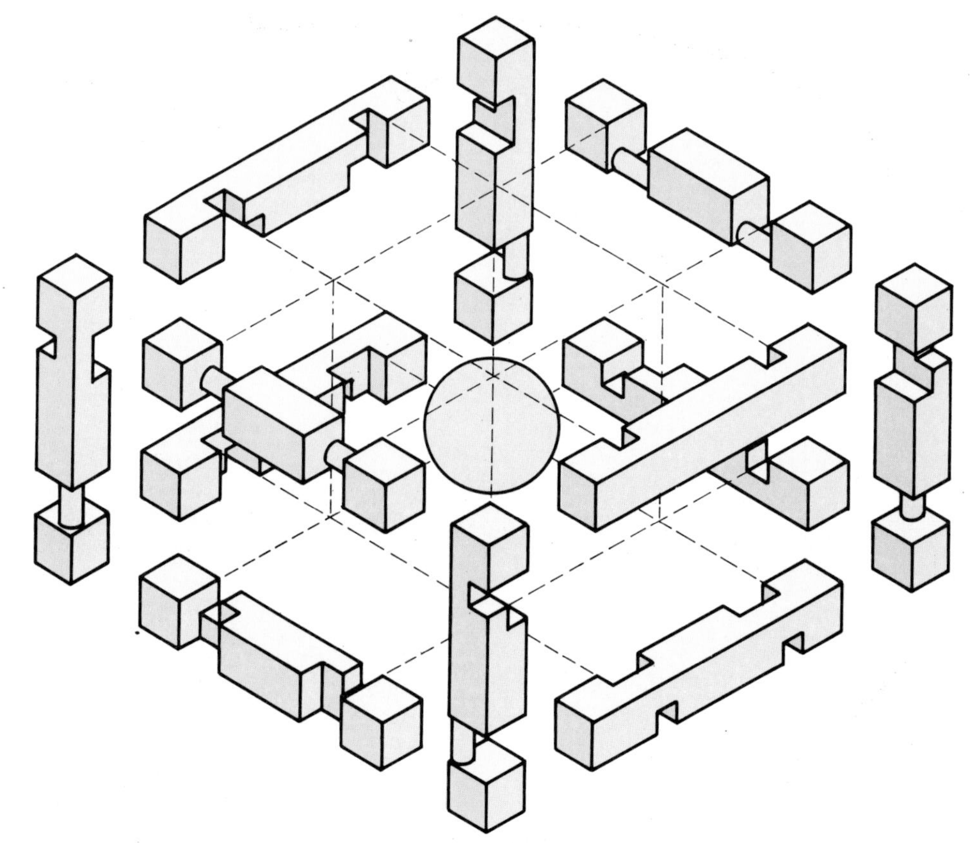

The Japanese Crystal

For the construction puzzle enthusiast this beautiful Japanese example is one of the most challenging. Its perfectly symmetrical, multifaceted structure is formed by the assembly of no fewer than 51 bars. Each bar has been carefully cut so that the pieces can interlock to make a solid core. Once assembled, no single piece can simply be pulled out of place in order to take the puzzle apart. As with many construction puzzles, the key lies in turning just one piece. Finding this key piece is no mean feat, for the surface cubes mask the internal differences of the bars. However, the key part is the small bar (marked *s* among the pieces shown on the next page) which lies directly below one of the six points of the octahedron. Twist this bar until you can lift it and release the two bars below. Continue lifting and removing bars until the puzzle is dismantled. Make the 51 bars following the patterns and dimensions given overleaf and the general instruc-

Once hand-carved, the bars which make up the Japanese crystal puzzle can now be machine-made with great accuracy. These puzzles, often made from the lightest hard wood, are now generally available in Japanese toy and game shops.

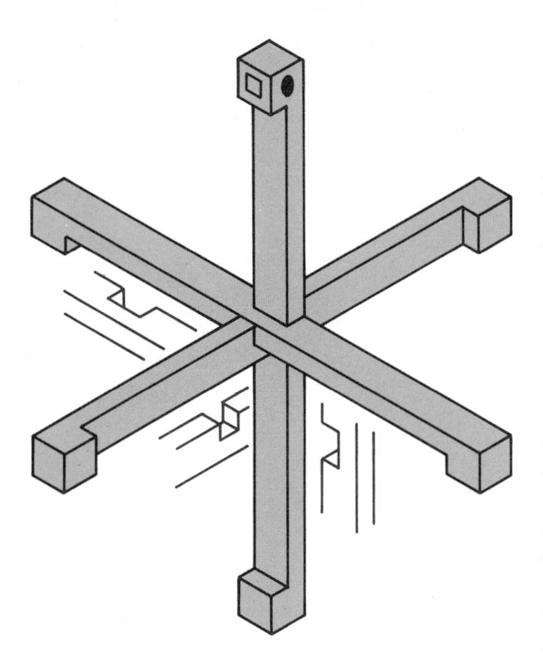

Interlock the three longest bars as above. The remaining bars, drawn and lettered below, should be laid out in the order given in the row of letters directly above the bars. Add these bars to the central cross, starting with the left-hand *a*. The positions of the bars and the order of placing them are given in the diagrams on the right, and arrows indicate in which direction the bars should be moved. A cross in a circle indicates that the bar is moved away from you. Each number in the diagrams refers to a different move — adding either one bar or several bars in symmetrical positions.

tions on page 79. Then assemble the crystal — the solution is also given below. Apart from the central cross bars, two of which are alike, and the special bar *s*, the bars have been lettered from *a* through *h*. The number of bars that are required is also indicated above the diagram of each bar below. Arrange the bars, apart from the three cross bars, according to the line of letters below. They are to be added to the central cross bars of the puzzle in this order, starting at the left hand *a*. Hold the cross bars as in the diagram on the left, slotting the notches together as shown. Note that the carved side of the vertical bar is marked with a dot, corresponding to those indicated in the diagrams on the right. Keep this marked end of the bar at the top of the puzzle throughout. With the top of the vertical bar marked with a square facing you, start to build up the first 14 bars on the central cross, up to and including the *s* bar, following the direction arrows on the top diagram. Turn the puzzle 90 degrees so that the side bearing the dot faces you. Add the bars from the two *h* bars (move 12) through the six *a* bars (moves 17 and 18). Turn the puzzle again and add the remaining bars, finally twisting the lock bar.

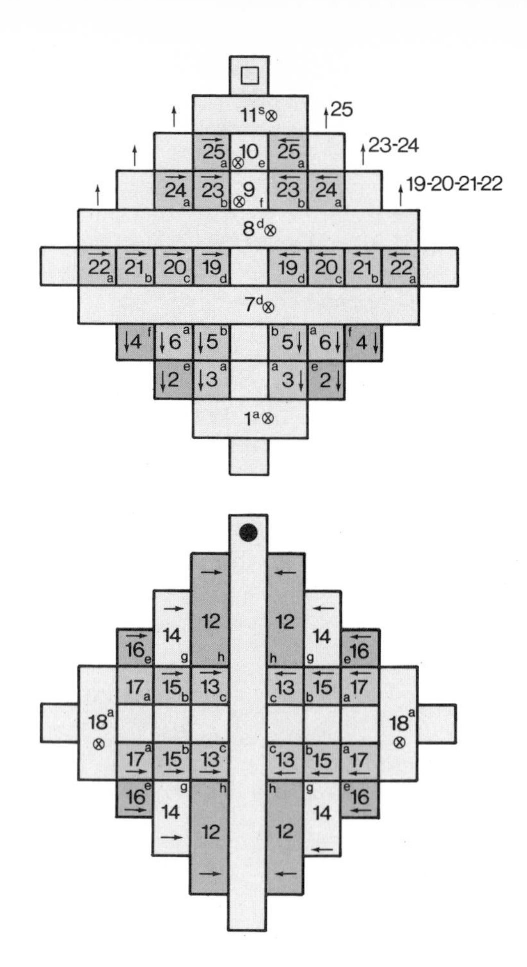

aeaafbbaaddfeshhccccggbbbbeeaaaaaaddccbbaabbaaaa

These letters, from the left, give the order in which the bars must be added to the central cross.

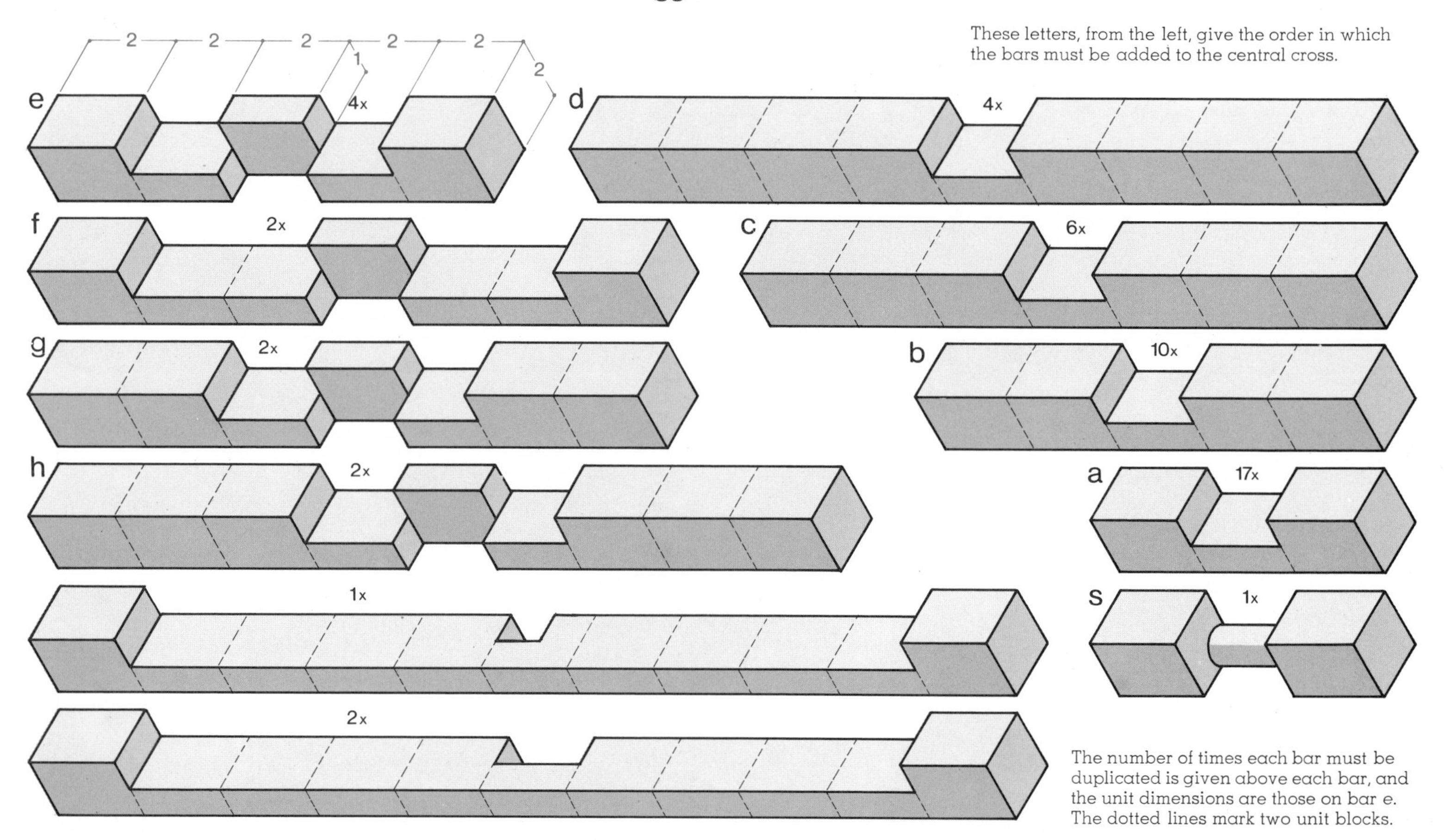

The number of times each bar must be duplicated is given above each bar, and the unit dimensions are those on bar e. The dotted lines mark two unit blocks.

How to Make the Burr Puzzles (pages 71, 72, 76, 77)

Scale drawings of the individual bars, with unit measurements marked, are given on the pages that illustrate each puzzle. Copy the guide lines from these drawings onto wood or acrylic bars with a pencil or scratching needle respectively, and shade the pieces to be cut from the wooden bars. Notches are cut into each bar, each notch half the thickness of the bar. When using wood, clamp each bar flat so that the backsaw can be used to cut vertically into the wood to make the sides of the notches (top diagram). Then use the chisels to chip out the unwanted pieces of wood (second diagram). To smooth the edges of the notches use a fine file (third diagram), and check that all angles are right angles. Sandpaper each bar until it is smooth; otherwise the bars may be difficult to interlock.

Materials for Van der Poel's Puzzle
Eighteen bars of beech wood, each 8 units long and 2 units square

Materials for De Boer's Puzzle
Twenty-seven bars of beech wood, each 6 units long and 2 units square

Materials for the Ball in the Cage
Twelve bars of acrylic, each 12 units long and 2 units square
A steel ball bearing 4½ units diameter

Materials for the Japanese Crystal
Beech wood, 2 units square as follows: 3 bars 11 units long; 6 bars 9 units long; 10 bars 7 units long; 14 bars 5 units long; 18 bars 3 units long

Tools
Backsaw; fine file; various chisels; hammer; clamp; fretsaw; sharp knife; scratching needle; ruler; pencil; fine waterproof and regular sandpaper

How to Make Van der Poel's Puzzle
Ten of the bars in this puzzle are similar; the remaining eight differ. On each bar draw a grid of 16 (8 × 2) unit squares, then copy the patterns for each bar from the exploded scale diagram on page 71. If the bars are to be less than 2" long, it is easier to cut out the notches with a sharp knife. For larger puzzles use the tools listed above. First cut vertically to make the sides of the notches (top diagram), and then turn the bar to chisel out the excess wood (second diagram). If a large piece of wood is to be removed, chisel it out little by little to avoid splitting the block. Smooth the sides of the notches with file and sandpaper, and correct badly fitting pieces by further filing.

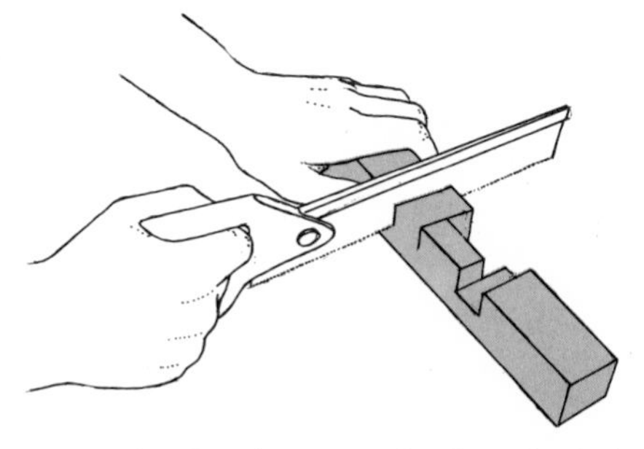

To cut notches from large wooden bars, begin by sawing through half the thickness of the bar, using a backsaw. This cuts the sides of the notches. Use a sharp knife to cut small bars.

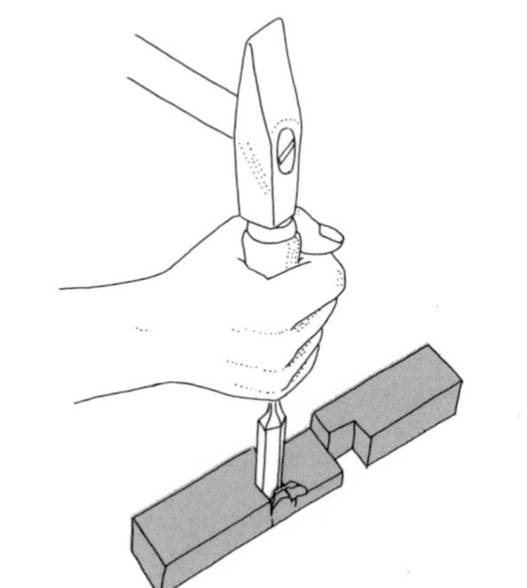

Turn the bar over and chip out the excess wood between the vertical cuts with a chisel. Tap the chisel head gently with the hammer to chip off small pieces of wood without splitting the bar.

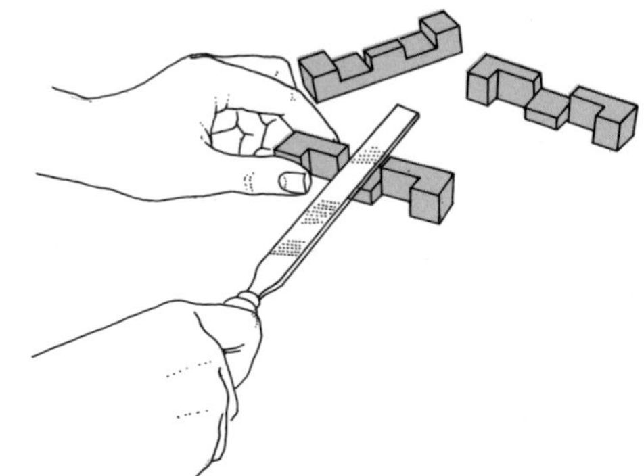

File the rough edges with a fine file. Make certain that the angles of each notch are 90° and that the width of each gap is exact. Adjust by careful filing along the sides of the notch if necessary.

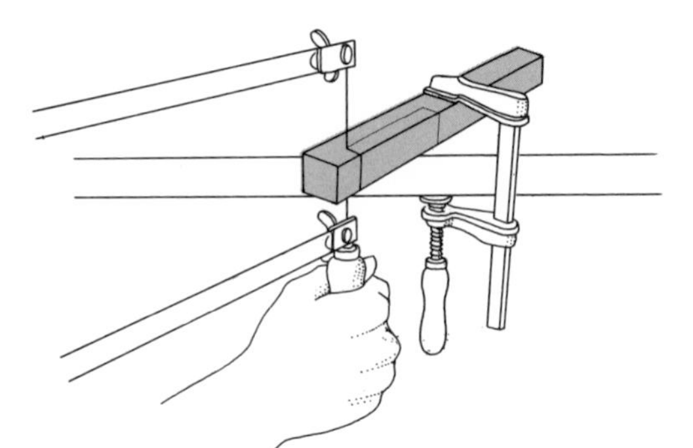

Cut a long notch from a wooden bar by using a fretsaw. Clamp the bar firmly before cutting the wood and make sure that the blade passes through the cutting line on both the top and bottom surfaces.

How to Make De Boer's Puzzle
The general instructions as well as those for making Van der Poel's puzzle apply also to the construction of this puzzle. To cut out the one-unit cubes, however, careful chiseling and a very sharp chisel are necessary. Drive the blade vertically into the wood for the six cuts necessary, taking care not to split the wood. If a small puzzle is being made, then a sharp knife may be more useful than a backsaw. Since this puzzle was originally made with bars only 1" long, some notches were filed out, not cut.

How to Make the Ball in the Cage
Use the patterns and units given on page 76 for the bars of this puzzle. Scratch the acrylic with a needle to indicate those areas that must be removed, but do not draw in the whole grid. This must be done very carefully to avoid scratching surfaces that will remain part of the puzzle. If a bar is accidentally scratched, sand the damaged area with the finest available waterproof sandpaper, and then buff it with a cotton polisher fitted onto an electric drill — or apply copper polish and buff well. To avoid damage to the sides of the acrylic when holding it steady, clamp it between two pieces of wood. Then saw the notches out, using a fretsaw, cutting through the acrylic alongside the scratch mark; if you cut through the scratch mark, the width of the blade will increase the measurement of the notch. File the cut edges smooth, rounding off those bars that must be able to turn. Polish the cut edges with fine sandpaper, leaving the square ends of the bars matt. If a bar is broken during preparation, glue the pieces together with acrylic glue.

How to Make the Japanese Crystal
As with previous puzzles, first draw the two-unit grid on the surfaces of the bars and shade in the areas to be cut away. Clamp the bars firmly and cut out the notches with the backsaw and chisels, or use a sharp knife if a small puzzle is to be made. However, a larger version of this puzzle is more attractive; the model in the picture (page 77) is 11 inches high. To cut the long flat pieces from the faces of the three cross bars, use the fretsaw as in the bottom diagram that appears on this page.

Each block of the puzzle is cut so that the pieces interlock to form a cluster with a solid center. Redwood, light and hard, and with a rich color, was used to make these blocks.

The Cluster

This solid, starlike cluster of wooden blocks is achieved by careful carving of two of the surfaces of each block, so that the individual pieces can interlock. Even if you know the shape of the blocks, you will find separating them, or reassembling the cluster, a very puzzling problem to tackle.

Materials
At least 2 feet of hard wood, 1¼" × 1¼"

Tools
Backsaw fitted with a fine-toothed blade; ruler; pencil; vise; sandpaper.

How to Make the Puzzle
Cut the wood into six 4" long pieces. Draw pencil lines to divide the upper surface of one piece into four 1" lengths. Draw a diagonal line to connect the far left corner with the first inch mark at the near edge. Draw another diagonal line from this near point to the far end of the center line (2" from either end of the piece). Connect the far end of the center line with the near end of the line drawn an inch from the right end. Then draw a final line from this point to the far right corner. Turn the block of wood 90° toward you. On the surface now on top pencil in the inch marks on both long edges. Connect these points in a similar zigzag way, but start the first line in the near left corner and take it to the far edge, meeting the mark drawn 1" from the left end. Clamp the wood in a vise with the common edge between the two marked surfaces uppermost. Cut along the pencil lines with the backsaw, following the heavy lines in the diagram below. While making each cut, the blade should pass through pencil lines on both marked surfaces. Discard the two wedge-shaped pieces. Sandpaper the wood, flattening the top of the central point a little. Repeat the above process on the other five blocks.

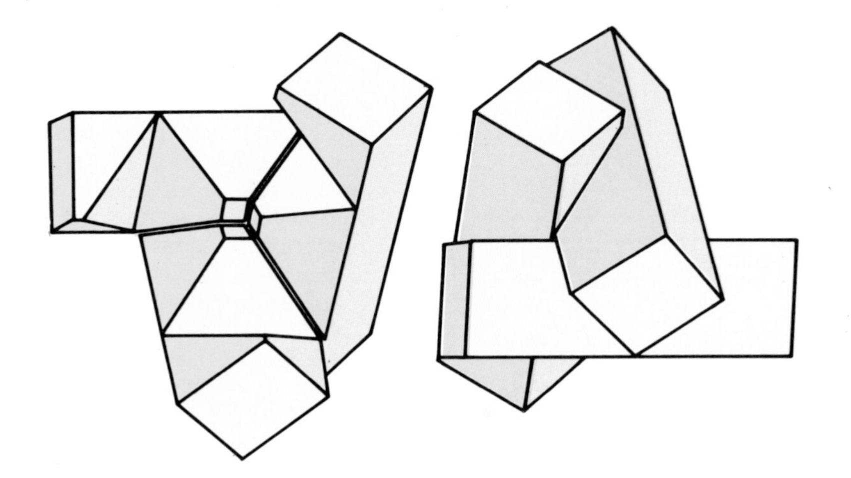

Assemble three blocks as in the diagram above, with the blunted pyramids meeting, and hold them in your left hand. One block should run vertically on the left of the horizontal blocks when looking toward the center of the puzzle. Arrange the other three blocks in your right hand to make a mirror image of the first group. Bring your hands together. Turning the right-hand group through 90° to the left, maneuver it onto the left-hand group.

To dismantle the cluster, stand it flat on the square ends of two vertical blocks. Turn it so that the top horizontal block runs from left to right. With your right hand grip the front vertical block, the top horizontal block, and the right middle block (also horizontal). Bring your left hand around the remaining blocks. Move your hands apart, and the cluster will separate into two halves. The individual pieces can now be separated from one another.

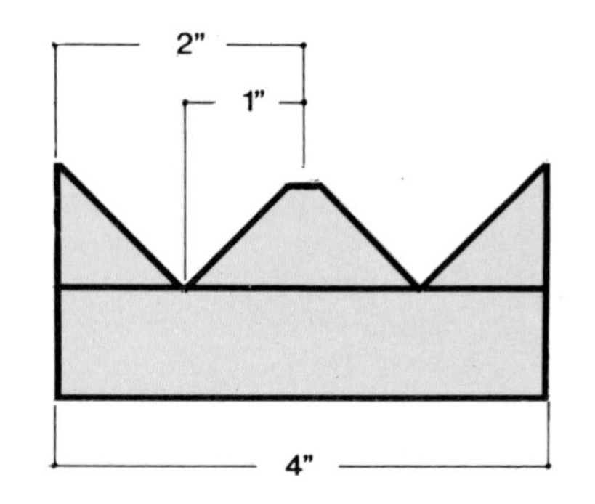

This block is lying on one edge. The lower faces are uncut, while the upper faces have been carved.

The Melting Block

Eight pieces of wood fit neatly into the rectangular interior of a wooden box in this puzzle created by T. H. O'Beirne. When the eight pieces are rearranged in the box, an extra piece miraculously can be fitted in. How is this possible when there were no spaces in the box in the first arrangement? Can you solve this mysterious puzzle?

Materials
Plywood, 36" × 12" × $^{19}/_{32}$"
Wood glue

Tools
Backsaw; clamps; ruler; pencil; sandpaper.

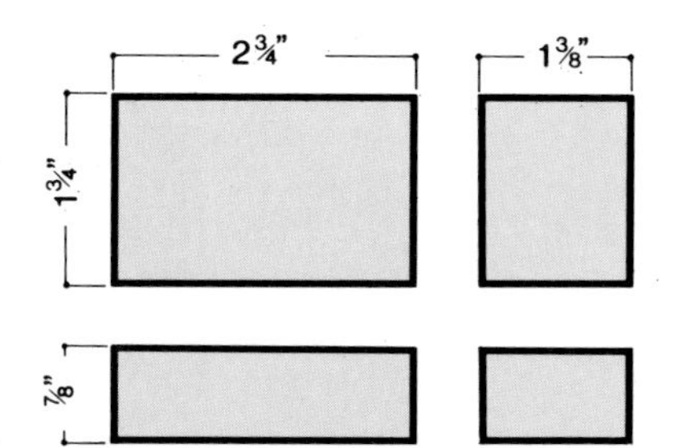

Cut through layers of plywood according to the dimensions above. Then cut an extra small block.

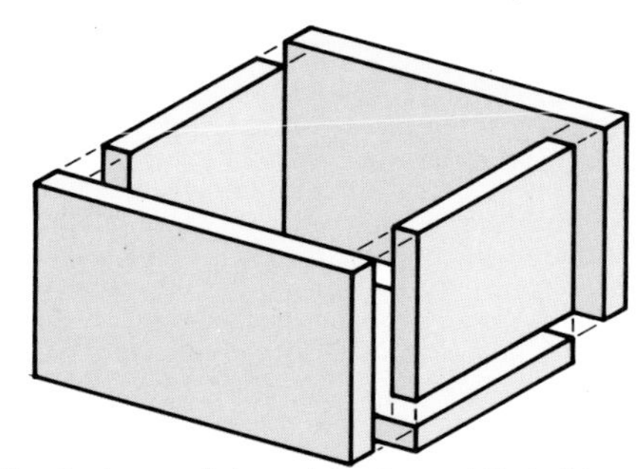

Glue the box and clamp it in place while it dries.

How to Make the Puzzle

Make the eight blocks first. Cut three pieces of the plywood board, each exactly 4⅛" × 2⅝". Lay two of these face to face and glue them together. On the third piece draw a line along its length one-third of the way from one long edge. Draw another line at right angles to the first, one-third of the way in from the right-hand end. Clamp this piece on top of the two glued together and cut along the lines marked through all three pieces, thus making eight blocks. Cut another piece exactly the size of the smallest block, that is 1⅜" × ⅞" × $^{19}/_{32}$". For the box cut two pieces of board 5⅜" × 2" and two pieces 2⅝" × $1^{13}/_{32}$" for the sides, and cut a 5⅜" × 2⅝" piece for the base. Assemble the parts as in the diagram above, and glue the sides to the base.

Fitted exactly into a wooden box are eight pieces of this packing problem. How can the small block now resting on the edge of the box also be fitted in? Amazingly, this is possible.

Each block in this puzzle has been given a letter in the diagrams below. In addition, the order in which the blocks are added to the box is also marked. To arrange the original eight blocks in the box, reconstruct the large block from which they were cut, as in the left-hand diagram below. Thus the first piece to go in the box is the largest of the blocks. Tip them out, and then arrange them with the extra block H, as in the right-hand diagram. In this example, all of the blocks are laid on their edges in order to fit them into the box.

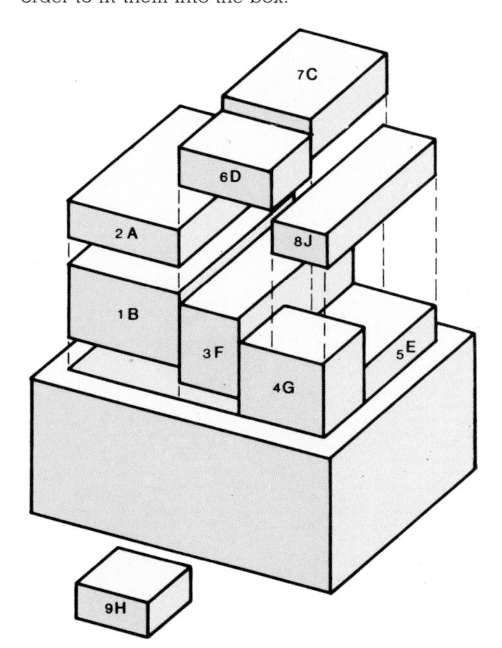

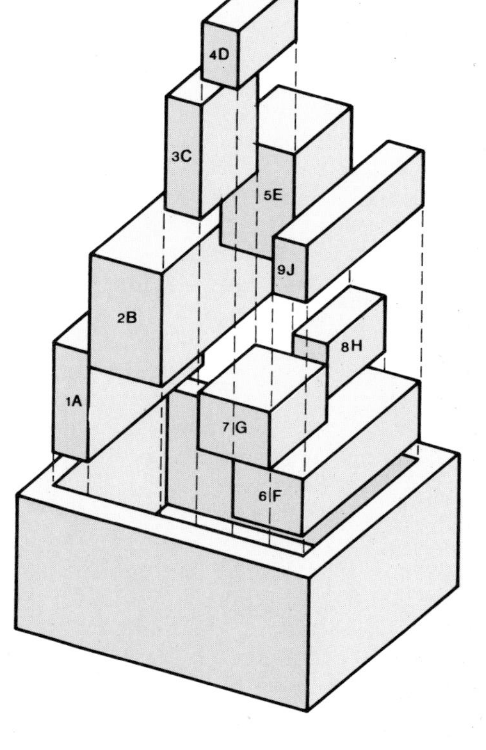

The Conway Packing Problem

This tantalizing puzzle was thought up by J. H. Conway, a Cambridge University mathematician. Seventeen pieces of wood are cut to various sizes so that their total volume is that of a 5 × 5 × 5 unit cube. The aim of the packing problem is to assemble this cube, which can then be fitted into a 5 × 5 × 5 unit box, as in the picture on the right. Although quite possible, correctly arranging the different-sized blocks to make the cube is a remarkably difficult task. Indeed, this puzzle is almost impossible to solve by trial and error alone. When the puzzle is done, all six faces of the completed cube show the same pattern, for the packed puzzle is totally symmetrical. Make your own model of this packing problem, following the directions below. Since the pieces will stack to make a cube that will stand unaided, it is not essential to make a box to contain the puzzle.

Seventeen blocks of the Conway puzzle can be packed in a cubic box. Without the box the puzzle can still be stacked into a cube, with each face of the cube bearing the same pattern of blocks.

Materials
Plywood, 48 × 10 × 1 units for the cube and 25 × 12 × 1 units for the box

Tools
Backsaw; ruler, pencil; sandpaper.

How to Make the Puzzle
The size of the pieces for this puzzle depends on the thickness of the plywood that is used. The thickness of the board is considered to be one unit in the following instructions.

Cut out six pieces from the board, each of 2 × 4 units; also cut out five cubes, each 1 × 1 × 1 unit. Now cut out 12 pieces, each 2 × 3 units. Glue two of these 2 × 3 units together, face to face, to build a 2 × 3 × 2 unit block. Repeat this for the remaining ten blocks, ending up with six 2 × 3 × 2 unit blocks. When the glue is dry, sandpaper all of the blocks, and the puzzle is ready.

To make a box for the cube, cut the bottom and sides out of the plywood so that a box with internal dimensions of 5 × 5 × 5 units can be built. The dimensions of the pieces will depend on the thickness of the board. Two pieces should measure 5 × 7 units, and three 5 × 5 units. Assemble the box according to the diagram on page 81.

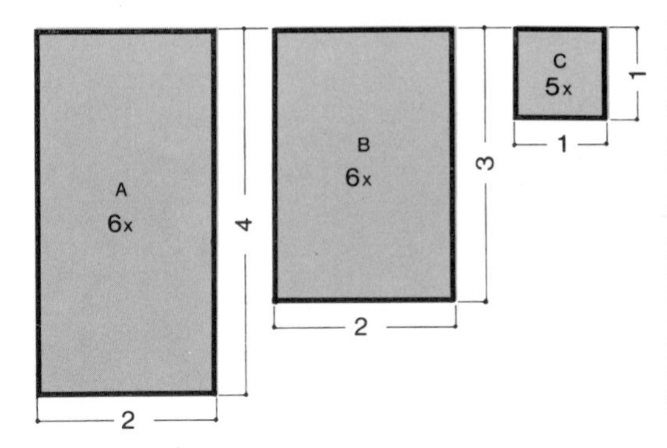

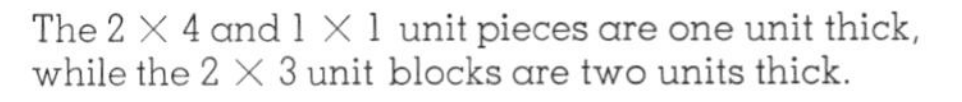
The 2 × 4 and 1 × 1 unit pieces are one unit thick, while the 2 × 3 unit blocks are two units thick.

To build the 5 × 5 × 5 unit cube, follow the diagrams below. The 2 × 4 × 1 unit blocks are labeled A, the 2 × 3 × 2 unit blocks are B, and the unit cubes are C. The face of the cube in the final arrangement has an area of 25 units, and since only the unit cubes have faces whose areas are an odd number of units (1), each face of the large cube must include the face of a unit cube. To do this, the unit cubes must run diagonally across the large cube, from top left to bottom right. To make the large cube such that each face is identical, with a unit square in each corner, first lay out the three A and two B blocks as in the left diagram. On these arrange the five cubes, stepwise, across the blocks. Finally add the remaining A and B blocks as in the right diagram.

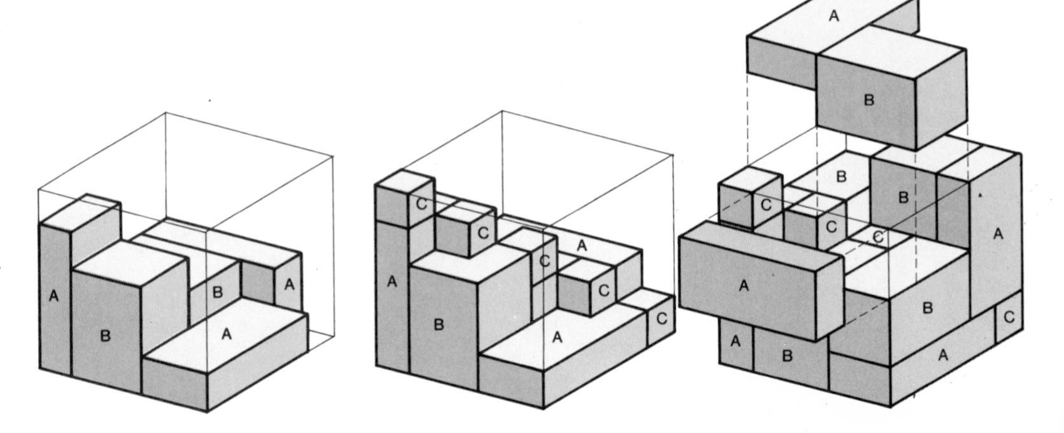

The Haselgrove Box

The H-shaped piece at the top of this magic box is held securely in place by an invisible internal mechanism, which is made up of interlocking blocks. The only way to release this piece is to discover how to shift the blocks within the box. To complete the initials of its creator, Jenifer Haselgrove, the H-shaped piece forms a J on one side.

In order to secure this magic box puzzle, the protruding piece of the P-shaped lock must drop into place, flush with the box top.

Materials

A piece of redwood, $2\frac{1}{2}$ yards × $\frac{3}{4}'' \times \frac{3}{4}''$
A piece of beech, $12'' \times \frac{3}{4}'' \times \frac{3}{4}''$
Wood glue

Tools

Backsaw; medium file; clamps; ruler; sandpaper.

How to Make the Puzzle

Cut the redwood into the following lengths: 16 pieces $3\frac{3}{4}''$ long; ten $\frac{3}{4}''$ pieces; two $2\frac{1}{4}''$ pieces; one 3" piece; four $1\frac{1}{2}''$ pieces. Glue five of the $3\frac{3}{4}''$ pieces side by side to make one side of the box. Make a second side the same size. Then make the two other sides of the box from three $3\frac{3}{4}''$ pieces each. Clamp the parts securely until the glue is dry. Glue eight $\frac{3}{4}''$ cubes and one $1\frac{1}{2}''$ piece together to make the base, with the $1\frac{1}{2}''$ piece upright in the center. Sand all of the parts and then construct the box. Glue a $\frac{3}{4}''$ cube inside the rim of the box, centered along one side as in the diagram below. Make the H-J shapes from the following pieces of redwood: two $2\frac{1}{4}''$ pieces; two $1\frac{1}{2}''$ pieces; a $\frac{3}{4}''$ cube. Glue and clamp the pieces together, as in the diagrams below. Glue the remaining $1\frac{1}{2}''$ piece alongside one half of the 3" piece to make the P-shaped lock. Saw the beech into seven $1\frac{1}{2}''$ pieces and one $\frac{3}{4}''$ cube. Glue the cube to one of the pieces to form an L. Sand everything smooth, using the file between the pieces.

Arrange the beech blocks in the box (two diagrams below). The L-shaped piece (one end shaded dark) lies flat in one corner (left diagram). Drop the J-H and P-shaped pieces into the box. One piece of the P will protrude, and in order to secure the lock this part must eventually drop into place. Tilt the puzzle thus moving the beech blocks one by one, each time filling the empty space in the box. Start by moving the block that lies under the rim cube, in the direction shown in the left diagram below. The block will slot into space A. Move each block until the lock drops.

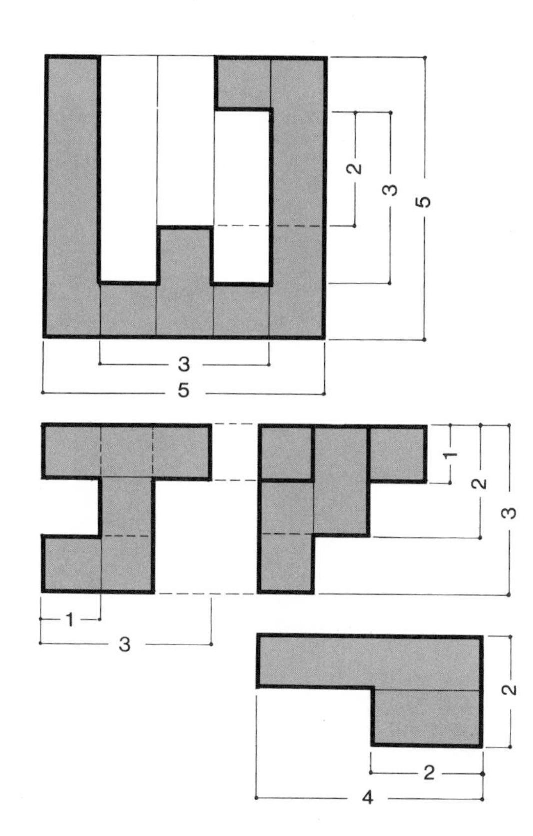

Dimensions above refer to unit lengths. The section cuts through the box side bearing the fixed cube.

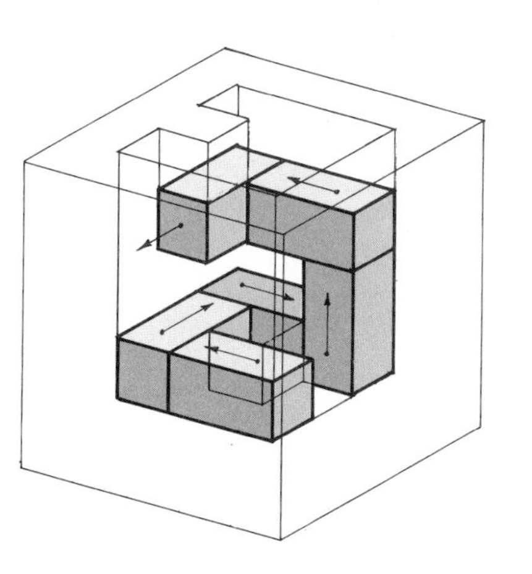

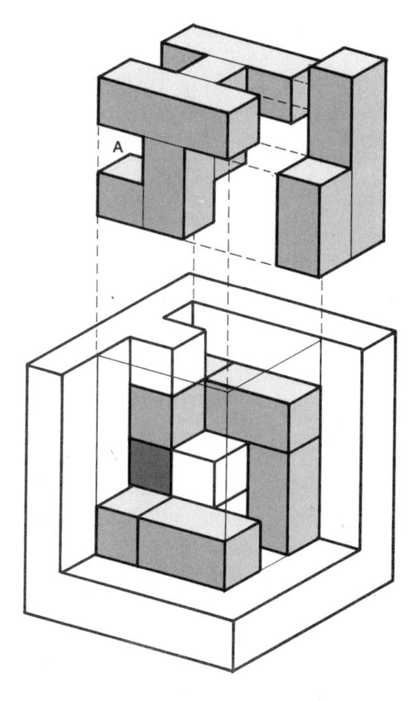

The Chinese Cube

A cube of wood or ivory and a box which just holds the cube are the starting materials for this packing problem. The cube can be cut into pieces of various shapes, and the puzzle is then to pack these pieces back into the box. Many different versions exist; the instructions below are for one example, that of the ivory puzzle on the right. When making any cubic puzzle, the first cut, which bisects the cube, must be made accurately. The half-cubes can then be cut randomly.

Carved from a block of ivory, the pieces from this 19th-century packing problem fit neatly into a delicately carved ivory box. Modern packing problems use readily available and cheaper materials in their construction, such as wood.

Materials
A block of beech wood, 2" × 2" × 2"
Two pieces of 3/8" board, 2" × 2 3/8"
A piece of 3/8" board, 2" × 2"
Two pieces of 3/8" board, 2 3/8" × 2 3/4"
Wood glue

Tools
Small hacksaw; sandpaper.

How to Make the Puzzle
Draw a corner-to-corner diagonal across one face of the cube. Cut along this line with the hacksaw, all the way through the block, making sure that the blade passes through opposing corners. Lay one half of the cube on its cut face, and saw through it a third of the way along its length, along line A. Saw through the resulting piece, along line B, cutting it in half. Stand one of these halves on a short face, and cut diagonally through its long face, following line C. This cut need not pass through the corners of the wedge. Return to the larger piece made by cut A, and lay it with one small face down. Cut diagonally through this block along the long face, following line D. Place one of the wedges made by cut D with its long side down. Cut through it along line E. Lay the second half of the original cube cut face down and saw through it, following line F. Take one of the pieces thus made, and saw through it along line G. Cut through the other piece, along line H. Make the box by gluing together the pieces of board.

To solve the puzzle and pack the pieces of the cube back into the box, you must reassemble the original cube. If you have used your own design in cutting the cube, then clearly you will also have your own solution. To pack any cube into its box, start by building up the half cubes, beginning with the last pieces to be cut. For the ivory cube shown in detail below, place together the two parts made by cut H, and add them to the two pieces made by cut G. This forms the half cube lying to the left of the diagonal in the assembled cube on the left. Beginning with the last pieces made by cut E, build up the other half cube. Drop both of the completed half cubes into the box, which they will fill up snugly.

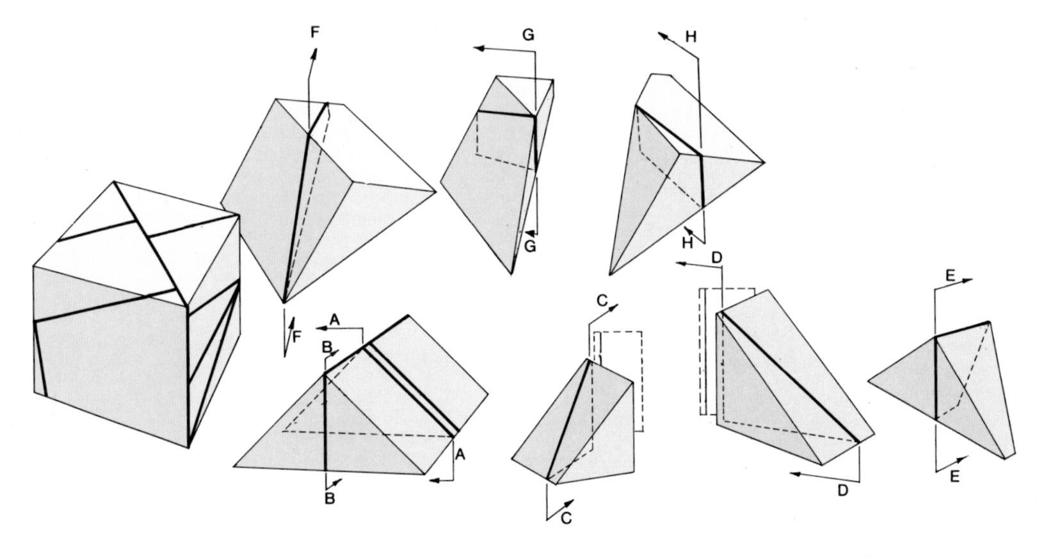

The Vanishing Space

Based on Stewart T. Coffin's Pyracube, this puzzle calls for the fitting of five shapes — formed with 14 balls — into a small cubic box. The shapes can then be placed — with the balls arranged symmetrically — so that the box is filled with only 13 of the balls.

Materials
Fourteen balls, each 1" in diameter
$1/8$" wooden dowel, 9" long
Acrylic sheet, $12\frac{1}{2}$" × $2\frac{1}{2}$" × $1/16$"
Wood glue and acrylic glue

Tools
Drill; $1/8$" bit; backsaw; fine sandpaper.

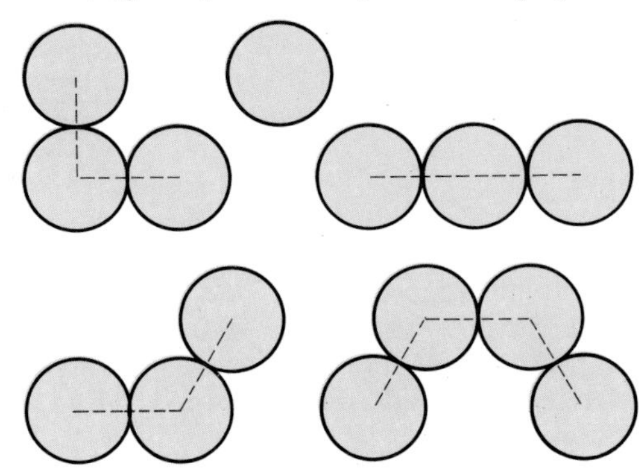

The dotted lines between the balls show where the holes must be drilled and the dowel inserted.

The wooden balls lie neatly in a clear plastic box — yet it is quite a problem to fit them in.

How to Make the Puzzle
Drill $1/8$" diameter holes into the balls, in the directions marked by the dotted lines in the diagram. A hole is drilled straight through one ball, but in the others the holes are $1/2$" deep. Saw the dowel into nine 1" pieces. Insert the pieces of dowel into the balls along the dotted lines. The angle made in the top left figure is 90°, and it is 120° in the lower two. Glue the dowels in place. To make the box, saw the acrylic into five $2\frac{1}{2}$" squares. Four edges of one square (the base of the box) and three edges of the other four squares must be beveled at 45° angles. To do this, take a spare block of wood, and saw it to make a wedge shape that has 45° corners. Clamp it to the acrylic so that the sloping face runs toward the sheet. The edge of the sloping face must be parallel to one edge of the acrylic and $1/16$" in from it. Glue sandpaper to a wooden board, and sand the edge of the acrylic with lengthwise strokes, keeping the sanding block in contact with the sloping face of the wedge, until the edge is worn down to a 45° angle. Repeat this on the remaining edges of the squares. Glue the squares together, angled edges touching.

To pack all of the balls into the box, start by laying the straight triplet diagonally across the base. Place the angled quadruplet over the triplet so that all four bottom corners of the box are filled with balls. Push the two top balls of this quadruplet toward the upper right corner in order to fit the 120° angled triplet into the front of the box. Add the right-angled triplet so that its two end balls fill the upper left and right corners of the box, with its middle ball in the center. Place the single ball in the lower left corner.

To fill the box symmetrically with only 13 balls, place the triplet with 120° angles in the base of the box. Two of its three balls touch the base and the third rests a little way up in the lower right corner. Add the quadruplet of balls so that one ball is near the base of the box, two are toward the upper left corner, and the fourth is in the middle of the back wall. Maneuver the straight triplet to drop between the upper balls of the first triplet and the quadruplet. Lay the right-angled triplet horizontally to fill the box.

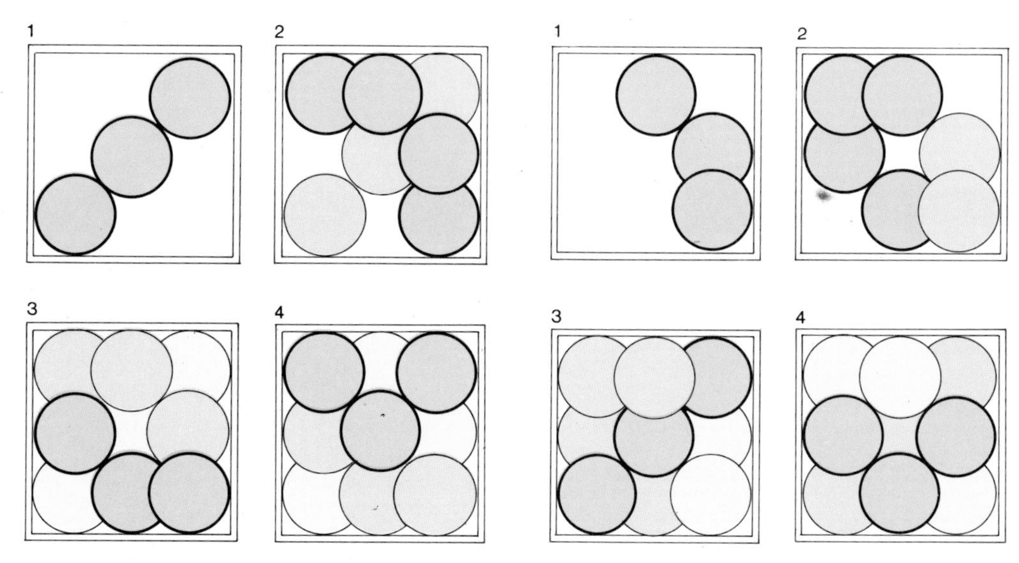

Magic Squares

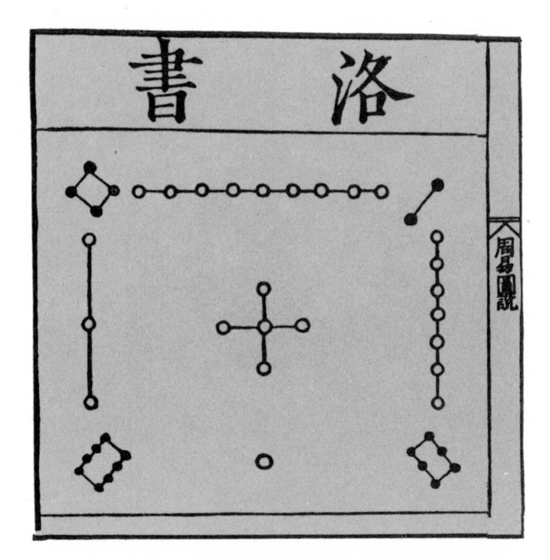

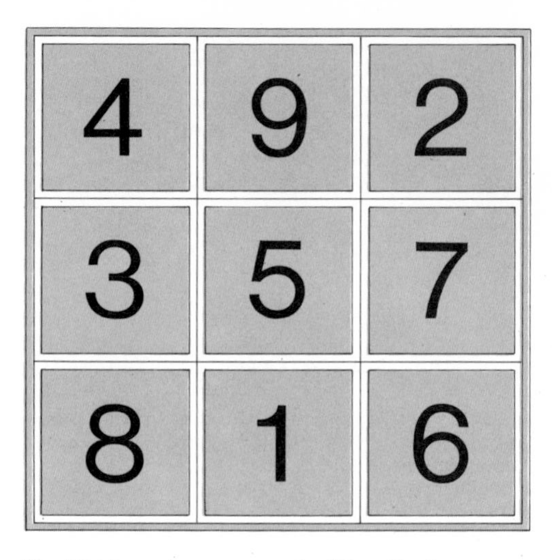

The 3 × 3 magic square, as traditionally drawn by the Chinese, and in arabic numerals. Every row, column, and diagonal adds up to 15. The diagram dates from the 12th century, but the mystic significance of the *lo-shu*, as the Chinese called the square, is much more ancient. The odd numbers were held to represent *yang*, the male principle in the universe, and even numbers to represent the female, *yin*.

Opposite: Symbols of the sciences surround the figure of Melancholy in Dürer's famous engraving. On the right is a magic square whose columns, rows, and diagonals all add up to 34. The central numbers of the bottom row provide the picture's only straightforward symbol: the date of the work.

Apparently it was the ancient Chinese who first developed magic squares — those beautifully balanced arrays of numbers in which all the rows, columns, and diagonals add up to the same total. The Chinese regarded them as symbolizing the harmonies and opposing principles that underlie the universe. Their complexity still challenges mathematicians today.

According to Chinese legend, the first magic square appeared to the mythical emperor Yü while he was walking beside the River Lo. The emperor spotted the square in a pattern on the back of a tortoise. The traditional symbolic form of the *lo-shu*, as the square was called, is shown on the left, together with its equivalent in arabic numerals. To the Chinese, the even numbers of the *lo-shu* represented *yin*, the female principle of the universe, and the odd numbers represented *yang*, the male principle. Other groupings of the numbers symbolized the five elements (earth, fire, metal, water, and wood).

There are only a few terms you need to know. The *lo-shu* is a "standard" square because it uses consecutive integers from 1 upward. Its "order" is 3 because there are three "cells" on each side of the square, or nine cells in all ($3 \times 3 = 9$). Every row, column, or diagonal adds up to 15, which is called the "constant."

The square can be rotated so that what is now a column becomes a row. Furthermore, each of the four squares obtained by rotating can be reflected in a mirror to get a reversed array. Altogether there are seven additional versions of this or any other magic square, derived from it by rotation and reflection. These trivially different versions aside, the *lo-shu* is unique; it is the only third-order, or order-3, standard magic square. Things are very different in the higher orders: not counting rotations and reflections, there are 880 order-4 squares and over 275 million order-5 squares.

The sum of the rows in a magic square equals the sum of all the numbers in the square. To obtain the constant of a standard order-4 square, add the integers from 1 to 16 and divide the sum by 4. The constant is 34. The constant of an order-5 square is the sum of the numbers from 1 to 25 divided by 5, which is 65. An easy formula to use is: *constant* $= \frac{1}{2} \times$ (*order cubed* + *order*); for order 6, *constant* $= \frac{1}{2} \times (6 \times 6 \times 6 + 6) = 111$.

If you add, say, 4 to every number in the *lo-shu*, the square remains "magic." Its constant is increased by 12 because you have added three 4s in each row, column, or diagonal. Any magic square remains magic when all its terms are increased, reduced, multiplied, or divided by the same number. However, it becomes nonstandard, because its numbers no longer begin at 1, or else are no longer consecutive integers.

The study of magic squares passed from the Chinese to the Moslems and later to the Hindus. New methods were found. Moslems, like the Chinese, were able to find religious significance in magic squares. Squares with 1 occupying the central cell were popular because the 1 represented the centrality and unity of God. Often this central position was, respectfully, left empty.

Europe was as fascinated by magic squares as Asia. In the 16th century the squares were still regarded as magical, and they were used in working spells. There were exceptions, however. The order-4 square in Albrecht Dürer's engraving *Melencolia* (opposite) was not a magic symbol. It probably represented arithmetic, one of the sciences that seem temporarily to have lost their attraction for the brooding thinker.

During the Age of Reason, magic squares became a pastime for mathematically inclined people. Ben Franklin amused himself in constructing them during his boyhood. As an adult he described one of his squares as "the most magically magical of any magic square ever made by any magician."

On the following pages you will find a variety of methods that will enable you to make numerous magic squares of any order. You could easily spend a lifetime on the delights of constructing magic squares. But spare a few hours for the puzzles at the end of this section.

MELENCOLIA I
16 3 2 13
5 10 11 8
9 6 7 12
4 15 14 1

Magic Squares of Odd Order

Staircase Method

Follow the sequence for constructing an order-3 square in figure A. First draw an array of nine blank cells. Write 1 *outside* the square, above the center top cell. Next, put 2 inside the square in the top right corner. Then write 3 below and to the right, outside the square. Place the next three numerals, 4, 5, and 6, in the diagonal from the top left corner to the bottom right. Finally, 7, 8 and 9 fall on the diagonal one row below and to the left of the numerals 4, 5, and 6.

We now have a square with five of its cells occupied. The rest are filled by transposing the numerals on the outside of the square to the empty spaces on the opposite side, inside the square. Thus 1 goes to bottom center, 3 to center left, and so on. The result is the standard 3 × 3 magic square. Basically the same method is used to construct an order-5 square. There are five numerals in each diagonal row, and the first 1 is placed *two* cells above the center top cell (figure B). The result is one of the many order-5 squares, with a magic constant of 65.

Continuous Numbering Methods

Here's one way in which odd-order squares can be filled sequentially, without the final transposition step. Follow it in figure C at the right.

Imagine that the array of nine cells is surrounded by identical arrays. Place 1 in the top center cell of the main square. Then place 2 *above* and *right* of 1. This takes you into the *bottom right-hand* cell of the square above. So transfer 2 into the *bottom right-hand* cell of the main 3 × 3 cell square.

Go one place up and right of 2. That puts you in the *center left-hand* cell of the neighboring square. So 3 goes into the *center left-hand* cell of the main square, as the diagram shows.

The next numeral, 4, should go one place up and to the right of 3, but this cell is occupied by 1. So, instead, go *down* one cell from 3 to the position shown. This is called a "break move."

Numerals 5 and 6 go in the diagonal begun by 4. Place 7 in the bottom left-hand cell of the neighboring square above and to the right. Since the corresponding cell of the main square is already filled, a break move is needed,

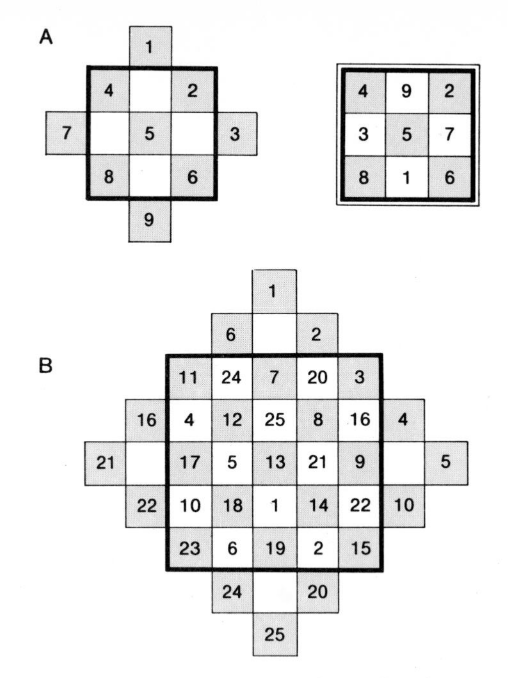

A. The staircase method for making a 3 × 3 magic square. B. Constructing a 5 × 5 square.

C

		2	
	1	6	
3	5		3
4		2	

	9		7
8	1	6	8
3	5	7	
4	9	2	

C. A 3 × 3 magic square partly filled by continuous numbering (left) and the final square (right).

D

	18	25	2	9	16
17	24	1	8	15	17
23	5	7	14	16	23
4	6	13	20	22	4
10	12	19	21	3	10
11	18	25	2	9	

D. A 5 × 5 square made by continuous numbering.

E

				16	
11	24	7	20	3	↗
23	6	19	2	15	23
10	18	1	14	22	10
17	5	13	21	9	17
4	12	25	8	16	4
11	24	7	20	3	

E. An alternative way of continuously numbering a 5 × 5 square. This time 1 is placed just above the center and the break move is two squares upward for example, from 5 to 6 and from 15 to 16. This results in a different square from the previous one, but with the same constant, 65.

and the 7 goes below 6 (figure C, right). When 8 and 9 have been placed, a version of our previous order-3 square is obtained, turned upside-down.

When you use this method to make an order-5 square, begin as before in the center top cell and use the same diagonal move and vertical break move, as shown in figure D.

Alternatively you can begin the fifth-order square in the cell immediately above the central cell. Use the one-up, one-right move, but the break move must be two squares *upward* (figure E).

De la Hire's Method

Methods by which a magic square is made from two preliminary squares are named after Philippe de la Hire, a 17th-century Frenchman. We use a fifth-order square as an example.

The "primary" square is filled with the numbers 1 through 5 only. Write them in a diagonal from top left to bottom right. They can appear in any order, except that 3 must be in the center cell (figure F, left). Next, fill each diagonal sloping the other way with repetitions of the number that already appears in it (figure F, right). Most of these diagonals are "broken." For example, suppose you are filling in the diagonals going up and to the right. If you end the diagonal at the top of the square, continue at the foot of the next column to the right; if you end at the right-hand side of the square, continue at the left of the row above.

In the second, or "root," square, only the numbers 0, 5, 10, 15, and 20 are used. Write them into the diagonal from top right to bottom left (figure G, left). Again, they can be in any order except that 10 must appear in the center cell. Now fill each of the intersecting diagonals with repetitions of the number that already appears in it (figure G, right). Add the numbers in the corresponding cells in both squares to get the order-5 magic square shown in figure H.

To make an order-3 square by De la Hire's method, fill the primary square with the numerals 1, 2, and 3. In the root square put 0, 3, and 6. To make an order-7 square, use the numerals 1 through 7 in the primary square and 0, 7, 14 ,21, 28, 35, and 42 in the root square. In other words, the root square is always filled with 0 and multiples of the order of the square.

F

1				
	2			
		3		
			4	
				5

1	4	2	5	3
4	2	5	3	1
2	5	3	1	4
5	3	1	4	2
3	1	4	2	5

G

				0
			5	
		10		
	15			
20				

10	20	5	15	0
0	10	20	5	15
15	0	10	20	5
5	15	0	10	20
20	5	15	0	10

H

11	24	7	20	3
4	12	25	8	16
17	5	13	21	9
10	18	1	14	22
23	6	19	2	15

F. De la Hire's method: making an initial square.
G. Making the other preliminary square.
H. When added, they give this magic square.

Squares of Singly Even Order

Ralph Strachey's Method

A singly even number is one that is divisible by 2 but not by 4. Examples are 6, 10, 14, and so on. Magic squares of these orders are the hardest to construct. Strachey's method involves assembling four odd-order magic squares to make a larger, singly even square.

Divide the singly even array — 6 × 6 in our example — into four equal subsquares (figure I). In the top left-hand subsquare, write in the numerals 1 through 9 in the basic third-order magic square pattern. (Reflected and rotated versions lead to different, but equally good, results.)

In the bottom right-hand subsquare, write in the numerals 10 through 18. Put 10 in the cell corresponding to 1 in the first subsquare, 11 into the cell corresponding to 2, and so on. The result is a nonstandard magic square with a constant of 42.

In the top right-hand subsquare write the numerals 19 through 27. First, 19 goes into the cell corresponding to 1, then 20 into the cell corresponding to 2, and so on. The resulting nonstandard magic square has a constant of 69. Finally, fill in the fourth subsquare.

Your 6 × 6 array is now only partially magic; the columns add up to 111, but the top three rows total only 84, and the bottom three total 138. You now make exchanges that add 27 to each upper row and subtract 27 from each lower row. At the same time, this increases the diagonal total from top left to bottom right by 54 and reduces the other diagonal by the same amount.

Exchange each number indicated in figure I: 4 is exchanged with 31, 5 is exchanged with 32, and 8 is exchanged with 35. Figure J shows the result: a magic square of the sixth order, with a constant of 111.

In figure K the construction of a tenth-order square is shown. The first subsquare is an arbitrary 5 × 5 magic square. The other subsquares follow this pattern. This time, different exchanges have to be made, as shown in the figure. For example, 17 exchanges with 92, 6 exchanges with 81, and so on. The result is the magic square shown in figure L, with a constant of 505.

I

8	1	6	26	19	24
3	5	7	21	23	25
4	9	2	22	27	20
35	28	33	17	10	15
30	32	34	12	14	16
31	36	29	13	18	11

J

35	1	6	26	19	24
3	32	7	21	23	25
31	9	2	22	27	20
8	28	33	17	10	15
30	5	34	12	14	16
4	36	29	13	18	11

I. The first step in making a 6 × 6 magic square: four 3 × 3 squares. J. The result after exchanges. Bottom: Exchanges in Strachey's method.

K

17	24	1	8	15	67	74	51	58	65
23	5	7	14	16	73	55	57	64	66
4	6	13	20	22	54	56	63	70	72
10	12	19	21	3	60	62	69	71	53
11	18	25	2	9	61	68	75	52	59
92	99	76	83	90	42	49	26	33	40
98	80	82	89	91	48	30	32	39	41
79	81	88	95	97	29	31	38	45	47
85	87	94	96	78	35	37	44	46	28
86	93	100	77	84	36	43	50	27	34

L

92	99	1	8	15	67	74	51	58	40
98	80	7	14	16	73	55	57	64	41
4	81	88	20	22	54	56	63	70	47
85	87	19	21	3	60	62	69	71	28
86	93	25	2	9	61	68	75	52	34
17	24	76	83	90	42	49	26	33	65
23	5	82	89	91	48	30	32	39	66
79	6	13	95	97	29	31	38	45	72
10	12	94	96	78	35	37	44	46	53
11	18	100	77	84	36	43	50	27	59

K. Strachey's method: make four magic squares.
L. Exchange numbers to make a large square.

There is a method for working out the pattern of exchanges for squares of any order. The first singly even square we made was of order 6. Now 4 divides into 6 just once (with a remainder of 2, of course). So 1 is the crucial number for this order. It tells us that we must focus attention on the *first* column on the left but on *no* columns on the right. So in the top left-hand subsquare mark the cells in the first column — *except* in the central row; there you mark the cell one place to the right, just as figure I shows.

The next square we made was of order 10. Since 4 divides into 10 twice, 2 is the relevant number. It tells us to make exchanges in the first *two* columns on the left and the *first* column on the right. In the top left-hand subsquare mark the first two cells in every row *except* the central one. In the central row the two cells to be marked are shifted one place to the right, as figure K shows. All the cells in the last column are marked for exchange, as the figure also shows.

The three squares (figure J, bottom) show exchange patterns for various singly even orders. However, you can find many other ways in which exchanges can be made successfully.

De la Hire's Method
We use a version of De la Hire's method to make an order-6 square. In the primary square write 1 through 6, in order, in the diagonals from top left to bottom right and from bottom left to top right, as shown in figure M.

The first column now has the number 1 twice. The complement of 1 is 6 — which means that 1 and 6 are the first and last numerals in the series 1 through 6. Fill the empty cells in the first column with three 1s and three 6s in any order. Figure M shows one way of doing this.

Now fill the sixth column. Each cell must contain the complement of the number in the corresponding cell of the first column; 1 in the last column matches 6 in the first column, and so on. (Each number in the first column is said to be *horizontally paired* with its complement, and vice versa.)

The second column has the number 2 twice. The complement of 2 is 5 (they are, respectively, second from the beginning and second from the end of the series 1 through 6). These numbers can appear in any order in the second-column, but they must appear equally often. Fill each cell of the fifth column with the complement of the corresponding cell of the second.

In the third column, write in 3s and 4s in equal number. Match each with its complement in the horizontally paired cell in the fourth column.

Fill the root square with the numbers 0, 6, 12, 18, 24, and 30. Write them into the two main diagonals from top to bottom, in sequence (figure N).

Now it is time to fill the rows. Fill each with a number and its complement. (The complementary pairs are 0 and 30, 6 and 24, 12 and 18.) A number and its complement must occur with equal frequency in a row. And each number must be *vertically* paired with its complement. That means that if you write 24 in the second row, you must write its complement 6 in the fifth row, and so on throughout the square.

There is an important restriction on the placing of numerals in the root square. Look at the top cell of the second column of the primary square. It contains the numeral 5, which by chance is vertically paired with its complement 2 at the bottom of the column. In such a case the corresponding cell of the root square (first cell of the second column) must contain the *same* numeral as its horizontally paired cell (first cell of the fifth column). In figure N this numeral happens to be 30. This rule must be applied twice more: for the second cell of the primary square's third column and for the third cell of its first column. Add the primary and root squares to obtain the final magic square (figure O).

M

1	5	4	3	2	6
6	2	3	4	5	1
6	5	3	4	2	1
1	5	3	4	2	6
6	2	4	3	5	1
1	2	4	3	5	6

N

0	30	0	30	30	0
24	6	24	24	6	6
18	18	12	12	12	18
12	12	18	18	18	12
6	24	6	6	24	24
30	0	30	0	0	30

O

1	35	4	33	32	6
30	8	27	28	11	7
24	23	15	16	14	19
13	17	21	22	20	18
12	26	10	9	29	25
31	2	34	3	5	36

De la Hire's method: M. Primary square. N. Root square. O. The final magic square.

P

1	9	3	7	5	6	4	8	2	10
10	2	8	7	5	6	4	3	9	1
10	9	3	7	6	5	4	8	2	1
1	9	8	4	6	5	7	3	2	10
10	9	8	4	5	6	7	3	2	1
10	2	3	7	5	6	4	8	9	1
1	2	3	4	6	5	7	8	9	10
10	9	3	4	6	5	7	8	2	1
1	2	8	7	6	5	4	3	9	10
1	2	8	4	5	6	7	3	9	10

Q

0	90	0	90	90	0	90	0	90	0
10	10	10	80	80	80	80	80	10	10
70	20	20	70	20	70	70	20	70	20
30	60	60	30	60	30	30	60	60	30
40	50	50	40	40	40	40	50	50	50
50	40	40	50	50	50	50	40	40	40
60	30	30	60	30	60	60	30	30	60
20	70	70	20	70	20	20	70	20	70
80	80	80	10	10	10	10	10	80	80
90	0	90	0	0	90	0	90	0	90

Combine P and Q to get a 10 × 10 magic square.

Figures P and Q show primary and root squares for an order-10 magic square. This time there are even more alternative ways of filling rows and columns.

Squares of Doubly Even Order

Diagonal Method
Magic squares are extremely easy to construct when the order is a multiple of 4, or "doubly even." Follow the making of an order-4 square in figure R.

First, write the numerals 1 through 16 in consecutive order, four numerals to a row. Then draw two lines marking the diagonals, to pick out the squares that are shaded in figure R, bottom left. Now: *either* reverse the numbers along the main diagonals — 1 and 16, 6 and 11, and so on — while leaving the rest fixed (figure R, bottom left); or leave the numbers on the diagonals undisturbed and switch the rest — for example, 2 with 15 and 3 with 14 (as in the bottom right square of figure R).

Things are only slightly more complicated with a larger square. First fill it with the numbers from 1 upward in consecutive order. Divide the square into its 4 × 4 constituent subsquares and draw the diagonals in each of these (figure S). The numbers lying on the diagonals now have to be exchanged among themselves; for example, 1 exchanges with 64, 14 with 51, and 25 with 40, as shown in figure S. Alternatively, leave these numbers undisturbed and interchange the others — for example, 2 and 63, or 31 and 34.

De la Hire's Method
Doubly even squares can be constructed by precisely the same method described for singly even squares. The primary and root squares for an order-8 square are shown in figures T and U. The primary is filled with the numbers 1 through 8. The root is filled with 0, 8, 16, 24, 32, 40, 48, and 56 — that is, with 0 and multiples of 8, the square's order.

R

1	2	3	4
5	6	7	8
9	10	11	12
13	14	15	16

16	2	3	13
5	11	10	8
9	7	6	12
4	14	15	1

1	15	14	4
12	6	7	9
8	10	11	5
13	3	2	16

R. Reverse either the diagonal or off-diagonal numbers in the square at the top to get the two versions of a 4 × 4 magic square below it.

S

1	2	3	4	5	6	7	8
9	10	11	12	13	14	15	16
17	18	19	20	21	22	23	24
25	26	27	28	29	30	31	32
33	34	35	36	37	38	39	40
41	42	43	44	45	46	47	48
49	50	51	52	53	54	55	56
57	58	59	60	61	62	63	64

S. The pattern of exchanges needed to make an 8 × 8 magic square. Switch the shaded numbers among themselves; or do the same for the unshaded ones.

T

1	7	6	5	4	3	2	8
8	2	6	5	4	3	7	1
8	7	3	4	5	6	2	1
1	2	3	4	5	6	7	8
8	7	6	4	5	3	2	1
1	2	3	5	4	6	7	8
8	2	6	4	5	3	7	1
1	7	3	5	4	6	2	8

U

0	56	56	56	0	56	0	0
48	8	48	48	48	8	8	8
16	40	16	40	40	16	40	16
24	32	32	24	24	32	32	24
32	24	24	32	32	24	24	32
40	16	40	16	16	40	16	40
8	48	8	8	8	48	48	48
56	0	0	0	56	0	56	56

T. Primary 8 × 8 square. U. 8 × 8 root square. When these two are added, the result is magic.

Constructing Bordered Squares

A bordered magic square is one that remains magic when the outer border of numbers is removed. Figure V shows an order-5 magic square that remains just as magic when its outer border is stripped off, reducing it to order 3. In figure W, two orders can be removed to leave a magic core. Following is a surprisingly easy method of constructing this square.

The numerals 1 through 49 are used to make the square. The middle nine numerals of this sequence — that is, 21 through 29 — go into the 3 × 3 core. Position them according to the pattern of the standard third-order magic square: but put 21 in the cell normally occupied by 1, and so on. The result is a third-order square with 20 added to each term. The constant is, therefore, 15 + (3 × 20), which is 75.

The first, or inner, border contains 16 cells. Write in the eight numerals preceding and following the core sequence — that is, 13 through 20 and 30 through 37. Arrange them so that each number lies at the opposite end of a row, column, or diagonal from its complement — 13 opposite 37, 14 opposite 36, and so on. Each line of numerals in the 5 × 5 square should add up to 125 (50 + 75 = 125). We show only one such arrangement, but there are many others that you can find.

It then remains to put the rest of the numbers — 1 through 12 and 38 through 49 — into the outside border in complementary pairs (1 opposite 49, 2 opposite 48, and so on). Again we show only one of the possible arrangements.

Figure X shows a sixth-order square with a fourth-order core. The twenty-square border is occupied by the first ten and the last ten numbers of the sequence 1 through 36. The others — 11 through 26 — are arranged in a magic square patterned on a standard 4 × 4 square made by the diagonal method.

(A helpful tip: the corner cells of an even-order bordered square can be filled by the numbers that would fall there if the entire sequence were written out in normal order. In this case the "natural" corner numbers of the 6 × 6 square are 1, 6, 31, and 36.)

Figures Y and Z show two 8 × 8 squares with 6 × 6 magic cores. The second of these has, in turn, a 4 × 4 magic core.

V

21	1	2	22	19
23	16	9	14	3
6	11	13	15	20
8	12	17	10	18
7	25	24	4	5

V. Both the large square and its core are magic.

W

46	1	2	3	42	41	40
45	35	13	14	32	31	5
44	34	28	21	26	16	6
7	17	23	25	27	33	43
12	20	24	29	22	30	38
11	19	37	36	18	15	39
10	49	48	47	8	9	4

W. Three magic squares nested inside each other.

X

1	35	34	5	30	6
33	11	25	24	14	4
8	22	16	17	19	29
28	18	20	21	15	9
10	23	13	12	26	27
31	2	3	32	7	36

X. A 6 ×6 magic square with a magic square core.

Y

1	63	62	4	5	59	58	8
56	15	49	18	47	46	20	9
55	44	22	41	42	25	21	10
11	38	37	29	30	28	33	54
53	27	31	35	36	34	32	12
13	26	40	24	23	43	39	52
14	45	16	48	17	19	50	51
57	2	3	61	60	6	7	64

Y. An 8 × 8 magic square with a 6 × 6 magic core.

Z

1	63	62	4	5	59	58	8
56	15	49	48	19	44	20	9
55	47	25	39	38	28	18	10
11	22	36	30	31	33	43	54
53	42	32	34	35	29	23	12
13	24	37	27	26	40	41	52
14	45	16	17	46	21	50	51
57	2	3	61	60	6	7	64

Z. An 8 ×8 magic square with two magic cores.

Diabolic Squares

These devilish squares are simply "pan-diagonal" magic squares: their broken diagonals, as well as their rows, columns, and main diagonals, add up to the square's constant. Because of this, if an area is covered with identical fifth-order squares side by side, as on the right, any 5 × 5 square area that can be picked out is magic.

Diabolic squares are also known as "Nasik" squares, after the town in India where an English magic-square enthusiast came across them. They have long been regarded as the most "perfect" of magic squares. The fifth-order square that appears here with 13 at its center is also *associative* — each pair of numbers that are symmetrically placed around the center total twice the central number (that is, 10 + 16 = 26, 20 + 6 = 26, and so on.) Only 16 fundamentally different associative diabolic squares of the fifth order exist.

There are complicated methods of making diabolic squares, which we won't discuss here. Instead, it is more interesting to modify squares made by one of the methods previously described in this section, to increase their devilishness.

1	15	24	8	17	1	15	24	8	17	1	15	24	8	17	1	15	24	8	17
23	7	16	5	14	23	7	16	5	14	23	7	16	5	14	23	7	16	5	14
20	4	13	22	6	20	4	13	22	6	20	4	13	22	6	20	4	13	22	6
12	21	10	19	3	12	21	10	19	3	12	21	10	19	3	12	21	10	19	3
9	18	2	11	25	9	18	2	11	25	9	18	2	11	25	9	18	2	11	25
1	15	24	8	17	1	15	24	8	17	1	15	24	8	17	1	15	24	8	17
23	7	16	5	14	23	7	16	5	14	23	7	16	5	14	23	7	16	5	14
20	4	13	22	6	20	4	13	22	6	20	4	13	22	6	20	4	13	22	6
12	21	10	19	3	12	21	10	19	3	12	21	10	19	3	12	21	10	19	3
9	18	2	11	25	9	18	2	11	25	9	18	2	11	25	9	18	2	11	25
1	15	24	8	17	1	15	24	8	17	1	15	24	8	17	1	15	24	8	17
23	7	16	5	14	23	7	16	5	14	23	7	16	5	14	23	7	16	5	14
20	4	13	22	6	20	4	13	22	6	20	4	13	22	6	20	4	13	22	6
12	21	10	19	3	12	21	10	19	3	12	21	10	19	3	12	21	10	19	3
9	18	2	11	25	9	18	2	11	25	9	18	2	11	25	9	18	2	11	25
1	15	24	8	17	1	15	24	8	17	1	15	24	8	17	1	15	24	8	17
23	7	16	5	14	23	7	16	5	14	23	7	16	5	14	23	7	16	5	14
20	4	13	22	6	20	4	13	22	6	20	4	13	22	6	20	4	13	22	6
12	21	10	19	3	12	21	10	19	3	12	21	10	19	3	12	21	10	19	3
9	18	2	11	25	9	18	2	11	25	9	18	2	11	25	9	18	2	11	25

In this array, you can pick out any square area with five cells on a side and find that it's magic.

Making the Square Magic

The attempt at a magic square shown here leaves a great deal to be desired. The constant for an order-4 square should be 34, but as the square now stands only a couple of the columns and one of the diagonals add up to this. See if you can "fix" the square by cutting it into *four* pieces and rearranging the pieces. An end result that is totally magic — and also totally square — can be achieved after a little effort.

1	15	5	12
8	10	4	9
11	6	16	2
14	3	13	7

Reassemble this square to make it magic.

The Sliding Block Square

Sliding block puzzles can be bought or made (page 181). Try to make as many magic squares as you can, each with a constant of 30. An example is shown below; the vacant space represents 0. (Hint: a magic square of constant 30 results when you subtract 1 from every number in a standard 4 × 4 square.)

Can you make other sliding block magic squares?

Squares of Playing Cards

Playing cards make a colorful way of laying out magic squares, especially when they are as attractive as the ones shown opposite. The cards from ace through 9 of any suit can be used to make a straightforward *lo-shu*. To make an order-4 square, use the 13 cards of one suit and 4, 5 and 6 of the opposite color suit to represent 14, 15 and 16. On the right we show an unusual square of order 4. It uses the ace through 7 of hearts, the ace through 8 of clubs and the king of diamonds. It looks quite unmagical at first. And what are we supposed to do with the red king? In fact, this is a perfectly good magic square provided you *subtract* the hearts values and add the clubs. The red king represents zero. What other order-4 squares can you make from these cards? (Hint: bear in mind that a magic square results when you subtract a given number from each number in *any* standard fourth-order square.)

(See solution page 193)

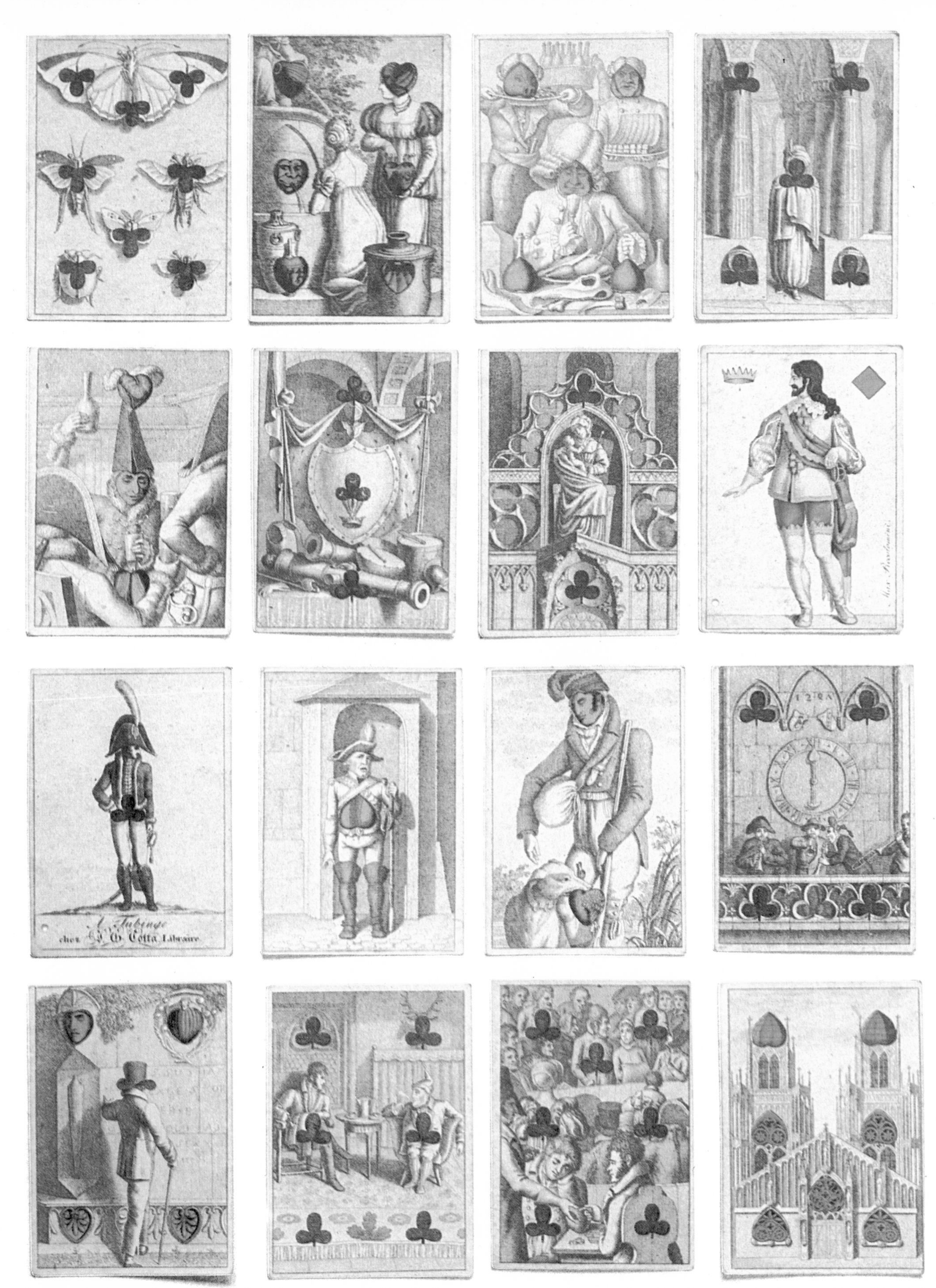

German playing cards from the early 19th century are laid out to form an unusual magic square, in which the red card values must be subtracted.

A Bordered Square

Illustrated here is an order-3 core square with a constant of 123 and two borders that form an order-5 square of constant 205 and an order-7 square of constant 287. If you study the borders, you will see that they were built up on a different pattern from the ones previously described. Can you add another border, incorporating the numbers in the range of 1 to 81 that have not already been used? The final square, like all standard order-9 squares, will have a magic constant of 369.

	20	55	30	57	28	71	26	
	14	31	50	29	60	35	68	
	58	46	38	45	40	36	24	
	65	33	43	41	39	49	17	
	64	48	42	37	44	34	18	
	10	47	32	53	22	51	72	
	56	27	52	25	54	11	62	

See if you can complete this 9 × 9 magic square.

A Fractional Square

You are probably getting familiar with the *lo-shu* by now. If so, you will immediately see that the array below cannot be filled out to make the *lo-shu*, or any reflected or rotated version thereof, because the 4 is not in a corner, as it would need to be. You could, of course, make a highly nonstandard magic square by the desperate expedient of filling the array with repetitions of 4. However, a magic square with a constant of 15 can be formed by replacing the numerals with *fractional* ones. In fact you can do it by finding two numbers, one of which you divide into each number of the *lo-shu*, and the other of which you add to the results. You can find two different solutions.

Fractions are needed for this magic square.

The Cross in the Square

When you find magic squares becoming too easy, you can always impose some extra restriction on yourself. In the diagram below, the central cross-shaped pattern contains 13 squares and should be filled with the odd numbers of the sequence 1 to 25. Try to make a standard order-5 square with only odd numbers in the center and even numbers in the corners, outside of the cross. (Hint: look for an "associated" solution in which pairs of numbers symmetrically placed on opposite sides of the center total 26.)

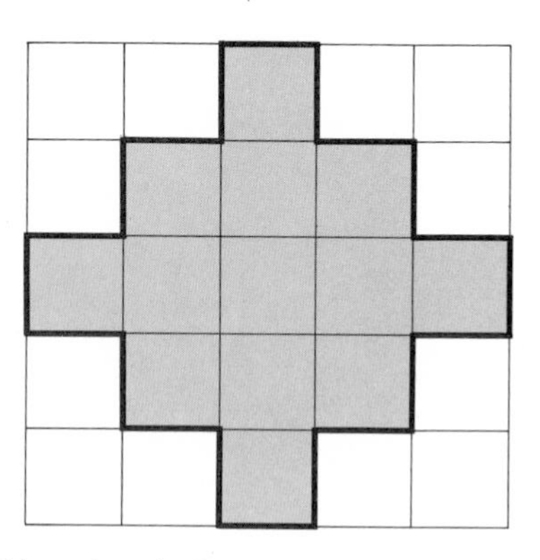

Put odd numbers in the cross, even ones around it.

A Magical Tour — With a Mystery

The chess knight moves one square parallel to any side of the board and then one square diagonally ahead. In the figure, each square is numbered consecutively as the knight visits it. Can a standard 8 × 8 magic square with the usual constant of 260 be formed in this way? Many puzzlers have tried and failed. The figure shows the first moves of the best solution known. The square formed is almost magic, but its diagonal sums are slightly wrong.

					9		7
					6		10
				12		8	
				5		11	
	3		13				
			4				
2		14					
		1					

Continue the tour to make an almost-magic square.

Magic Strips

Imagine that you have seven cardboard strips, each bearing the numerals 1 through 7 in order. Cut them up and arrange them to make a nonstandard magic square. The strips must not be turned around to lie vertically (or turned upside-down, for that matter). The final square will have a constant of 28. Of course it's easy to do the problem if you allow yourself any number of cuts. Try to do it in the smallest possible number — the minimum is a surprisingly small figure.

1	2	3	4	5	6	7
1	2	3	4	5	6	7
1	2	3	4	5	6	7
1	2	3	4	5	6	7
1	2	3	4	5	6	7
1	2	3	4	5	6	7
1	2	3	4	5	6	7

Cut and move the strips to make a magic square.

Franklin's 8 × 8 Square

In 1769 the American colonies' most notable intellect, Benjamin Franklin, published some remarkable magic squares. Below is one of his order-8 squares. One of the many interesting things about the square is the fact that its rows and columns add up to 260. Also, every half-row and half-column adds up to 130. And furthermore, the four corner squares and the four cells in the center add up to 260, and so on. How many such groups with sums of 260 or 130 can you find?

52	61	4	13	20	29	36	45
14	3	62	51	46	35	30	19
53	60	5	12	21	28	37	44
11	6	59	54	43	38	27	22
55	58	7	10	23	26	39	42
9	8	57	56	41	40	25	24
50	63	2	15	18	31	34	47
16	1	64	49	48	33	32	17

Many number patterns lie hidden in this square.

(See solution pages 193-194)

Franklin's 16 × 16 Square

In his *Letters and Papers on Philosophical Subjects*, Benjamin Franklin tells how "... in my younger days, having once some leisure (which I still think I might have employed more usefully) I had amused myself in making these kinds of magic squares, and, at length had acquired such a knack of it, that I could fill the cells of any magic square of reasonable size with a series of numbers as fast as I could write them." As an adult he bent his mind again to these "trifling and useless" activities (as he called them) and made, for one, this order-16 square. It is not totally magic; its diagonals do not add up to the constant of 2056. But plenty of other 16-cell groupings do. If you do not wish to employ your leisure more usefully, why not hunt them out?

The Underlying Pattern

When the cells of a magic square are joined by straight lines in the order in which they are numbered, a beautifully balanced pattern emerges. Further patterns appear when successive oddly or evenly numbered cells are linked. These harmonious networks give insight into the method of construction of the square and make pleasing objects of contemplation in their own right.

200	217	232	249	8	25	40	57	72	89	104	121	136	153	168	185
58	39	26	7	250	231	218	199	186	167	154	135	122	103	90	71
198	219	230	251	6	27	38	59	70	91	102	123	134	155	166	187
60	37	28	5	252	229	220	197	188	165	156	133	124	101	92	69
201	216	233	248	9	24	41	56	73	88	105	120	137	152	169	184
55	42	23	10	247	234	215	202	183	170	151	138	119	106	87	74
203	214	235	246	11	22	43	54	75	86	107	118	139	150	171	182
53	44	21	12	245	236	213	204	181	172	149	140	117	108	85	76
205	212	237	244	13	20	45	52	77	84	109	116	141	148	173	180
51	46	19	14	243	238	211	206	179	174	147	142	115	110	83	78
207	210	239	242	15	18	47	50	79	82	111	114	143	146	175	178
49	48	17	16	241	240	209	208	177	176	145	144	113	112	81	80
196	221	228	253	4	29	36	61	68	93	100	125	132	157	164	189
62	35	30	3	254	227	222	195	190	163	158	131	126	99	94	67
194	223	226	255	2	31	34	63	66	95	98	127	130	159	162	191
64	33	32	1	256	225	224	193	192	161	160	129	128	97	96	65

Benjamin Franklin's "most magically magical" square, with a constant of 2056. Tracing successive numbers leads to the pattern shown here.

(See solution page 194)

Decorated with mother-of-pearl and metal inlay depicting traditional Chinese scenes, this black lacquer box contains an excellent selection of ring-string-ball and other puzzles. Many of the ivory puzzles within the box are intricately hand-carved with figures, delicate flowers and trees, and the graceful curves of pagodas. Although the box and puzzles were produced in China, in the middle of the 19th century, they were made for export to Europe — for wealthy ladies to while away their leisure hours.

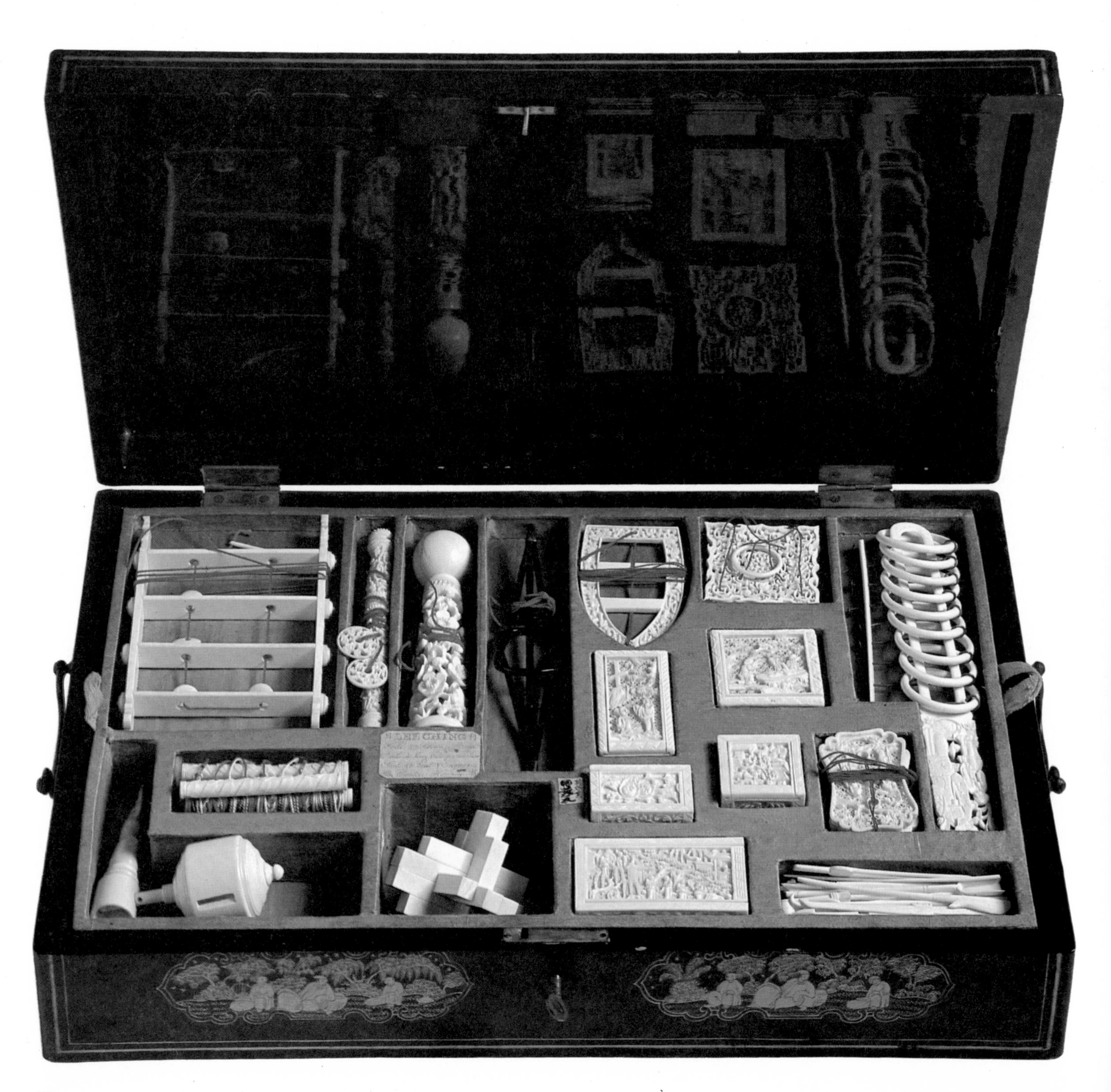

Ring-String-Ball Puzzles

This Victorian ivory puzzle, taken from the Chinese puzzle box (opposite), differs from many by the absence of a central disk threaded between the two main components. Yet the principle of releasing the individual pieces remains the same.

This meleda puzzle, or Tålamodsspel ("patience game"), is one of a collection of folk puzzles from the Nordiska Museet in Stockholm. Such puzzles are still occasionally found in Scandinavia and Britain.

A whole range of varied and intriguing puzzles are made up of the elements of ring, string, and ball. A few puzzles use all of these items, but in many there are only two of them. All of these puzzles follow a similar pattern of construction and solution, although the puzzles with parts connected by cord are far more flexible than those linked by solid rods.

The aim in ring-string-ball puzzles is either to remove one element from the puzzle or merely to move it with respect to the main component. In some puzzles the solution depends on the serial repetition of a small number of basic moves until eventually one part is removed or repositioned. While such puzzles require patient manipulation, they are often relatively easy to do, once the basic moves are known. There are other puzzles that can be solved only by a series of dissimilar moves in the correct order. One mistake may complicate such a puzzle even more.

Before attempting any of the puzzles that are linked by string, take heed of the Reverend J. G. Wood's advice to young gentlemen confronted with such problems. In his book *The Boy's Modern Playmate*, written in 1890, he suggests that "when a string is used, the key is generally to be found in a loop which can be drawn over a knot or ball." This maneuver of moving a small part in order to release a larger component is useful in all ring-string-ball puzzles.

Ring-string-ball puzzles have been played for such a long time that their exact origins remain a mystery. Possibly they can be traced to Africa, for today in many parts of the continent ring-string-ball puzzles are popular amusements. Certainly some of the simplest puzzles must be of African origin, such as the *djibilibi* — a piece of bamboo with a loop of creeper running through two holes in a way closely resembling the method of attaching price tags used in many stores. Other African puzzles are more complex. They often include seeds or stones, through which holes are bored, or specially prepared clay beads strung on the creeper. Similar puzzles are made by Eskimo societies, using the materials close at hand; the base and beads are usually made of bone, threaded with gut and sinew from seals or caribou. The Chinese, with characteristic artistry, have produced some of the most beautiful of all ring-string-ball puzzles, particularly during the boom in the ivory trade. These exquisitely hand-carved puzzles were often intended for export to Europe. The Norwegians seem to have treated these puzzles in the most practical manner, however, using versions of the meleda puzzle, or "tiring irons," as baggage locks.

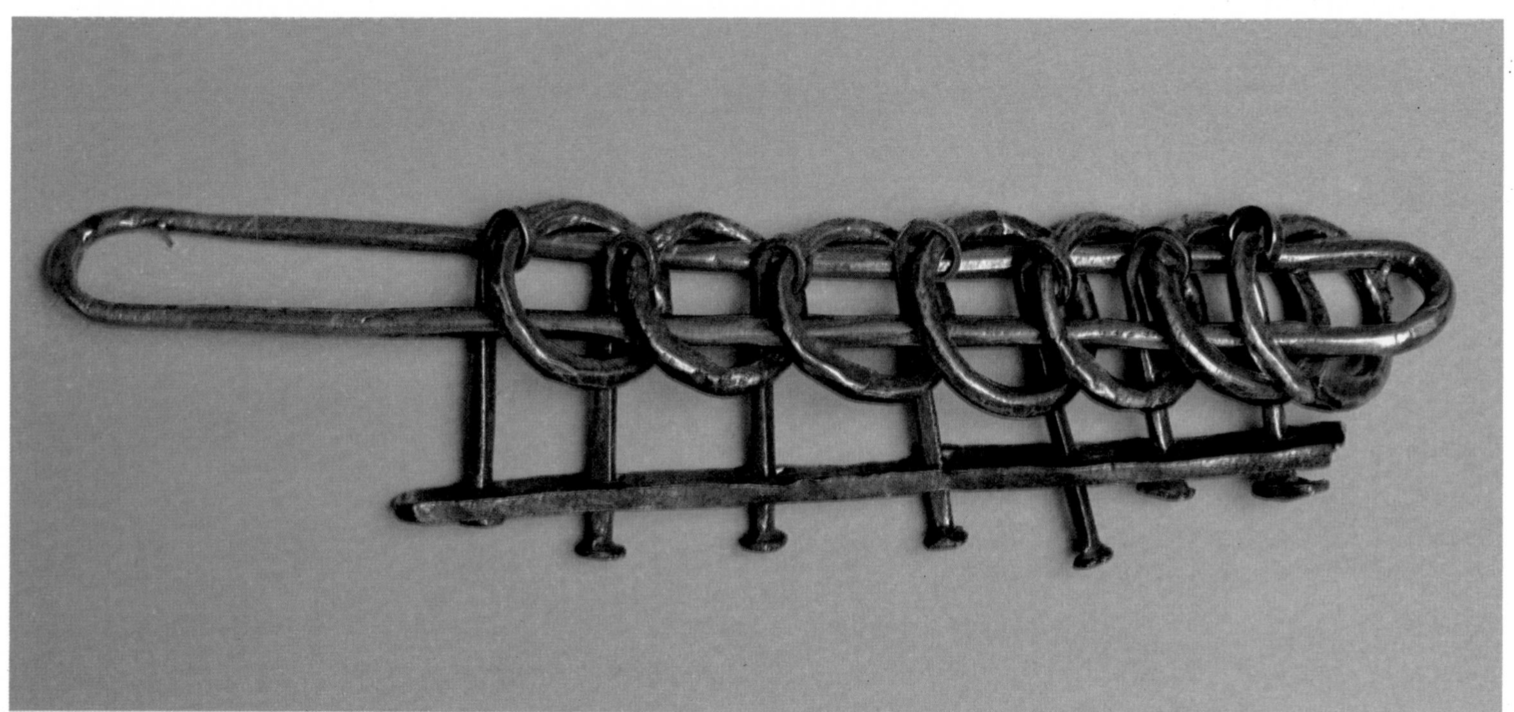

The Crown Puzzle

The crown puzzle features all of the components of ring, string, and ball arranged about a circular wooden board. To solve the puzzle requires a truly logical mind, for the aim is to transfer all the balls to the underside of the circle and the rings to the top side. The balls and rings are threaded on a continuous loop of string.

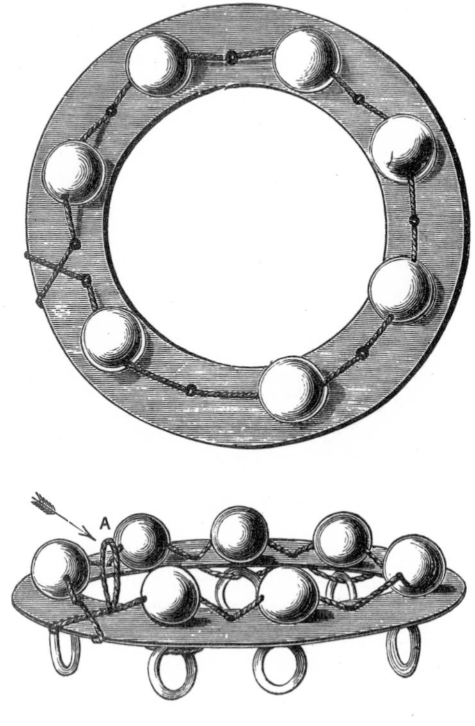

Loop A, indicated in the diagrams, is the starting point for all moves in this puzzle.

How to Solve the Puzzle

This puzzle is solved in four stages, each of which starts at loop A. First the balls are transferred to a single loop of cord; then the rings are transferred to another loop; then the balls are placed in their new positions; and finally the rings are placed on top. To do this, pull up loop A from the underside to the top of the ring. Pass the ball that is adjacent in the counterclockwise direction through loop A. Pull up the next loop and pass the second ball through this loop and loop A. Continue around the board until all of the balls are on one loop. Now pull loop A to the underside of the board and pass the adjacent ring through it. Continue as you did with the balls, but each time pull a loop downward through the board. Continue until all the rings are on one loop. Still pulling the loops to the underside, pass the balls along the cord and through the loops, but now work in a clockwise direction. All the balls must pass through the first loop, but only six go through the second and so on, each time leaving a ball in position. Repeat this stage with the rings, pulling the loops up.

Materials

Plywood board, at least 4" square
Seven balls, 1" diameter with 1/8" holes
Seven rings, 1" diameter
At least 1 yard of 1/16" nylon cord
Varnish

Tools

Fretsaw; drill with 1/8" bit; matches; brush; compasses; ruler; pencil; and sandpaper.

How to Make the Puzzle

Keeping the point of the compasses in one position on the board, draw three circles of 4", 3", and 2" diameter, respectively. Set the compasses to 1 1/4". Put the point on the circumference of the 3" diameter circle and mark two points, each 1 1/4" on either side of this point. Place the point of the compasses on each of these marks in turn and draw another line to cross the circumference of the circle, also 1 1/4" away. Repeat this once more. Put the point of the compasses on one of the last marks to be made, and mark off one more point, also 1 1/4" away. There should be eight marks on the circle, including the original mark made by the compasses. Through each mark drill a 1/8" hole. Cut around the 4" circle with the fretsaw. Drill a 1/8" hole just inside the 2" circle, insert the fretsaw and cut out this circle. Sand and varnish the ring. Burn the ends of the cord, pinch them into points, and then thread all seven balls onto the cord. Place the puzzle in front of you as in the diagram (bottom right), with the two holes that are closer together at the top. Thread one end of the cord — the head end — through the left top hole, from the upper to the lower side of the ring. Pull through just enough cord to be able to thread the head end back through the hole, to the top, keeping a loop on the underside. Move one ball along the cord, so that it lies over the top left hole. Thread the tail end of the cord through the head end loop, then string a brass ring onto it. Now thread the tail end up through the second hole, immediately to the left of the first hole. Draw the tail over the cord, trapping the first ball between the first and second holes, and then thread the tail down through the second hole. Repeat these movements, positioning one ball and one ring at a time. When the tail has been threaded through the last hole, seal the ends together.

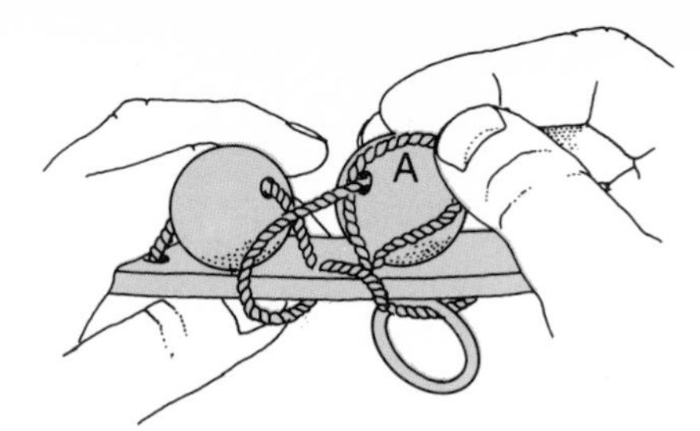

For the first move lift loop A over the first ball, which will then slide off the wooden ring and leave a space that the next ball can be moved to fill.

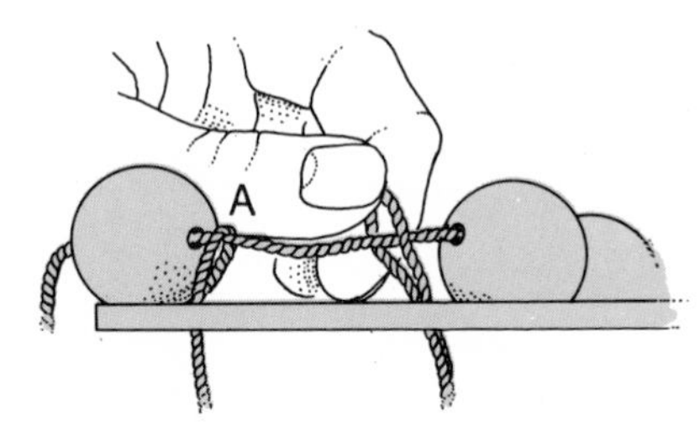

Lift up the second loop and pass the second ball through it and through loop A. Continue in this way around the board until all balls are together.

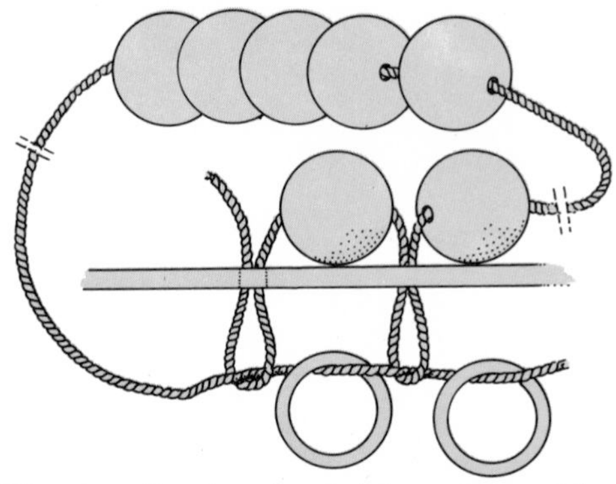

When threading the tail end of the cord around the puzzle, pull the rings down occasionally and check that the cord is exactly following this diagram.

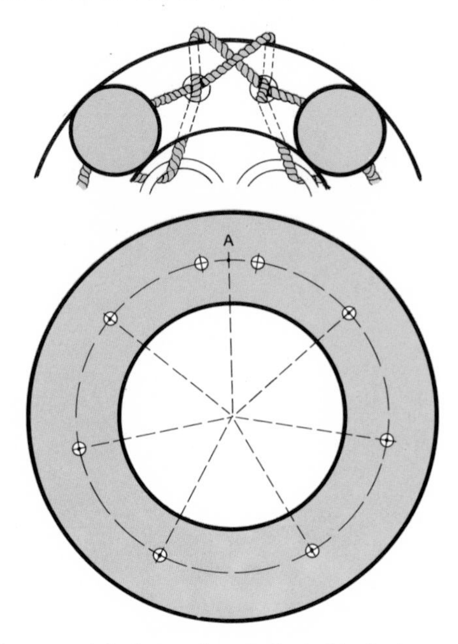

Cut around the heavy lines indicated in the lower diagram, and drill 1/8" holes in place. Thread the puzzle and connect the ends as in the top figure.

The strong grain of the waxy larch makes it a very attractive wood to use when constructing the intriguing block and tackle puzzle.

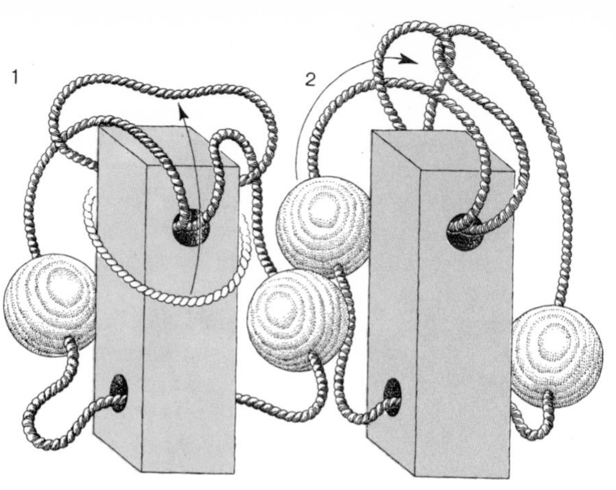

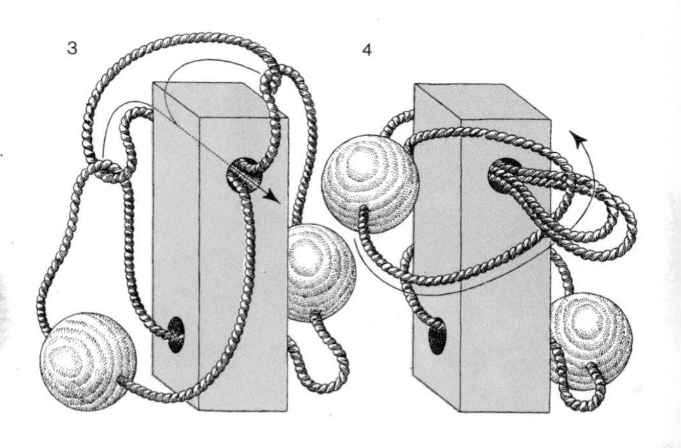

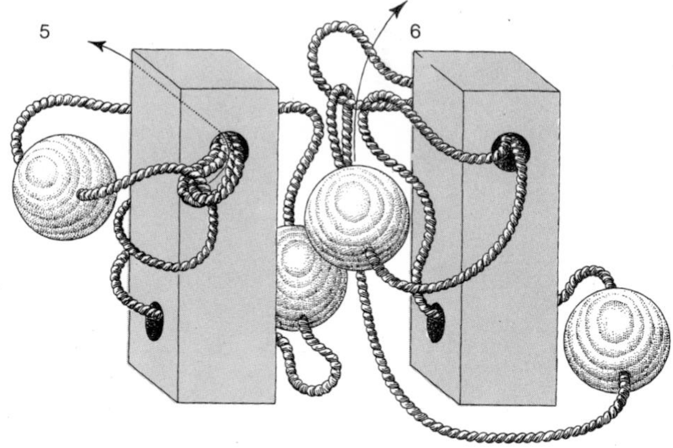

The Block and Tackle

A block of larch, cord, and a pair of wooden balls are combined to make this unusual puzzle. It was developed by combining the ideas and design of a traditional African puzzle with the Sleeper Stopper of Stewart T. Coffin. In the Sleeper Stopper the cord is glued into the lower hole in the block, while in the block and tackle puzzle it is free to slide through the hole. The point of the puzzle is to maneuver both balls to one side of the block, a task requiring several deliberate steps.

Materials
A block of wood, 1″ × 1″ × 4″
2 feet of cord, $\frac{1}{8}$″ diameter
Two wooden balls, $1\frac{1}{2}$″ diameter, with holes of at least $\frac{3}{16}$″ diameter
Varnish
Cotton thread

Tools
A drill with $\frac{3}{8}$″ bit; brush; ruler; pencil; needle; sandpaper.

How to Make the Puzzle
On one long side of the block mark a point $\frac{1}{2}$″ from the long sides and $\frac{3}{4}$″ from one end. Center the $\frac{3}{8}$″ bit of the drill on this point and bore a hole through the block. Turn the block 90° so that the hole lies in the horizontal plane. Now drill another hole at the opposite end to the first hole, $\frac{1}{2}$″ from the long sides and $\frac{3}{4}$″ from the end. Sandpaper and varnish the block. Thread the block with the cord, as shown in the model above. First take one end of the cord, and thread it through the top hole from back to front, and then through the right-hand ball. Pass the cord through the lower hole from right to left, then through the left-hand ball. Thread it through the top hole, from front to back, and counterclockwise round the top of the block. Bind the ends together.

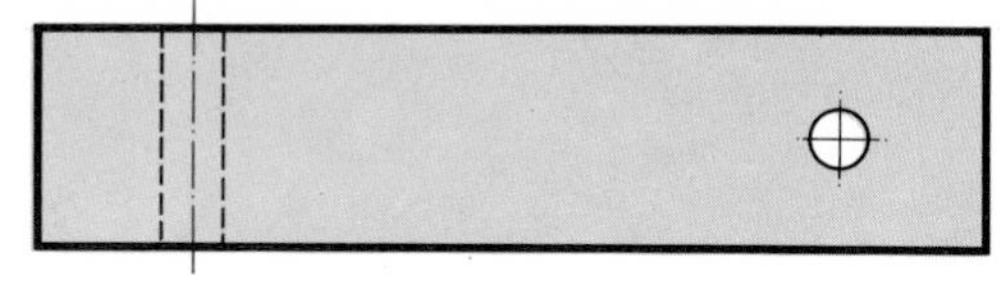

Drill the holes at right angles to one another.

Before attempting to solve this puzzle, stand it in front of you with the cords arranged as in the model.
1. Pull this top loop out toward you, and then pass it back over the top of the block.
2. Run the left wooden ball up the cord until it passes through the top loop, following the direction arrows in the second diagram.
3. Now tug at the two cords which run through the top hole, bringing them toward you. This movement will drag the loops which carry the two wooden balls through the top hole as well.
4. Keep pulling the double loop through the hole until the left wooden ball can be passed along the cord and through the loops.
5. Pull the loops back through the hole, tugging on the cords at the back of the block.
6. Arrange the puzzle as in this diagram, and then slide the left ball up the cord and through the loop at the back, until both balls are at the same side.

Meleda

Known in China as Ryou-Kaik-Tjyo — the "delay guest instrument" — the meleda is one of the oldest mechanical puzzles in existence. Its origins are still unknown. According to Chinese legend it was invented by the soldier-hero Hung Ming (A.D. 181-234), who gave it to his wife when he went to war. In trying to solve the puzzle, she forgot to grieve for her husband.

Meleda first appeared in Europe in the mid-16th century and was described by the Italian mathematician Geronimo Cardano. In 1693 it was mentioned in an English book, and around that time it gained popularity in many European countries. Early examples are found in England and Scandinavia.

In Norway these puzzles have even been put to practical use, for they were found to be very effective luggage locks. Made of iron, meleda certainly warranted the alternative name "tiring irons," a name which still persists. It would surely be a determined or desperate thief who could manage to open a trunk locked with this puzzle.

Meleda puzzles can be bought in toy and game shops in many countries. They are usually made of wood and aluminum and are often called Chinese rings or puzzling rings. However, it is much more enjoyable to construct your own meleda puzzle. This is a fairly simple task, given the necessary tools and materials, and a free afternoon or evening. Full instructions are given on page 102.

How to Solve the Puzzle

The object in meleda is to try to remove all seven rings, and the accompanying balls and bars, from the hairpin-shaped loop around which they are linked. After you succeed in this, they must be replaced on the loop. To take the rings off the loop, the first ring, *a*, or *a* and *b* (see diagrams) together, can be dropped simply, by taking them over the end of the loop and dropping them through the central space. But any other ring can be removed only when it is second from the leading end of the loop. To remove ring *c*, you must drop ring *a*, slide *b* temporarily over the end of the loop, and follow it with ring *c* which can then be dropped through the central space. Then replace *b* on the loop. To replace the rings, reverse the procedure.

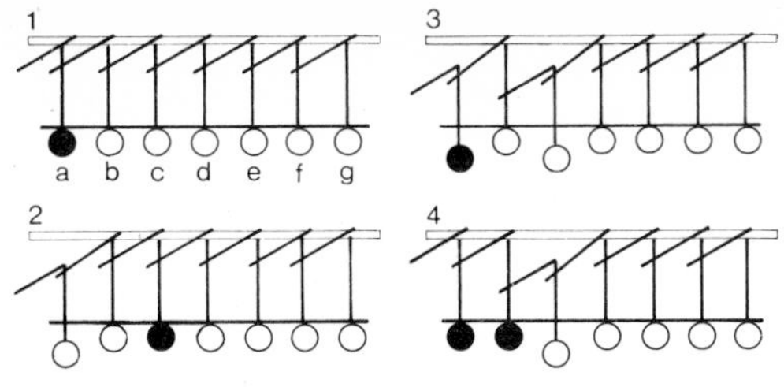

Drop ring *a*, and then ring *c*; replace ring *a* before dropping rings *a* and *b* together from the loop.

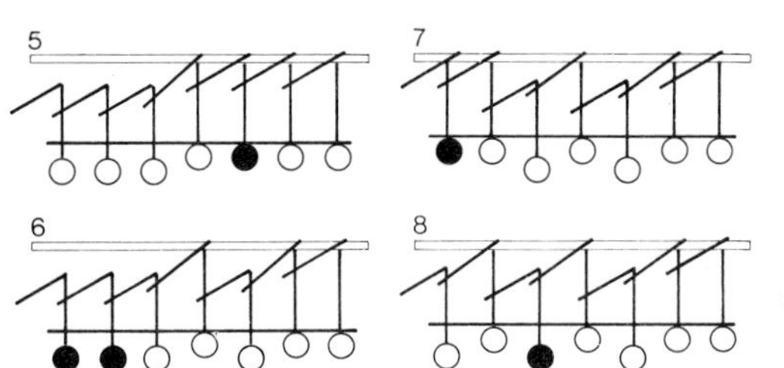

Drop ring e, and then replace rings *a* and *b*. Drop ring *a*, which allows you to replace ring *c*.

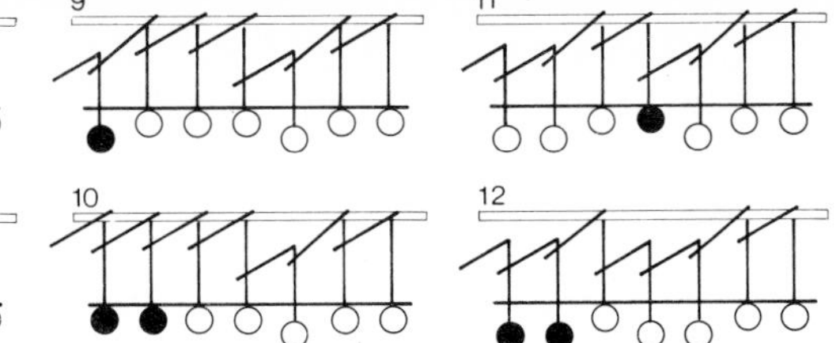

Replace ring *a*, then drop rings *a* and *b* together. Remove ring *d* before replacing rings *a* and *b*.

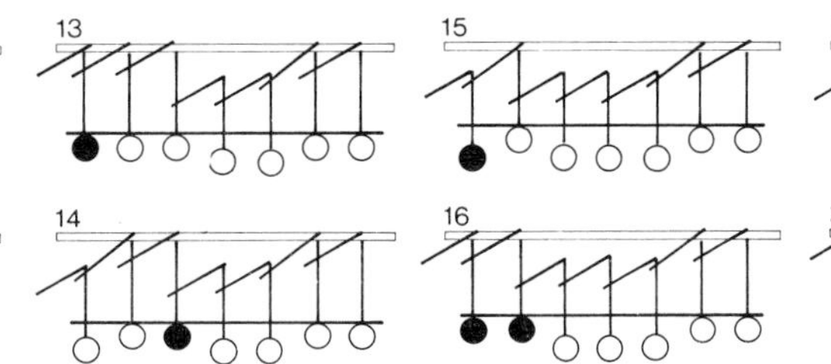

Drop ring *a*, then drop ring *c* from the loop. Replace ring *a*, and then drop rings *a* and *b* again.

In the diagrams above the letters run from *a* to *g*, from the head to the handle of the meleda. Balls filled in black indicate the next rings to be manipulated — either dropped or replaced on the loop — in the course of dismantling the meleda.

This brightly painted example of a home-made meleda shows how attractive they can be. The fixed part of this puzzle comprises the hairpin loop and handle, while the assemblage of balls, rods, and rings make up the movable part.

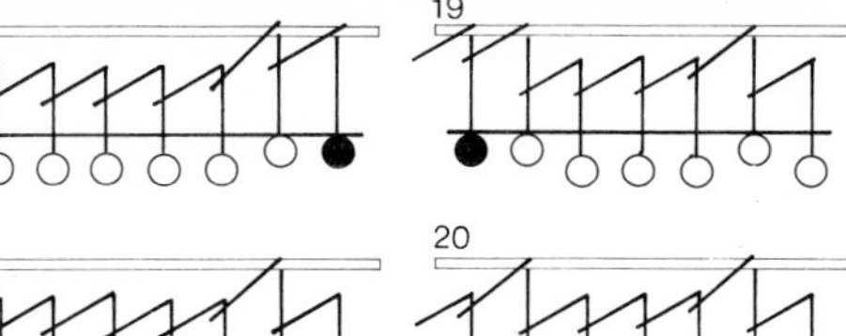

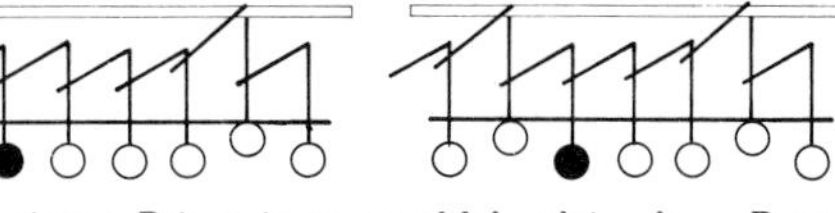

Drop ring *g*. Bring rings *a* and *b* back in place. Drop ring *a*, and then replace ring *c* on the loop.

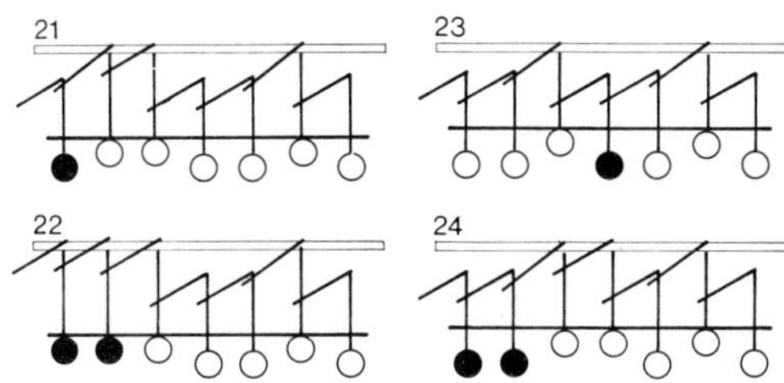

Replace ring *a* on the loop, and then drop both *a* and *b*. Replace ring *d*, then rings *a* and *b*.

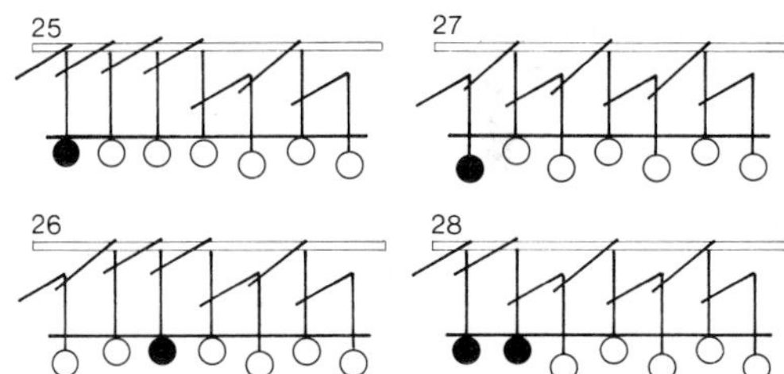

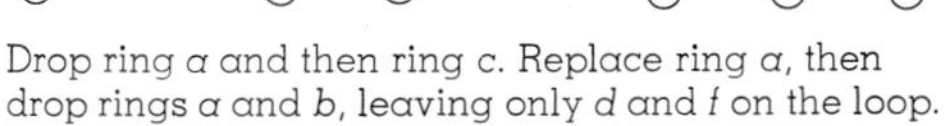

Drop ring *a* and then ring *c*. Replace ring *a*, then drop rings *a* and *b*, leaving only *d* and *f* on the loop.

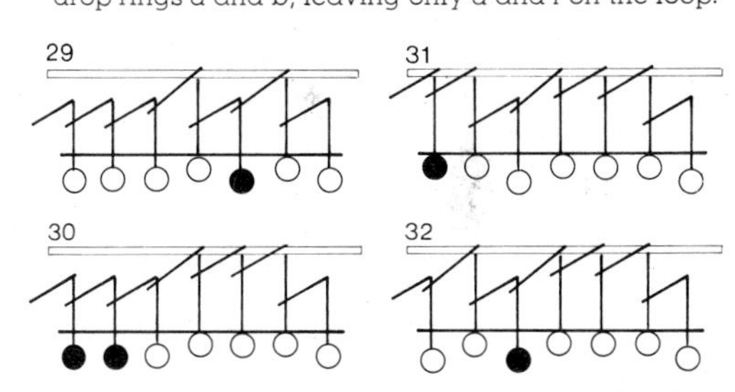

Replace ring e, then *a* and *b*. Drop ring *a* and replace ring *c*, so only *a* and *g* are off the loop.

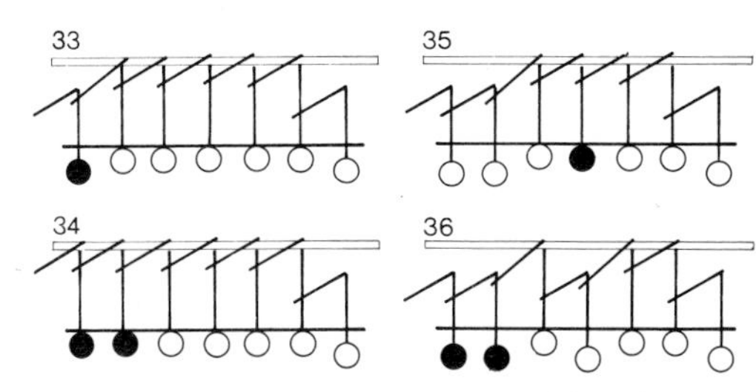

Replace ring *a*. Then drop rings *a* and *b*. Drop ring *d*, and then replace rings *a* and *b*.

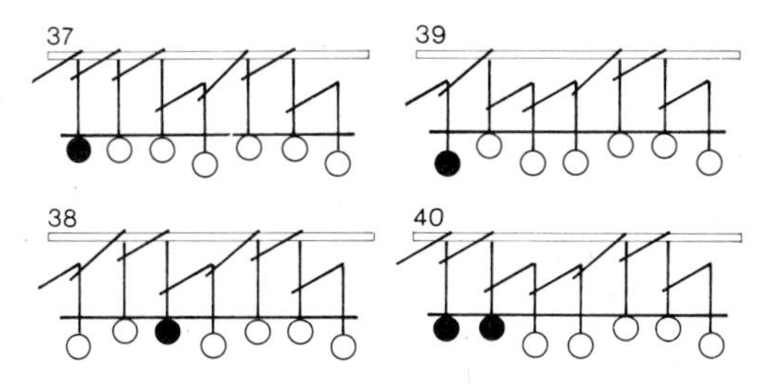

Drop ring *a* and then ring *c*. Replace ring *a* before dropping both rings *a* and *b* together.

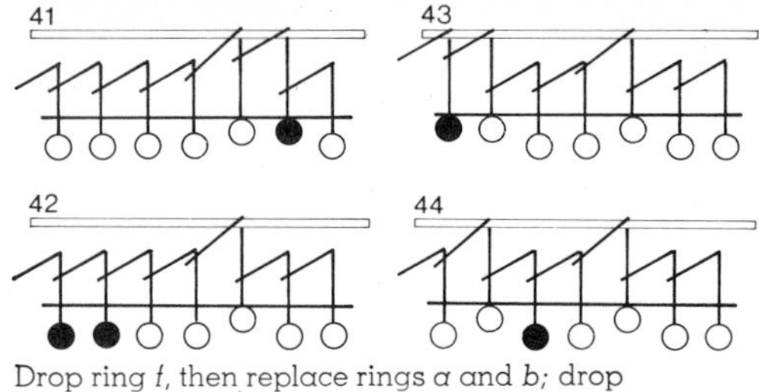

Drop ring *f*, then replace rings *a* and *b*; drop ring *a*, and then replace ring *c* on the loop.

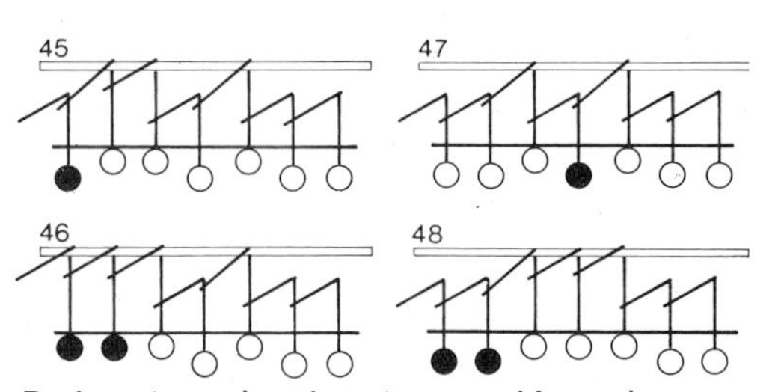

Replace ring *a*, then drop rings *a* and *b* together. Replace ring *d*, and then bring back rings *a* and *b*.

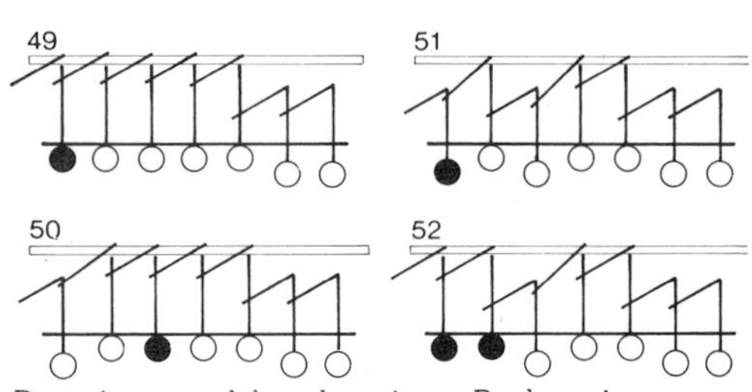

Drop ring *a*, and then drop ring *c*. Replace ring *a* before dropping both rings *a* and *b* together.

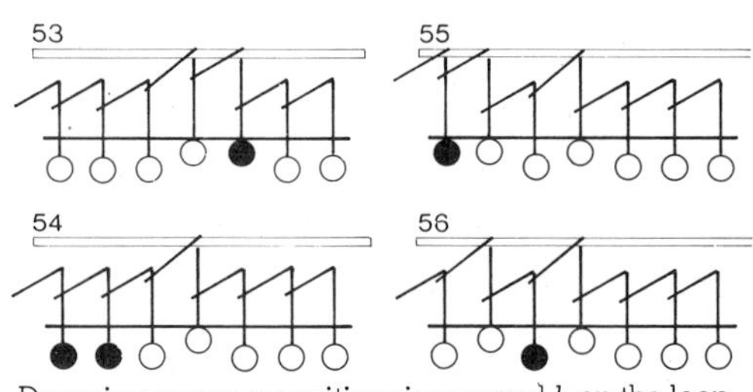

Drop ring *e*; now reposition rings *a* and *b* on the loop. Drop ring *a*, so now ring *c* can be replaced.

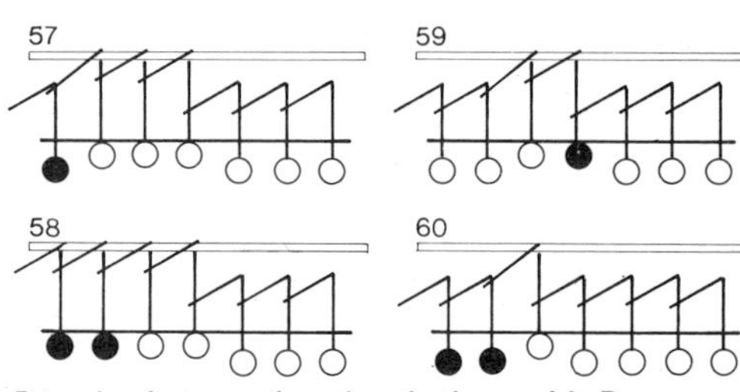

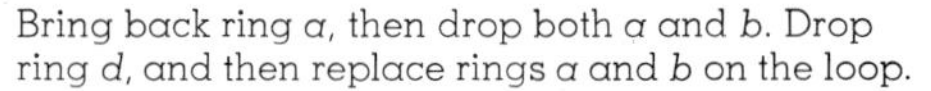

Bring back ring *a*, then drop both *a* and *b*. Drop ring *d*, and then replace rings *a* and *b* on the loop.

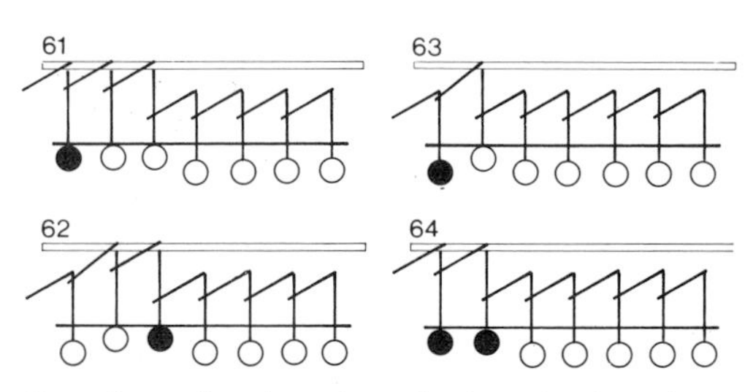

Drop ring *a*, then drop ring *c*. Replace ring *a*, and then drop rings *a* and *b*, thus solving the puzzle.

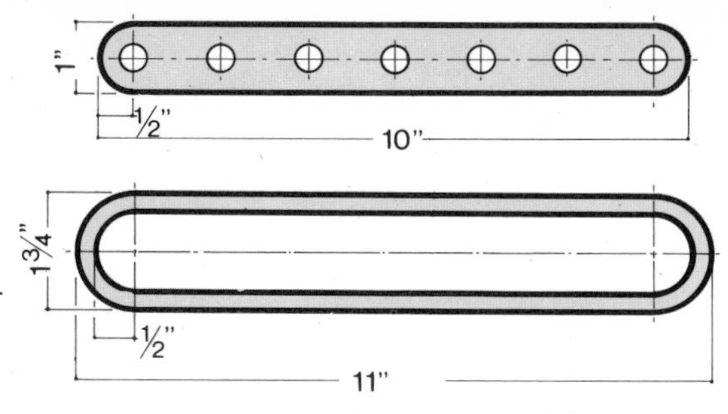

The top diagram gives the dimensions of the seven-hole platform of the meleda, while the lower diagram shows the exact shape of the loop frame.

Materials

Plywood board, 1¾" × 11" × ⅜"
Plywood board, 1" × 10" × ⅛"
Seven wooden balls, 1" diameter
A wooden handle, 4" long
Seven steel rings, 2⅜" diameter
1 yard of wooden dowel, ⅜" diameter
Seven screw eyes, ⅝" long with a diameter slightly larger than the thickness of the steel rings
One wood screw, 2" long
Wood glue
Paint

Tools

Ruler; pencil; electric drill or brace with ⅛", ⅜", and 7/16" bits; vise; fretsaw; compasses; pliers; paintbrushes; sandpaper.

How to Make the Puzzle

To make the loop, mark midway points at the two ends of the thicker plywood (⅞" from the long sides). Connect these two points with a straight pencil line. Measure and mark a point ⅞" from each end on this line. Set your drawing compasses to ⅞", center them on each of these points in turn, and draw an arc at both ends. Reset your compasses to ½", place the point on the same marks and draw two circles. Connect the tops and bottoms of the two circles by drawing horizontal lines, thereby creating an elongated ellipse. Bore a hole inside this ellipse, near its inner edge. Unfasten the blade of your fretsaw and insert it into the hole. Now refasten the blade to the frame, saw out the center of the ellipse and discard it. With the fretsaw follow the lines of the arcs drawn at the ends of the loop, trimming off the board's corners. With one end of the loop in a vise, bore a ⅛" hole at one end for the handle. Sandpaper the loop until it is smooth. Insert a 2"-long wood screw through the bored hole in the frame end and into the wooden handle.

To make the lower bar, mark the midway points at the two ends of the thinner plywood board (½" from the sides). Connect these two points by drawing a straight line. Measure and mark a point ½" from each end along this line. Set your compasses to ½", then place the point on each of these two marks in turn, and draw an arc at both ends. Using the fretsaw, follow the lines of the arcs, and trim off the board's corners, creating an ellipse. Place the ruler on the center line of the board and divide the section of the line between the two circle centers into six equal lengths. With the 7/16" auger bit fitted in the drill, bore seven holes in the board, centering on the points marked. Sandpaper the board until it is smooth.

Place one of the wooden balls in a vise. Drill a hole ⅜" wide and ⅜" deep. Repeat this with the other six balls. Cut the dowel into seven equal pieces. At this point paint the wooden parts of the meleda in whatever colors you choose. Then glue the seven dowels into the balls. Pass the dowels through the holes of the lower bar. With pliers fasten the partly opened screw eyes onto the free ends of the dowels. Fasten the rings, beginning with the one nearest the handle. Slip this ring into the screw eye and close the eye. Loop the ring over the next dowel before inserting the next ring into its screw eye. Continue in this way through to the first dowel, where the ring is free. When these stages are completed you have only to link the rings and loop. The only way to do this is to reverse the solution process, starting at diagram 64 and working back to diagram number 1.

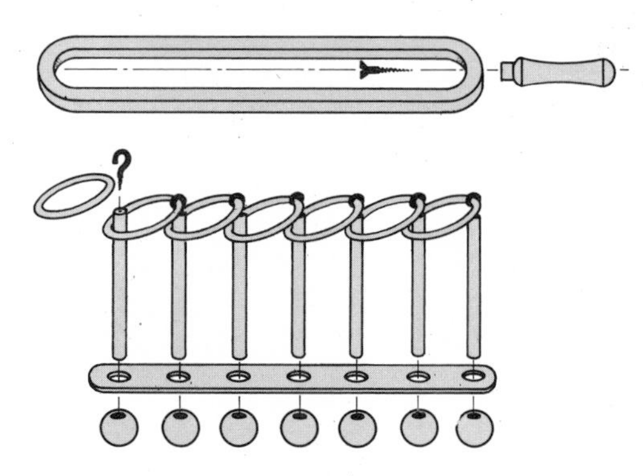

Screw the loop to the handle as above top. The rings, balls, and dowels fit as shown.

The Pancake Puzzle

Hanging from a loop of cord in this puzzle is a wooden button. The cord is threaded through the flat pancake in an unbroken ring, so that the two components seem to be interlocked. Yet there is a way of manipulating the cord and removing it from the pancake with the button attached and the cord intact.

Materials
Plywood board, 6" × 7" × 3/8"
Paint or varnish
2 yards of 1/8" thick cord

Tools
Fretsaw; drill with 3/8" and 1/8" bits; compasses; pencil; ruler; brush; needle; sandpaper.

How to Make the Puzzle
Draw a 2"-diameter circle and a 5"-diameter circle on the board. On the larger circle draw in the diameters AB and CD at right angles to one another. With the compasses set at 2 1/2" radius, place the point on A and make two marks on the circumference. Move the point of the compasses to C and mark the circumference between A and C. Then place the point of the compasses at D and make a mark on the circumference between A and D. Draw diameters through the four new points. There are now six diameters drawn, all at angles of 30° to one another. On each diameter drill two 3/8" holes, each 1/2" from the circumference. Drill a 1/8" hole just outside the circle, and insert the blade of the fretsaw into it. Cut out this large circle. Move to the smaller circle, and draw in a diameter. On this line drill two 3/8" holes, each 1/2" from the edge of the circle. Drill a small hole just outside the circle, and cut it out in the same way as the larger one. Sandpaper both pieces and then paint or varnish them. Thread a strand of cord through each hole in the small circle, and bind the free ends of the cord together with thread. Do not use a knot here or the puzzle will not work. Take the cord loop and thread it through the small holes in the large circle, as in the model. When you have passed it through the last hole, turn and thread it back the way it came, skipping the eleventh hole. When the cord has again passed through the first hole, four strands run through all the holes except the eleventh. Loop the cord over the small wooden disk. Now pull the cord back through the holes, so that only a double strand runs around the large disk. Adjust the loop, as in the top model.

Here is a puzzle that can be made simply from leftover pieces of plywood and a length of cord.

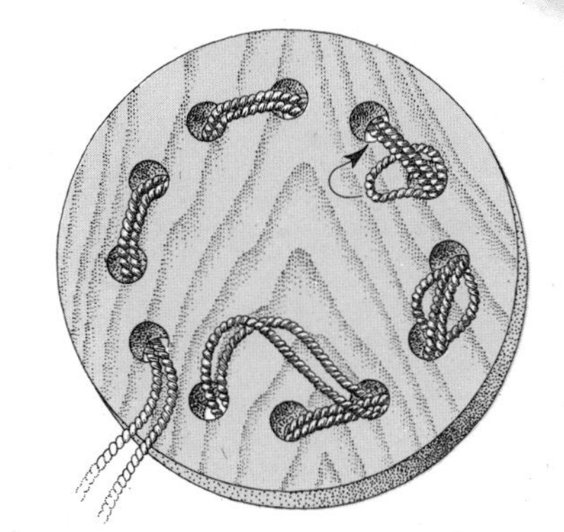

Bring the button close to the pancake. Work the excess cord around the puzzle, through the holes, to the point where the cord interlinks with itself. Now thread this long loop back around the puzzle, through the holes, as in the diagram.

Loop the cord over the button as shown above. Retrace the movements of the cord, through the holes in the pancake, away from the button. When you reach the last hole again, you will find that the cord and attached button can be slipped free.

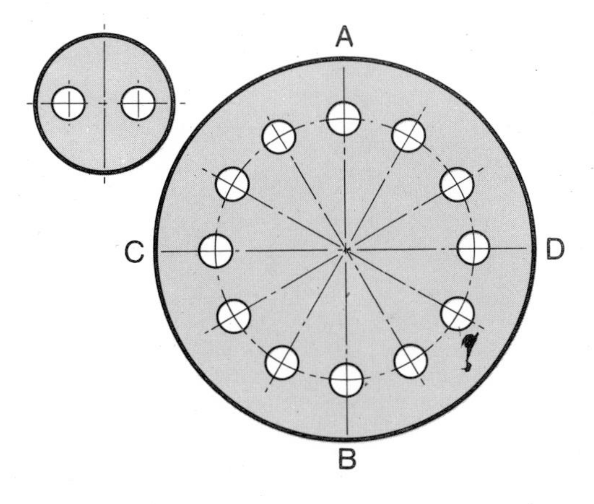

There is room for the two circles in one 6" × 7" rectangle of wood if they are both positioned as close as possible to opposite corners. After drilling the holes where marked, cut out the two disks.

After you have constructed your own Chinese ladder, why not experiment with the decoration? This model was colored with enamel paint and plastic tape.

The Chinese Ladder

This puzzle is one of the many to come out of China. It consists of eight disks lying on the steps of a small ladder, held in place by a long cord that passes through them and through the slats of the ladder. The aim is to take the disks off the ladder but to keep them on the cord like a string of beads, attached to the ladder only at the left-hand knot.

Materials

Four plywood slats, 4″ × 1½″ × ⅛″
Two plywood slats, 5″ × 1½″ × ⅛″
Wooden dowel, 4″ long and 1″ thick
Paint or varnish
1 yard of cord about 1/16″ thick
Wood glue

Tools

Dovetail saw; electric or hand drill with ¼″ bit; clamp; brush; ruler; pencil; a long wool needle; sandpaper.

How to Make the Puzzle

On one small slat draw a line ½″ from each end and another down the center, ¾″ from the long sides. Place this slat on top of the other three and hold them with the clamp. Where the lines cross drill holes through all four slats with the ¼″ bit. Take the two long slats and mark them off into five equal parts. Now glue the ends of the four slats to these side pieces at the marked positions, thus making the ladder. Saw through the dowel at ⅜″ intervals to make nine disks, and through the center of each drill a ¼″ hole. Sand and paint the puzzle. Assemble it by positioning the disks on the ladder as in the photograph. Thread them on the cord using the needle. Knot the free end of the cord.

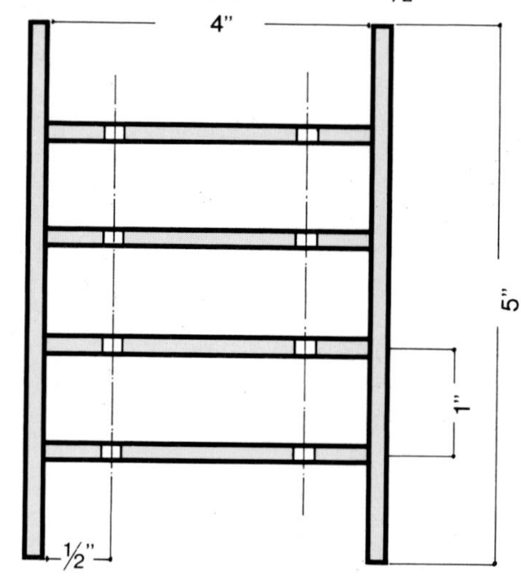

Follow the diagram to make the Chinese ladder.

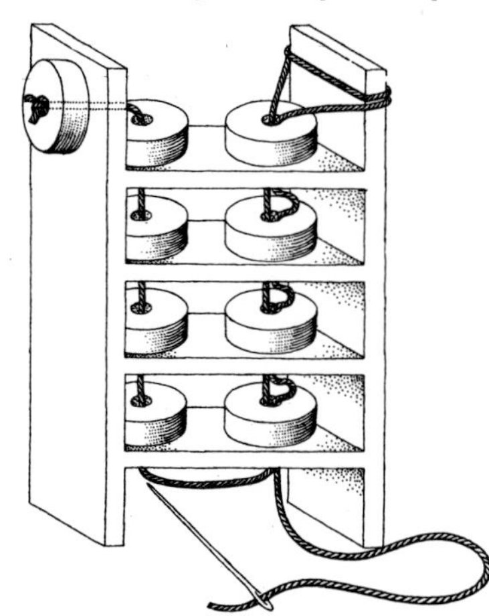

With the puzzle set up as above, wind the cord once around the top of the right-hand upright. Thread the cord down through the right-hand disks and the holes in the slats, and up through the disks and slats on the left-hand side.

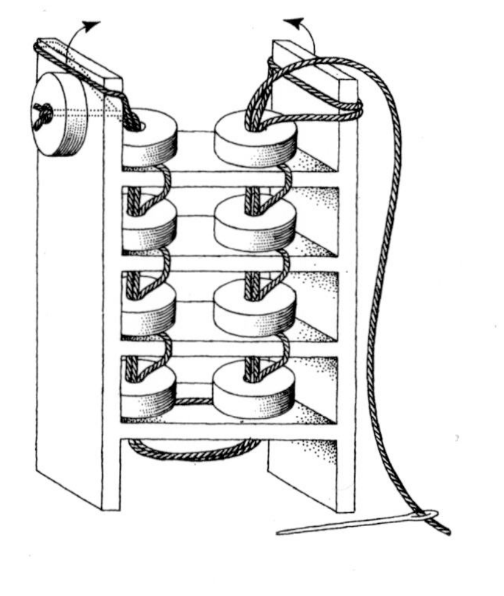

Wind the cord around the top of the left-hand upright. Thread the cord back the opposite way, but pass it only through the disks. Between the disks run the cord around the front of each slat. Slip the loops off the uprights, pull the cord and work the disks free.

The Cherry Tree

This beautiful and interesting puzzle was described in a Russian book of pastimes by E. Minskin. The cord bearing the tail piece has to be freed from the main component. What at first may seem a formidable task should pose no difficulty if you follow the principles common to most of these puzzles.

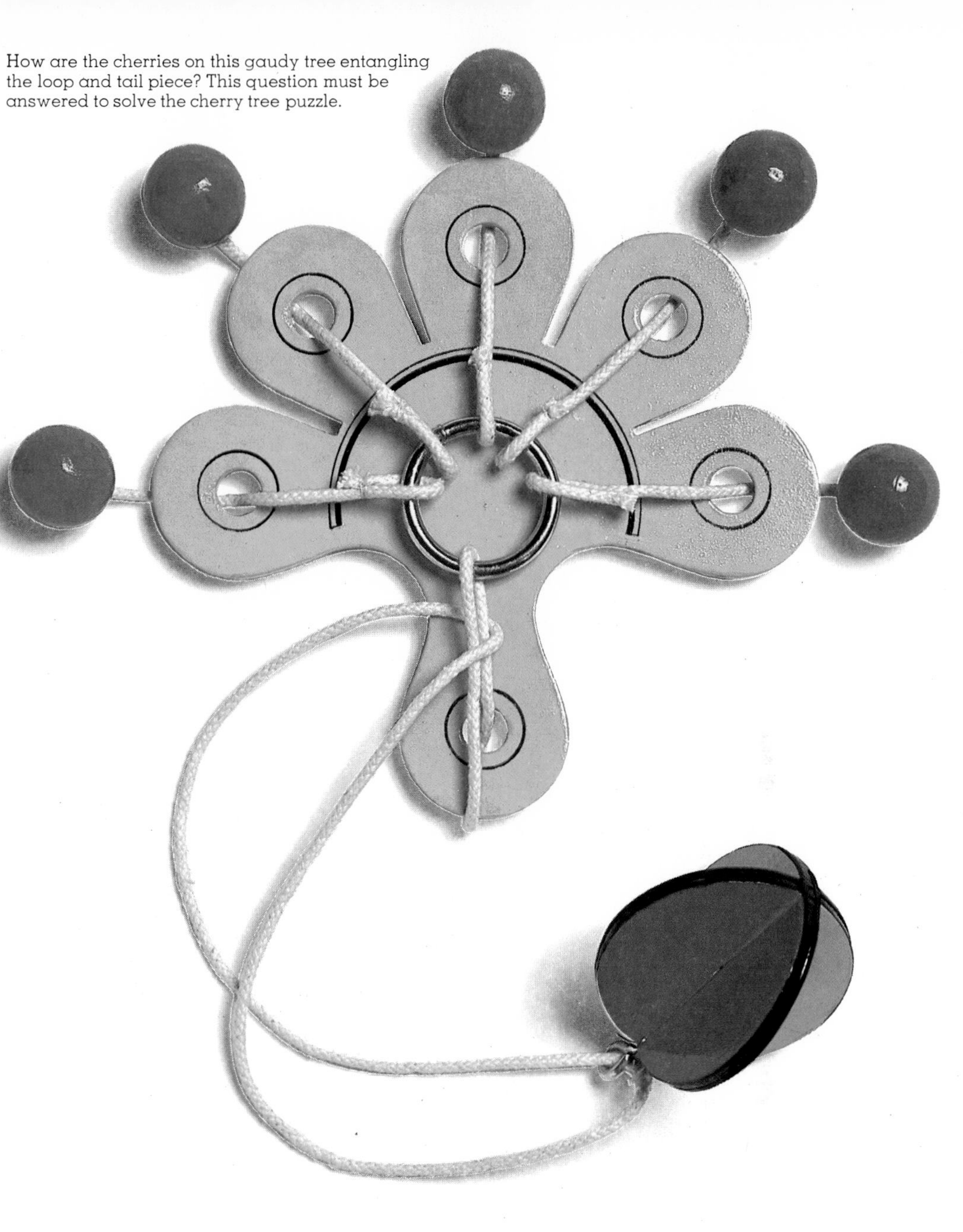

How are the cherries on this gaudy tree entangling the loop and tail piece? This question must be answered to solve the cherry tree puzzle.

Materials

One 8" square of 1/8" thick plywood
Five wooden balls, 1" diameter
One steel ring, 1 1/2" diameter
One screw eye
1 1/2 yards of cord, about 1/8" thick
Wood glue and paper glue
Paint
Thread

Tools

Fretsaw; drill with 1/8" and 3/8" bits; ruler; pencil; brush; needle; paper; sandpaper.

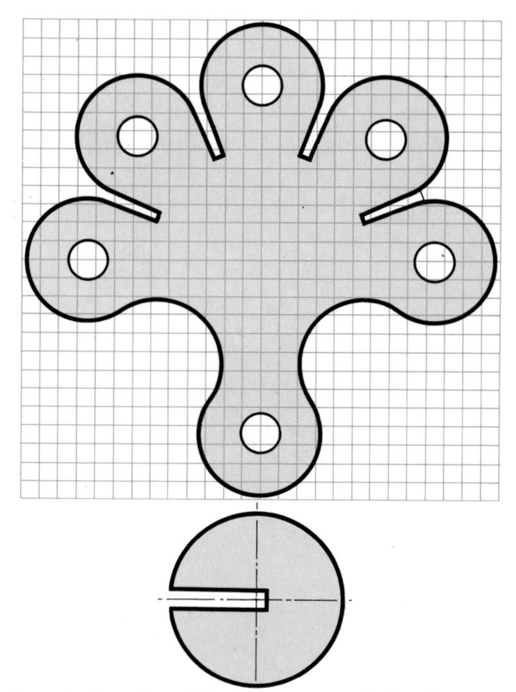

Draw in the grid and tree on paper, paste it to the plywood and cut around the heavy lines.

How to Make the Puzzle

Draw the grid of 1/4" squares on paper, and copy the tree. Glue this to the wood, and cut around the tree. Drill six 3/8" holes where marked. Also cut out two 2" disks, each with a slot 1 1/8" deep and 1/4" wide. Fit these together and glue them securely. Insert a screw eye into the tail piece, and bind on a cord. With the 1/8" bit drill a hole 1/2" deep in each ball. Insert and glue a piece of cord into each. Sand and paint the puzzle.

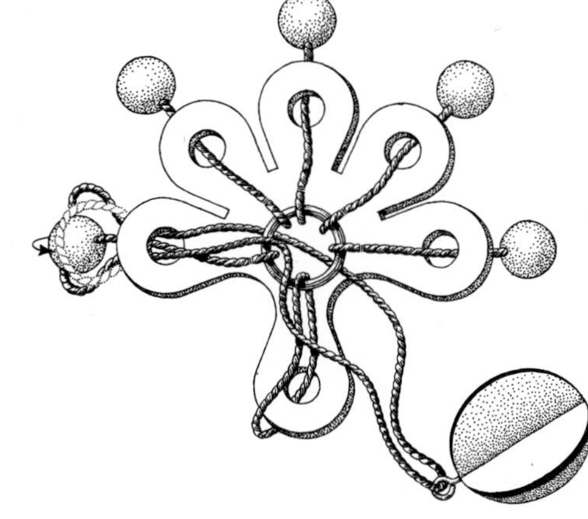

Take the loop of cord attached to the tail piece and, passing it under the steel ring, push it through the first hole on the left. Bring the loop of tail cord forward over the cherry and pull it out of the hole.

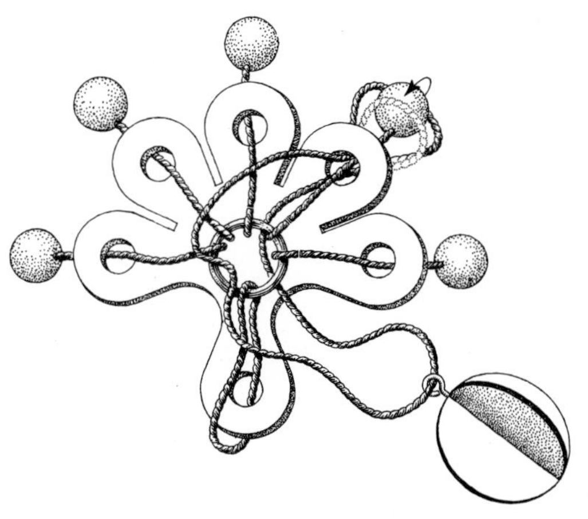

Repeat this procedure with each cherry in turn, moving clockwise. The cord must not be twisted or a knot will form — be sure to check this after each movement. When the cord is free, try to put it back by reversing the procedure.

African Ball Puzzles

The African ball puzzle is one of the most interesting and common of all ring-string-ball puzzles. It was once used in magic rites by tribes living in the jungles of the Ivory Coast. The puzzle is still used for amusement in this part of Africa, not only by the people who inhabit the remote outlying areas but also by city dwellers.

The most primitive versions of the puzzle consisted of a straight branch or twig cut from a tree and laced with vines woven to make a cord. One or more clay beads, or stones through which holes had been bored, were then added. The puzzles were not restricted to this part of Africa. Variations may be found in Guinea, and some of the most beautiful and elaborate of the puzzles were made in China. The Chinese ivory model laced with silk cords (below) was made over a century ago, probably for export to Europe. Its principle is essentially the same as that of the simple branch and vine versions.

From the most basic to the most sophisticated version of the African ball puzzle the aim is the same: to transfer a ring or ball from one hanging loop of cord to the other. The hole in the center of the board is too small for the beads to pass through, so some other way of manipulating the puzzle must be found.

A puzzle can be very easily produced from a cardboard rectangle in which holes have been punched. Use the plan on the opposite page for the shape of the board and the position of the holes. Then paint the cardboard or decorate it by covering it with colored paper. Hang curtain rings or large beads on the cord, and then thread them up as in the Chinese version below. To keep the ends of the cord in place behind the board, either knot them behind the small holes or bind the ends together into loops with thread.

1. Begin with the central loop lying in front of the bar, as in this figure. Pull the loop toward you.
2. Slide the left ring up the cord, and pass it through the central loop.
3. Keeping the ring in place, pull the left and right sections of the cord toward you through the hole in the bar by tugging the central loop.
4. Slide the ring along to the right and through the two central loops that are now at the center.
5. Pull the central loops back through the hole.
6. Let the ring slide onto the right-hand section of the cord. Readjust the lengths of the cord on the two sides of the puzzle so that they are equal. Make the corresponding movements, but working from right to left, to transfer the ring back to the left cord.

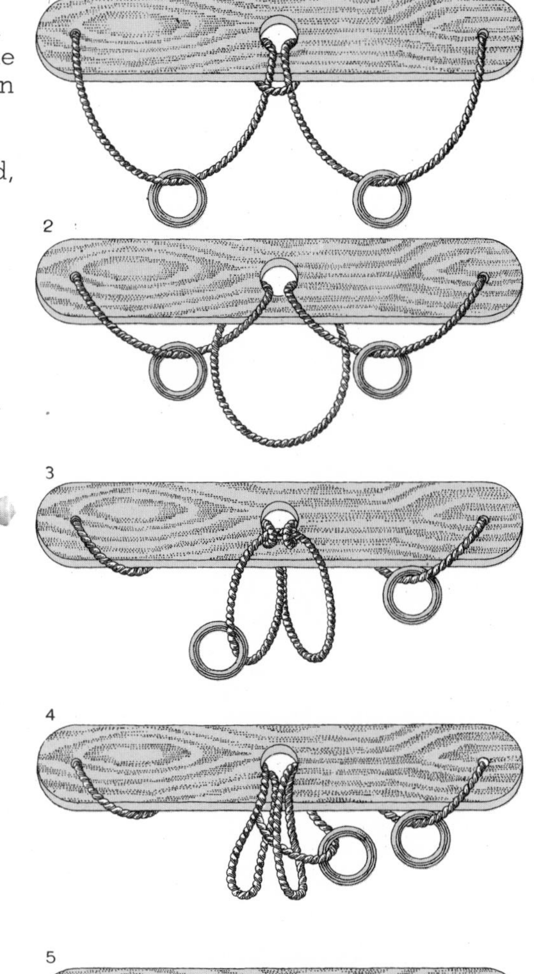

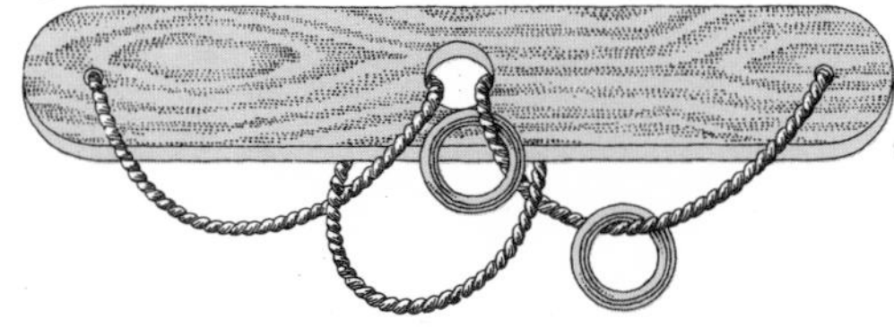

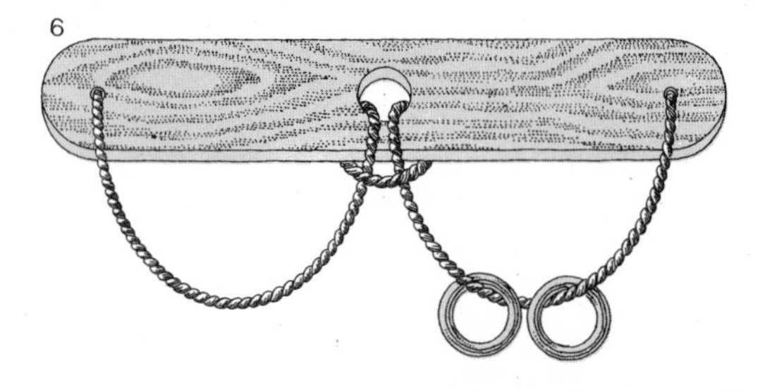

The solid piece of ivory which forms the bar in this Chinese version of the ball puzzle has three panels. Each is hand-carved with detailed scenes of family life, pagodas, and Chinese weeping willow trees.

This version of the African ball puzzle is an interesting variation on the original and is more difficult. In this puzzle seven wooden balls are threaded onto the cord, but an important difference from the original puzzle is that the cord passes through one of the balls twice.

Materials
One white pine board, 1½" × 10" × ⅛"
1 yard of cord, ⅛" thick
Seven wooden balls, 1" to 1½" diameter
Varnish or paint

Tools
Fretsaw; drill with ⅛", ⅜", and ¾" bits; ruler; pencil; sandpaper.

How to Make the Puzzle
Draw a 1½" diameter circle at each end of the pine board. Use these circles as a guide in trimming off the corners of the board with the fretsaw, leaving rounded ends as shown in the diagram (right). Where the point of the compasses was placed to make these two circles, drill holes ⅛" in diameter. Find the exact center of the board by drawing a crosswise line 5" from one end and another line lengthwise ¾" from either edge. Where these two lines cross drill a hole ¾" in diameter. Through six of the balls drill a hole of ⅛" in diameter; through the seventh drill a ⅜" hole. Sand the board, and paint or varnish it. When it is dry, thread the seven wooden balls on the cord, as shown in the model below. Lace the cord on, securing it by knotting the free ends behind the small holes in the board. Take care not to twist the cord when doing this, or you could create an unsolvable puzzle.

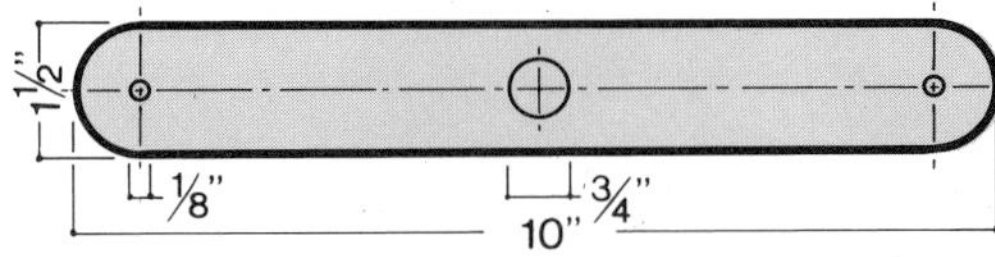

Cut along the heavy lines when making the board for the African ball puzzle. If you buy 1½" board, it will be necessary only to trim the ends.

1. Loosen the central loop. Slide the central ball and the first right-hand ball up through it.
2. Pull the two adjoining sections of the cord so that the central loop is forced through the hole in the bar, toward you.
3. Draw the newly appeared double-stranded loop through the central ball.
4. Pass the first ball through the double-stranded loop as it comes through the central ball. Pull the double loop back through the holes in the ball and the bar.
5. Loosen the loop that is now at the center, and pass the first ball through it and onto the left-hand cord.
6. Pull the central loop over the central ball and let the ball drop into place. Repeat this series of movements, each time transferring one ball.

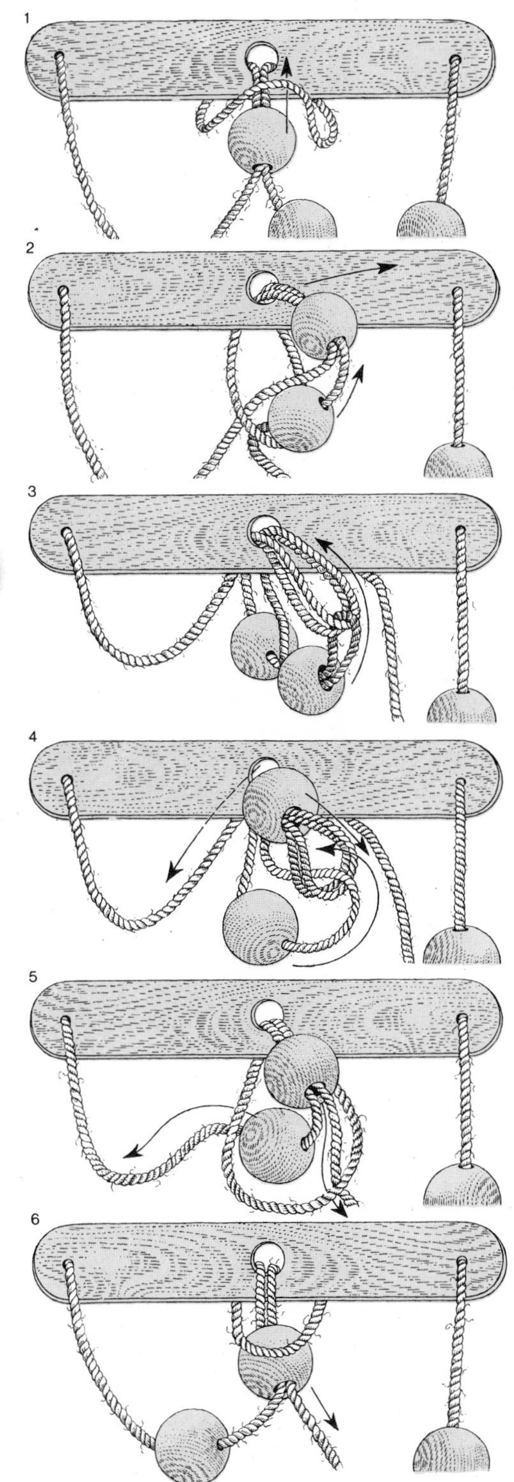

Varnished, painted, or left in its natural state, this version of the African ball puzzle can make an attractive wall hanging when not in use.

Look at this tricky problem with the eyes of a wise old owl, and release the trapped red ring from the puzzle.

The Wise Owl Puzzle

Staring down from his circular perch, this wise old owl is keeping a tightly closed beak about how to free the red ring. The ring encircles a cord, which in turn is knotted around the owl's tail. The ends of the cord pass through small holes and are then held in place around the bar of a dumbbell. Can you solve this ring-string-ball puzzle?

Materials
One piece of 1/4" plywood, 6" by 7"
Two wooden balls, 3/4" diameter
2" of wooden dowel, 1/4" diameter
18" of cord, 1/8" thick
Two nails
One steel ring (optional)
Wood glue
Paint
Thread

Tools
Fretsaw; drill with 1/2" bit; pincers; paintbrush; pencil; hammer; needle; paper; tracing paper; sandpaper.

How to Make the Puzzle
As this puzzle is cut in one piece from the plywood, the easiest way to begin is to make a direct copy of the model on this page. Lay tracing paper on the page, and draw around the owl and blue ring. If you want to make a larger puzzle, draw a grid of 1/4" squares onto the tracing paper before copying the puzzle. By transferring the pattern for the puzzle to a larger grid after you have traced it, you can make the puzzle any size desired. Transfer the final shape onto plywood, and cut around it with the fretsaw. After the outer shape has been cut, drill a hole just inside the inner circle. Insert the blade of the fretsaw into this hole and cut around the inner circle and the owl's tail. Drill three 1/2" holes where marked. From the remaining wood cut out the circle later to be painted red in the same way, or substitute a steel ring for this part of the puzzle. Sandpaper and paint the pieces. Hammer a nail into each of the wooden balls, and then clip the nailheads off. Drive the head ends of the nails into each end of the dowel, and glue them in place. Paint this dumbbell shape, and the puzzle is then ready to thread up, as in the model.

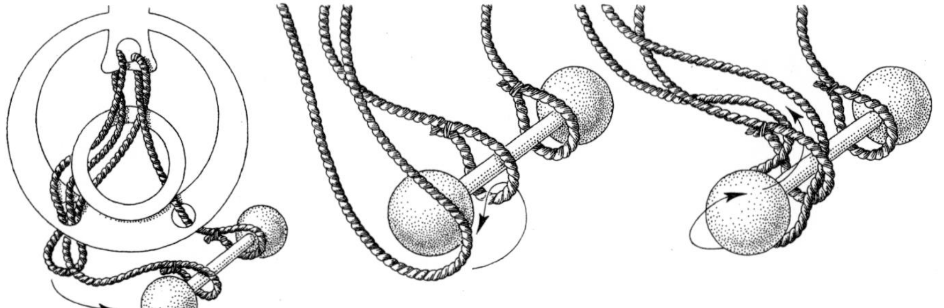

Take the loop of the knot from the owl's tail, and lead it through the small left-hand hole of the puzzle.

After you have made these moves on the left of the puzzle, repeat them on the right-hand side.

The Nimble Spindle

The aim in the nimble spindle puzzle, inspired by the meleda puzzle, is to free the elliptical wooden spindle from the main component; not an easy task when the ends of the rods and the upper bar are obstructed by large steel rings. But with correct maneuvers of the rings and spindle, the puzzle will soon be separated into two pieces.

Materials

One piece of 1/4" plywood, 10" × 3"
Six steel rings, 2 1/4" diameter
18" of wooden dowel, 1/4" thick
One 4" wooden handle
One wood screw
Four screw eyes (with eyes wider than the ring thickness)
Wood glue
Paint

Tools

Fretsaw; drill with 3/8" and 1/8" bits; metal saw; pincers; paintbrush; pencil; compasses; hammer; sandpaper.

How to Make the Puzzle

Draw a 10" × 1" rectangle on the wood, and a circle of 1" diameter at each end. Cut around the ends with a fretsaw, making the top ellipse of the diagram. Drill a 3/8" hole through both circle centers. Drill a 1/8" hole into the handle and into one end of the ellipse. Cut the head from the screw and insert the screw, head-end first, into the handle. Screw the other end into the ellipse, and glue both ends in place. On the remaining wood draw a 8" × 1 1/2" rectangle. At each end draw two concentric circles, of 1" and 1 1/2" diameters. Link the smaller circles, top and bottom, by drawing two lines, each 1/4" away from the edge of the rectangle. Trim the corners of the board away, leaving the rounded ends of the outer ellipse. Drill a hole just inside the inner ellipse, insert the fretsaw blade, and cut around this inner ellipse, following the heavy lines in the diagram. Cut the dowel in two, and drill a small hole into each end of the two pieces. Insert open screw eyes into each hole. Now sand and paint the puzzle. Loop four rings through the eyes, as in the model, and close the eyes. Cut through the other two rings and open them so that they can pass through the holes in the bar. Pinch them closed to complete the puzzle.

Suspended from both of the doweling rods, the nimble spindle is trapped by the closed steel rings.

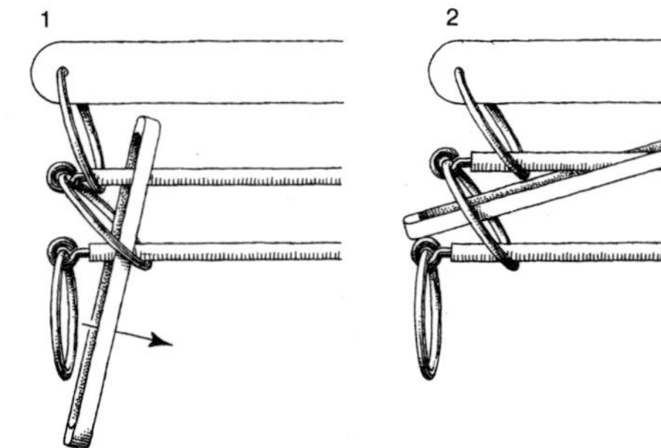

Work with the rings farthest from the handle. Push the spindle through the center ring, slide the lowest ring through the spindle, and then return the spindle.

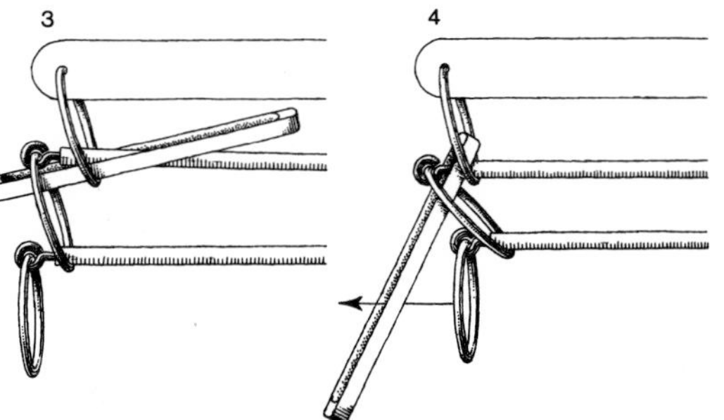

Lead the spindle through the lower part of the top ring and through the middle ring. Then slide the bottom ring through the spindle.

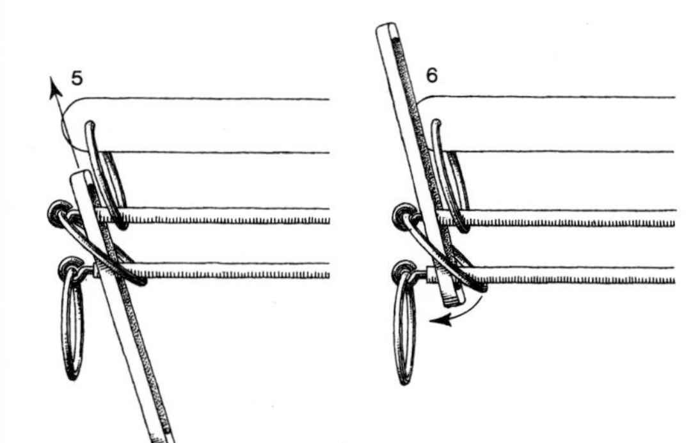

Pull the spindle up through the middle ring, and then let this ring slide to the left. Now the spindle can be passed over the rings and off the puzzle.

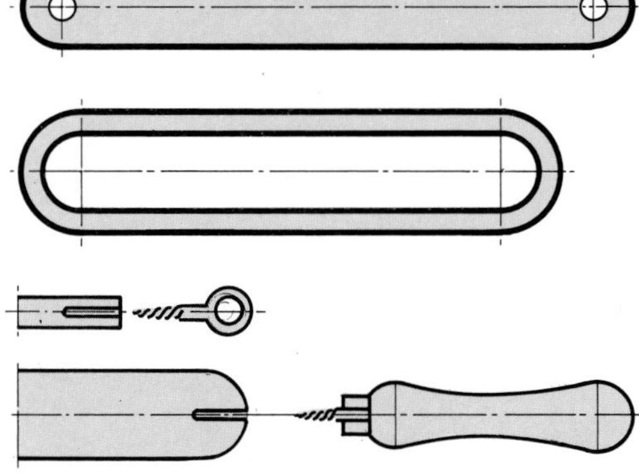

Cut around the heavy lines to make the solid bar and the open ellipse shown in the top figures. Drill holes (about 1/8" diameter) into the ends of the dowels and one end of the solid bar before inserting the screw eyes and wood screw.

The Victoria Puzzle

Named after the British Queen Victoria, this puzzle was invented over a century ago. For many years it was a popular parlor game, amusing children for hours before the days of radio and television. In the puzzle the double cord, which runs through the three wooden elements, must be removed completely.

Materials

One plywood rectangle, 2" × 14" × 1/4"
2 yards of nylon cord, 1/16" thick
Wood glue
Paint or varnish
The handle from a file
One wood screw, 1" long

Tools

Fretsaw; drill with 1/8" and 3/8" bits; compasses; hacksaw; matches; ruler; pencil; hammer; paintbrush; sandpaper.

How to Make the Puzzle

Draw a line down the length of the plywood, 1" from either edge. Draw two short lines crosswise, 6" from either end. Put the point of the compasses in the center of the board, and draw a circle 2" in diameter. Draw four more 2" circles: two touching the crosswise lines, and one touching each end of the board. Drill a hole 3/8" in diameter at the center of each circle except the central one. Drill two more holes of the same diameter, each 3" from one end of the board and on the center line. Using the same bit, drill two holes on the center line 1/2" from the center of the board. Draw in the heavy lines shown in the diagram, and cut out the three shapes with a fretsaw. Drill a 1/8" hole into the blade end of the handle, and also into one end of one of the elliptical plywood boards. Cut the head off the wood screw with an iron saw, and hammer the head end into the handle. Screw the other end carefully into the ellipse, and fix both with glue. Sandpaper and paint the pieces. Melt the ends of the cord together, then thread up the puzzle.

The handle in the Victoria puzzle makes it easier to hold and maneuver. It is not an essential part, however, and many early examples consisted only of two ellipses joined by cords through a disk.

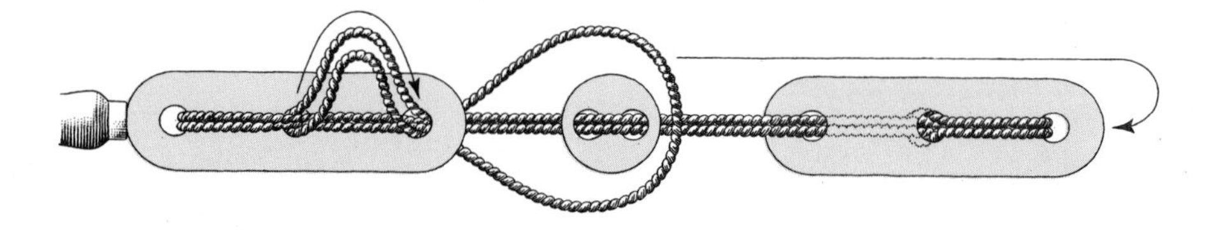

Take the loop at the center of the ellipse that is screwed to the handle, and pull it out of the hole. After you have pulled about four or five inches of the loop through the hole, push it away from you through the hole farthest from the handle.

After you have pushed all of the loop through the hole, pass it over the other two elements of the puzzle, following the direction arrow in the diagram above. Pull the loop back through the hole, and it will be possible to remove the cord.

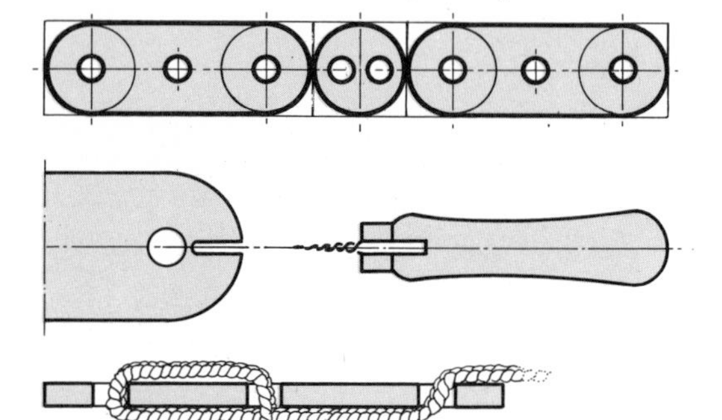

This diagram guides you in making the puzzle.

The Trefoil Puzzle

The aim of this puzzle is to remove the cord and attached wooden ball from the trefoil base and the entangling silver rings. The solution follows the principles of all ring-string-ball puzzles, but here appearances can be particularly deceptive. To construct your own trefoil puzzle, refer to the instructions below.

Materials

One 5" square of plywood, 1/4" thick
One wooden ball, 1 1/2" to 2" diameter
Four steel rings, 1" diameter
1 1/2 yards of cord, 1/16" thick
Varnish or enamel paint
Wood glue
Thread

Tools

Fretsaw; drill with 1/2" and 1/4" bits; ruler; pencil; compasses; needle; paintbrush; sandpaper.

How to Make the Puzzle

Mark the diagonals on the plywood square. Put the point of the compasses where the lines cross, and draw a circle of 2" diameter. With the same setting on your compasses mark off six equidistant points on the circumference. Draw three circles, also of 2" diameter, centering on alternate points on the circumference of the first circle, as in the diagram. Drill a 1/2" hole through the center of all four circles. Cut around the trefoil with the fretsaw. Sandpaper and varnish or paint the trefoil. Drill a 1/4" hole halfway into the wooden ball and glue both ends of a piece of cord, 1 foot in length, into this hole. Take two equal lengths of cord and arrange the rings and ball in place on the trefoil, following the picture and the diagram at the bottom right. Bind the four free ends of the cord with the thread.

Four steel rings and crossed cords imprison the ball and cord loop in this trefoil puzzle.

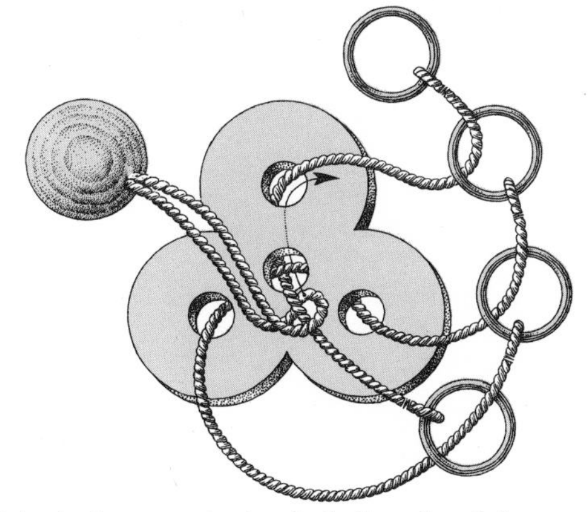

Take the loop attached to the ball, and push it through the center hole. It passes under the cross cord that is visible through the hole. Pull the loop along, following the cord leading to the first ring, passing through the second ring.

Loop the cord over the first ring and then pull it back along the same path, through the trefoil's top and center holes. That's it! You have freed the ball and loop without involving any of the other rings and cords in the solution.

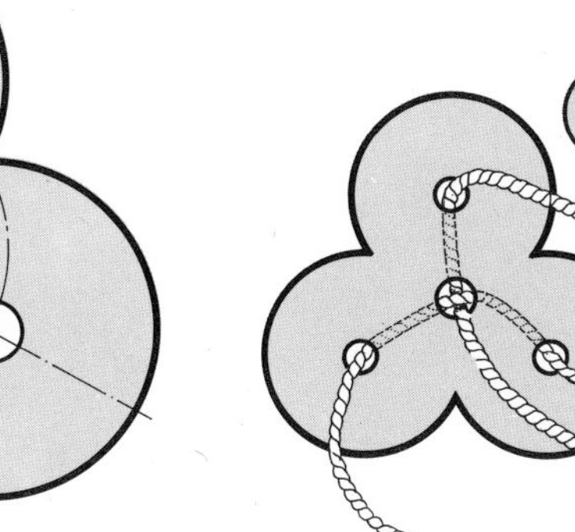

Draw the circles and cut along the heavy lines.

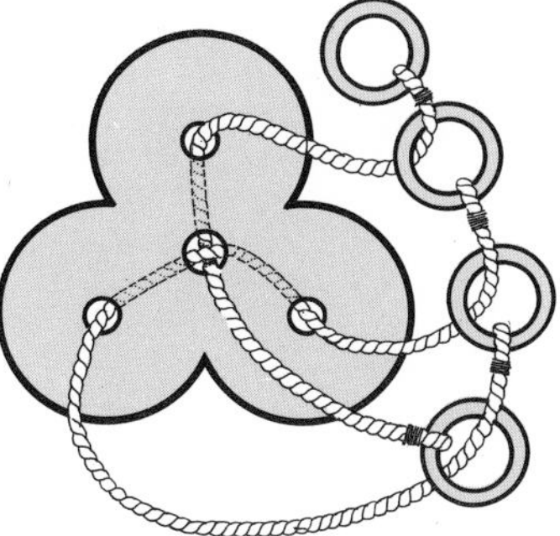

After making the loop for the ball, cut the rest of the cord into two pieces. Thread these pieces as shown in the figure, taking care to cross the cords correctly underneath the center hole.

Trouble with Bears

These two ferocious bears have good reason to be angry. Not only do they have rings through their noses, but they are also tied to one another by a long cord, which is prevented from coming free by two wooden balls. Make this puzzle, according to the instructions and diagrams, and then see if you can release the cord from the two steel rings. The bears may not appear happier, but it should give you great satisfaction to find the solution to this knotty problem.

Materials

One piece of plywood, 15″ × 4″ × 3/8″
Two steel rings, 1 1/2″ diameter
Two screw eyes, at least the width of the ring
2 yards of cord, 1/8″ thick
Two wooden balls, 1″ diameter
Wood glue
Paint

Tools

Fretsaw; drill with 1/2″ and 1/8″ bits; ruler; pencil; compasses; pliers; sandpaper; paintbrush.

How to Make the Puzzle

Start by making the wooden rings. Draw two 4″ diameter circles on the plywood. Inside each of these draw concentric circles with the compasses set first at 3/4″ radius, and then at 1 3/8″ radius. Mark two points, separated by 2″, on each circle drawn at the 1 3/8″ radius. Drill a 1/2″ hole at each point. Drill a small hole inside each inner circle in order to insert the fretsaw blade. Cut around the inner circles and then around the 4″ outer circles. Using the grid shown on page 113, make two

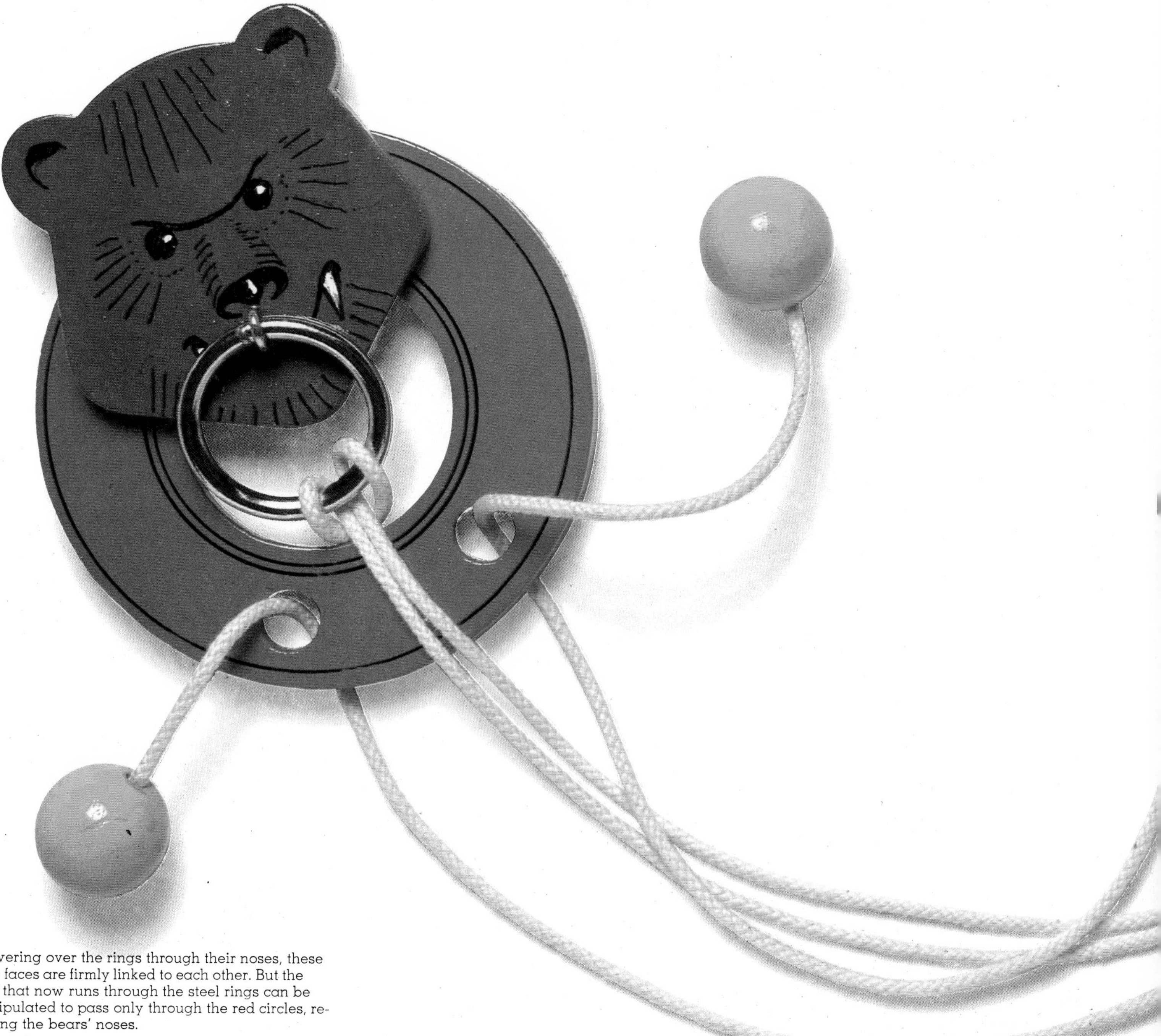

Glowering over the rings through their noses, these bear faces are firmly linked to each other. But the cord that now runs through the steel rings can be manipulated to pass only through the red circles, releasing the bears' noses.

copies of the bear head on the wood, making the width of the head about $2\frac{1}{2}$". Cut the heads out with a fretsaw. Now sand and paint all four wooden pieces. Push a screw eye into each head, just under the nose, and open the eye with pliers. Slip a steel ring into each eye, and close it again. Into each wooden ball drill a $\frac{1}{8}$" diameter hole, $\frac{1}{2}$" deep. Paint the balls. Take the cord and thread it through the heads, exactly according to the model. Insert a free end of cord into each wooden ball, and seal it with wood glue.

Copy this bear-face pattern onto a larger grid to make the heads the size you want for the puzzle.

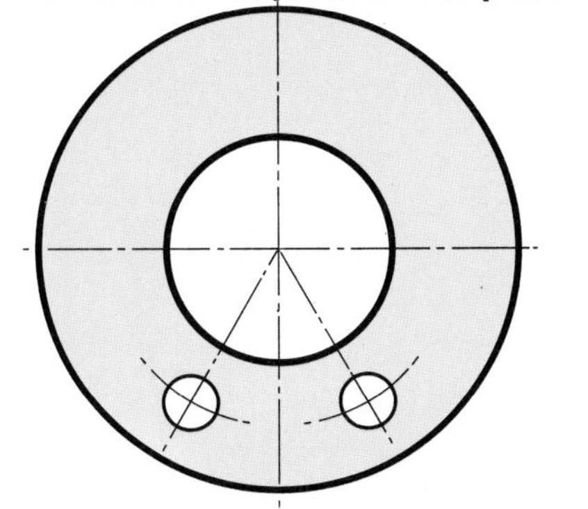

Make two circles like this one from plywood, and drill $\frac{1}{2}$" diameter holes at the points marked.

How to Solve the Puzzle

This puzzle is solved when the cord no longer runs through the steel rings but only through the two wooden circles. Beginning with the puzzle arranged as in the photograph, take the central loop of cord from the left-hand steel ring, and pull it to the right, under the right-hand wooden circle, and through the steel ring. Follow the first diagram and pass the cord loop through the top hole in the right-hand wooden circle. Pull the loop across to the left-hand wooden ring and through the top hole from the back to the front, as in the second diagram. Push the upper wooden ball through this cord loop before pulling the loop back out of the top hole. Pull the bears apart so that the cord retraces its path. When the central loop is free of the top hole in the right-hand circle, pull the loop through the right-hand steel ring, as in the third diagram, and then through the lower hole in the wooden ring. Repeat the above movements, leading the loop through the lower holes and over the lower ball. Pull the puzzle gently apart.

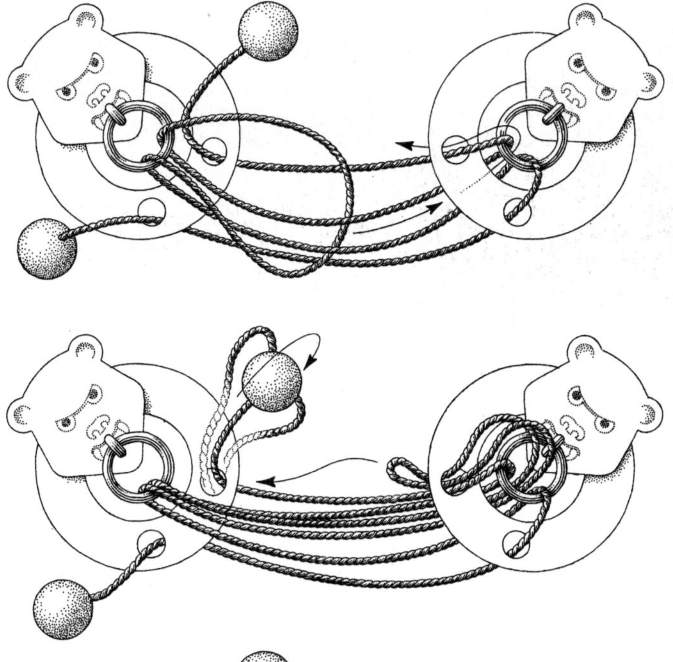

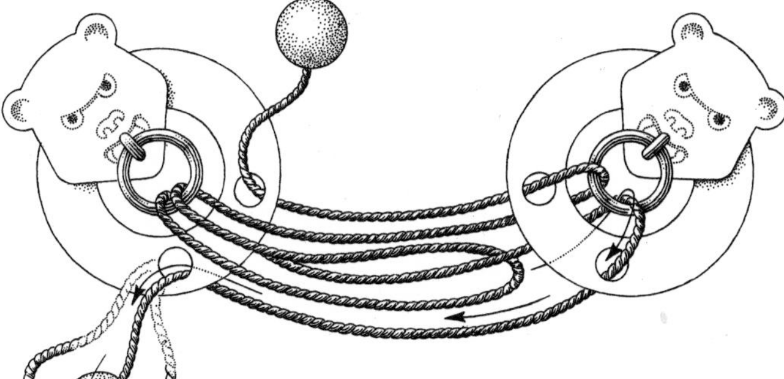

Hold the cord loop firmly between thumb and index finger, and draw it along the path marked by arrows.

The Imperial Scale Puzzle

The problem posed in this puzzle is to remove the ring from the cord without undoing any knots and then to replace it. While this model (right) may be too fragile to keep outside a glass case, a more practical version can be made.

Materials

One 4" × 4" square of $1/8$" plywood
1 yard of cord, $1/16$" thick
Four beads with holes of at least $1/16$"
One ring, 1" to $1\frac{1}{2}$" in diameter
Paint or varnish

Tools

Drill with a $1/8$" bit; ruler; pencil; paintbrush; sandpaper.

How to Make the Puzzle

Draw the square's diagonals on the wood. On each diagonal mark points $1/2$" from each corner and four others $1/2$" from the center of the square (as in the diagram). Drill a hole through all eight points. Sandpaper and then paint the wood. Attach a 1-foot length of cord to the base by threading the ends through two adjacent corner holes, and knotting each under a bead beneath the base. Tie another 1-foot length of cord in the same way on the opposite side of the base. Tie the two loops of these cords at the top. Tie one end of the remaining piece of cord to this knot, and thread the other end as in the diagram: down through a center hole, under the base, up through the adjacent hole and the ring, around the descending strand and through the ring and the hole diagonally opposite to the first, up through the last hole, and its own loop. Tie it to the top knot.

This delightful puzzle, of Chinese origin, dates from 1850. The ivory base, intricately hand-carved with a pattern of leaves and flowers, is suspended on silken cords. Part of a set of ivory puzzles, its delicacy seems ideally suited to the gentle fingers of the highborn Chinese women for whom it was intended.

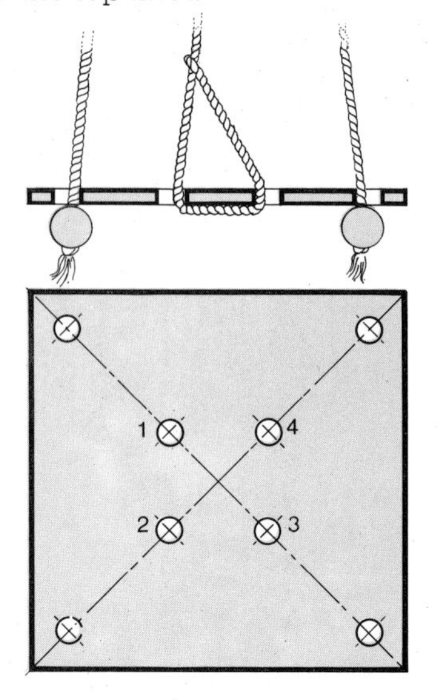

Follow the bottom diagram when drilling the holes and the top figure when threading the cords.

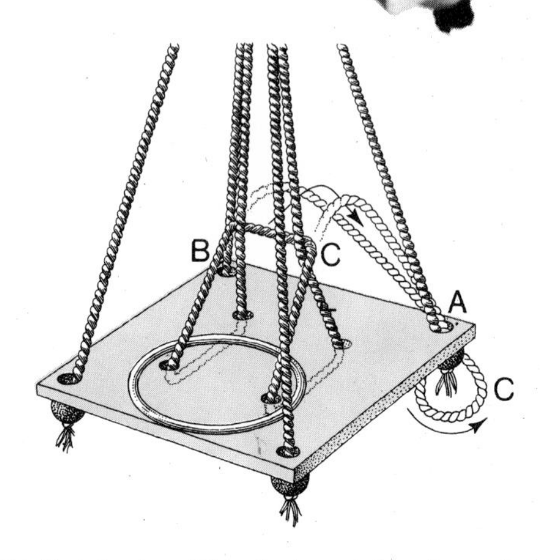

The first step in solving the imperial scale puzzle is to thread loop C down through hole A at the corner of the base, as indicated by the lightly drawn cord above. Pass the loop over the bead and pull it back to the top side of the base.

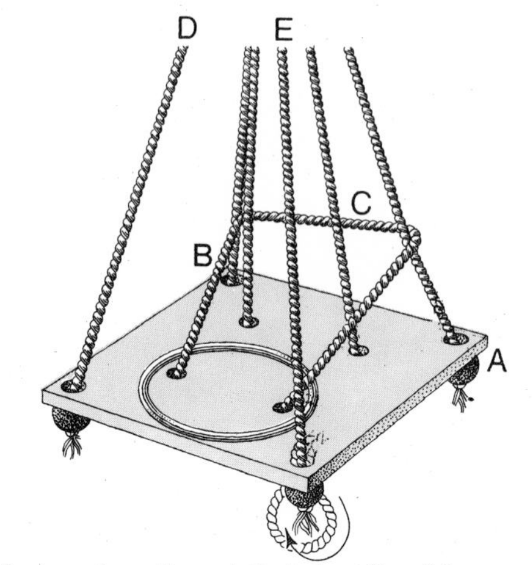

Pass the loop down through the hole at B, pull it over the bead and bring it back to the top side. Then pass the loop over the knot from which the base hangs, and bring it down around threads D and E. Repeat the previous steps at the remaining holes.

The Triplets Puzzle

This wood and string puzzle consists of three disks linked by a continuous loop of cord running through nine small rings. To solve the puzzle, you must separate the cord from all three disks, each of which carries three of the rings, without breaking the loop. Once you know the secret, it is easy — but watch for knots on the way!

Materials
Plywood, 4" × 12" and 1/8" thick
2 yards of cord, up to 1/8" thick
Wood glue
Varnish
Thread

Tools
Fretsaw; drill with a 3/8" bit; compasses; ruler; pencil; paintbrush; needle; sandpaper.

How to Make the Puzzle
On the plywood draw three circles, each 3" in diameter, and nine circles 1" in diameter. Using an electric or hand drill fitted with a 3/8" bit, drill a hole through the center of each of the small circles. Set the compasses to the radius of the large circle again — that is, 1 1/2". Place the point of the compasses on the circumference of one of the large circles, and mark off a point on the circumference at a distance of one radius. Move the point of the compasses to this mark and repeat the procedure. Continue this around the circle until you have six marks on the circumference, all equidistant from one another. Mark a cross at alternate points on the circumference so that there are three crosses on the the circle, all the same distance from each other. Repeat this with the other two large circles. These crosses mark the points that will be used in positioning the small circles. Cut out all of the pieces with a fretsaw, and sandpaper them well. Place each ring on a mark, as in the diagram. In this way, while the ring can be securely glued to a large disk, the central hole will not be obstructed. Glue all nine rings in place on the three large disks. Decorate and varnish the puzzle. When it is dry, loop the cord around the puzzle exactly as shown in the model. Do not knot the ends of the cord together or the puzzle will be difficult to maneuver. Instead, bind the ends by stitching them together with cotton thread.

One way of decorating this puzzle is by scorching circles on the small rings, as in the model shown here, using a soldering iron with its pin removed.

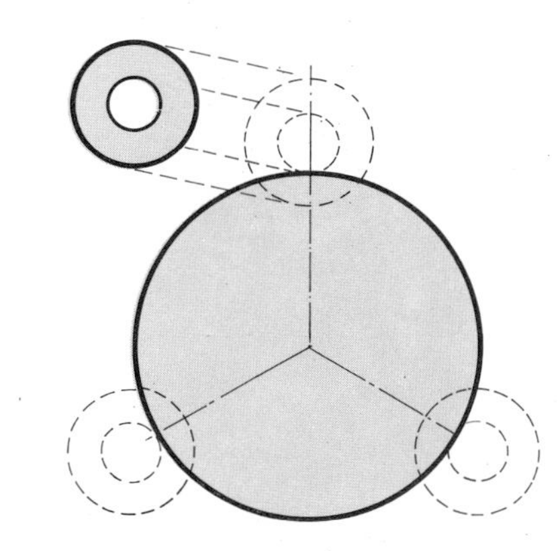

Place the rings as shown in the diagram above so that the inner edge of each ring is aligned with the outer edge of the wood circle. In this way the hole through which the cord passes is not blocked.

Take the loop from one of the three main disks and, exactly as shown, pass it through the ring marked in the diagram. Slide the other two disks through the loop. Take care not to twist the cord at any time. Pull the loop back through the ring to its original position, and the first disk will be free. Repeat these movements with the other two disks.

Whai, or cat's cradles, are traditionally played by New Zealand Maori children, and the intricate designs are passed on from one generation to the next. The children below have made a variety of patterns, frequently representing familiar objects from daily life. Some require two people to make and hold them. Other patterns, such as the one in the picture on the right, are passed around from one person to another, each time creating a new design.

String Puzzles

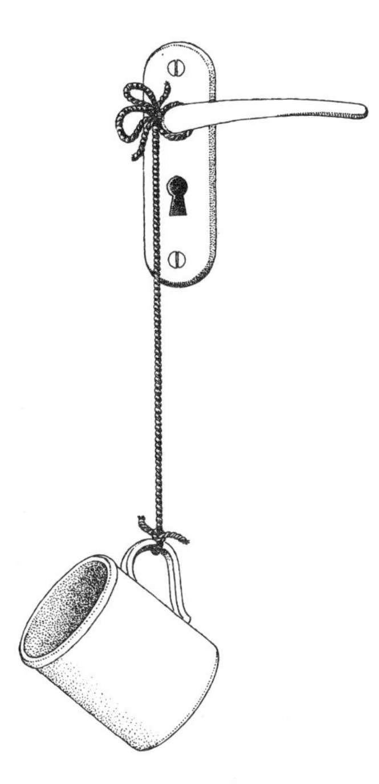

In contrast to the many intricate string puzzles, this trick is quickly and easily performed. A cup is tied to a door handle by a piece of cord. The challenge is to cut the cord without letting either the cup or string fall. The answer, truly a trick, is simply to cut through one of the loops of the bow on the door handle.

Few people can resist playing with a piece of string. Give a piece to someone with a few moments to spare, and soon it probably will be twisted, knotted, and frayed. Spare time and a little string are also all the materials you need for a variety of puzzles that can be done alone or with your friends.

Some string puzzles deceive the eye and challenge onlookers to discover how they work. They often involve the apparent rejoining of two ends of a cord cut during the puzzle or the sudden vanishing of complex knots when loose ends are pulled. Many of these puzzles are used by conjurors at children's parties and can be easily learned. More complicated effects with cord and rope were achieved by Houdini, the most expert and daring of all illusionists. Wrestling with cords tied around his wrists, neck, and ankles, or hanging suspended by his feet from a skyscraper, Houdini had an uncanny ability to release himself, which depended largely on his knowledge of knots and a careful arrangement of his bonds. Some less dangerous escape puzzles are given in the following pages.

Although conjurors and escapologists are relatively recent string puzzlers, in many parts of the world string has been twisted into complex puzzles and patterns for hundreds of years. String figures known as cat's cradles are familiar to schoolchildren and have been developed to a high degree among primitive peoples. During long, dark winter months in the north, Eskimo tribes pass the time telling stories. They illustrate these stories with a piece of string, or more often with a thin strip of hide or gut, weaving it around their fingers. With rapid, deft movements they produce patterns in string which represent objects in the story, such as harpoons, stars, canoes, and animals.

Similar patterns are made by people of the Pacific islands, where woven vegetable fiber, creepers, or plaited hair are used in creating the figures. In many of these figures a complex construction of string is devised which rapidly can be broken up by pulling on one part of the string. Indeed, many of these games with string utilize the same basic principles as some of the most puzzling effects of illusionists and conjurors.

An escapologist, seemingly tied securely with thick ropes, was once a common sight at country fairs. To attract the crowds, the escapologist, cunningly tied by his accomplice, would struggle and grimace to make it appear that this time he was really in difficulty. Once the crowd had gathered, he would make a few deft moves and free himself.

The Elastic Loop

Fold an 8" piece of cord in half, and thread the loop through your buttonhole. Thread the cut ends of the cord through the loop, and pull them taut. Thread and tie the cord through a hole made in the unsharpened end of a pencil that is six inches long. Now try to remove the pencil from the buttonhole without cutting the cord. The loop is too short for the pencil to pass through, so you must bunch up the cloth around the buttonhole and pass this upward through the loop. Then push the pencil up, through the hole.

The Elusive Midpoint

Baffle your friends with this puzzle, which they almost certainly will fail to solve. Wind a 36" piece of cord into a flat spiral, as in the diagram below. Ask a friend to push a pin through the cord exactly at its midpoint. Hold the pin firmly in place while you pull ends A and B, unraveling the spiral and revealing the pin to be off-center. When first winding the cord in a flat spiral, fold the cord in two — but be careful not to fold it at the midpoint. It is then impossible for your friend to predict the middle with any accuracy.

String the Ring

Handcuff a friend with a 36" piece of cord, the ends knotted around each wrist. Give him a metal ring and challenge him to knot the ring onto the length of cord between his wrists. To demonstrate how this is done, make a loop in the cord between your wrists. Pass it through the ring and then through one cord handcuff on the palm side, moving from the wrist in the direction of your fingertips. Pass the loop over the back of your hand and back through the handcuff. Pass it over the handcuff and your hand. Pull your hands apart.

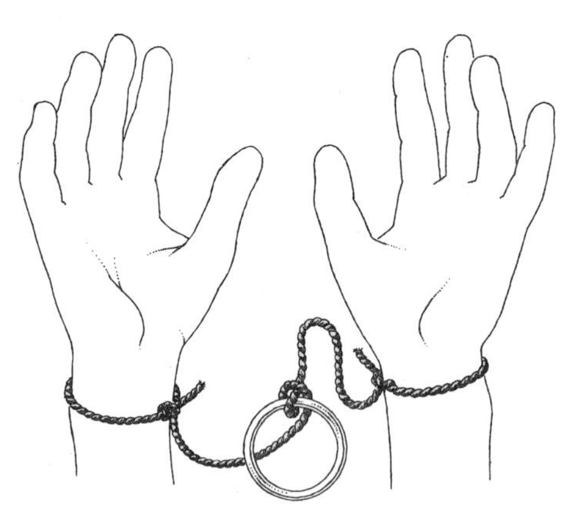

Cutting the Cord

Arrange the rings and cord as in the diagram and ask an assistant to hold the loose ends of the cord. Point out to onlookers that obviously the only way to release the rings without letting go of the free ends of the cord is to cut through the loop of the knot. Grasp the knot and the bottom ring and pretend to cut the cord. But, behind your hand, loosen the knot and pull the loop down over the ring, slipping it free. As the other rings slide off, ask your assistant to pull the intact cord taut.

A Knotty Problem

Try posing this teaser: how can you knot a metal ring onto a piece of cord while continuously holding both ends of the cord? The answer is remarkably simple. First thread the ring onto the cord and lay the cord on the table in front of you. Now fold your arms and pick up the left end of the string with your right hand and the right end with your left hand. Still holding the ends, unfold your arms and move your hands apart — the ring will be securely tied in place on the cord.

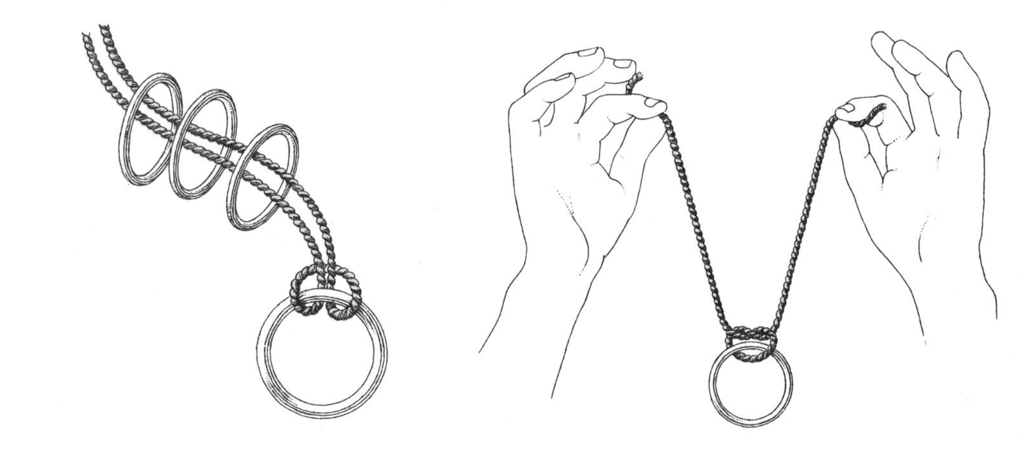

Releasing the Loop

Bewilder onlookers by removing a loop from around an assistant's finger without either lifting it over the fingertip, or cutting the string. Ask your helper to point his index finger upward. Take a piece of string, and knot the ends together. Holding the knot in your left hand throughout the puzzle, slip the loop over your assistant's finger. With your right hand, lift the left-hand section of the string and pass it over the right-hand section, crossing it at two points. Take up the section now on the left (originally on the right) and repeat the movement. Insert your right index finger down through the central loop of the string between the two crossover points. At the same time bring your thumb up through the loop nearest the knot. Twist your right thumb counterclockwise, so that it is pointing downward, similar to the index finger. Slide your right hand along the cord toward your assistant's hand. When it is as near his hand as possible, twist your hand clockwise, and place your right thumbtip on the tip of your assistant's finger. Pass the loop from around your thumb over your assistant's finger. Then let go of the cord completely with your right hand. Pull the knot toward you and the loop will come free.

Penetrating the Pencil

In this puzzle you appear to do the impossible, for you seemingly pass a string through a pencil without breaking either the string or the pencil. Begin with a pencil, a few inches of fine string, and a strip of paper about a quarter of an inch wide and as long as the pencil. Then proceed as follows.

1. Attach one end of the paper with a rubber band, at the pencil point.
2. Fold the paper forward, out of the way, and lay the string across the pencil. The left end is *a*, the right, *b*.
3. Wind the string around the pencil, and cross end *a* over *b* at the back.
4. Bring the two ends to the front of the pencil and cross *a* over *b*.
5. Lay the paper along the pencil and secure it with a rubber band at the unsharpened end.
6. Cross the ends of the string, *a* over *b*, in front of the paper.
7. Take the string behind the pencil, and again cross end *a* over end *b*.
8. Bring the cord to the front again and cross *a* over *b* on top of the paper.
9. Pull on both ends of the string. The paper will be torn, but the string will come free of the pencil.

Nonsense Knots

How can you tie three knots in a piece of cord and then make them disappear? Tie a loose, single knot in the cord, passing the right-hand end of the cord first over and then under the left-hand end. This forms the lower-left knot. Tie a second knot, passing the right-hand end over and then under the left-hand end to make the upper-left knot. Thread the right-hand end through the lower and then the upper loop, each time passing the cord away from you, to make the third knot. Pull both ends, and the knots will disappear.

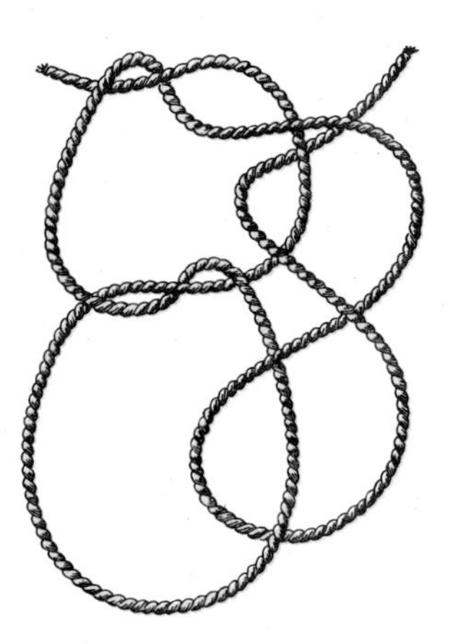

Release the Prisoner

With 30 feet of cord and an assistant you can demonstrate this escapology puzzle. Ask your assistant to stand with his hands clasped behind his back, palms facing outward so that he can point his thumbs upward. Place the cord horizontally across his chest. Throughout the trick, whenever the ends of the cord are crossed, the end now on your assistant's left, *a*, must pass over *b*, the end now on his right side. Bring the ends around his arms and behind him. Keeping the cord taut throughout, cross *a* over *b* behind your assistant's back. Keeping *a* in the same position, bring *b* in front of your assistant again, around his body and to his back once more. Cross *a* over *b* behind him. Now pass end *b* from right to left between your assistant's thumbs and his body. Loop end *b* around the thumbs, and lead it away to the right. Make the corresponding moves with end *a*, moving in the opposite direction. Your assistant must help here by keeping his thumbs upright so that the loops do not slip free. Cross the cords in front of him and then behind him once more. Knot the ends behind your assistant's back. Take the knot and ask your assistant to wriggle his thumbs free. Pull the cord and he will be free.

The Open Buttonhole

If you practice this string puzzle until you can execute it quickly and smoothly, you will be able to deceive even the sharpest eyes. The aim is to make a loop of string appear to cut through the cloth surrounding a buttonhole without damaging either the cloth or the string. To do this, make a loop with a piece of string about 36" long and thread one end of it through your buttonhole. Wihout twisting the string slip a thumb into each end of the loop and pull the string taut. Bring your hands close together in front of you with your thumbs uppermost. Turn your right hand palm upward, then hook your right little finger around the lower string held by your left thumb. With your left little finger pick up the lower string held by your right thumb, making sure that this string passes under all of the other strings. Pull all the strings taut, and then insert your left thumb downward into the loop on your left little finger, dropping the loop that was previously over your left thumb. Remove your left little finger from the loop now held on your left thumb. At the same time slip your right little finger free of the loop that it holds. With the string on your thumbs, part your hands and the string will slip free.

The Great Escape

This string puzzle is guaranteed to break the ice at any party. Give each of your guests who is wearing trousers a six-foot piece of cord tied to make a loop. Ask them to slip the loops over their right wrists and put their right hands into their right trouser pockets, or hold them firmly on their hips in the absence of pockets. Now challenge your guests to escape from the loop without moving their right hands at all. To demonstrate the solution, carry out the following moves, taking great care not to twist the cord at any stage during the solution. Lead one end of the cord loop down inside your right trouser leg, touching the outside of your leg. When the loop appears at the bottom of your trouser leg, slip it over your right foot, and then, by pulling on the other end of the loop that is still around your right wrist, draw the cord up along the inside of your right leg, still within your trousers. Keep pulling this end of the loop until you can pass it over your head. Then lead the loop down inside your left trouser leg, keeping it against the outside of your leg. Slip the loop over your left foot and then pull — the rest of the loop will be drawn down the inside of your left trouser leg. You will then have escaped from the loop.

Scissors and String

Thread a doubled cord through the handles of a pair of scissors, as in the diagram below, and tie it to a chair or ask a friend to hold it. How can you get the scissors free without cutting the cord? Pull on the end of the loop knotted around the left handle. As this loop lengthens, thread it through the scissors following the path taken by the rest of the double cord. When you have passed a sufficient length through the right handle, slip the scissors through the loop, taking care not to twist the cord. Pull the scissors and they will come away from the cord.

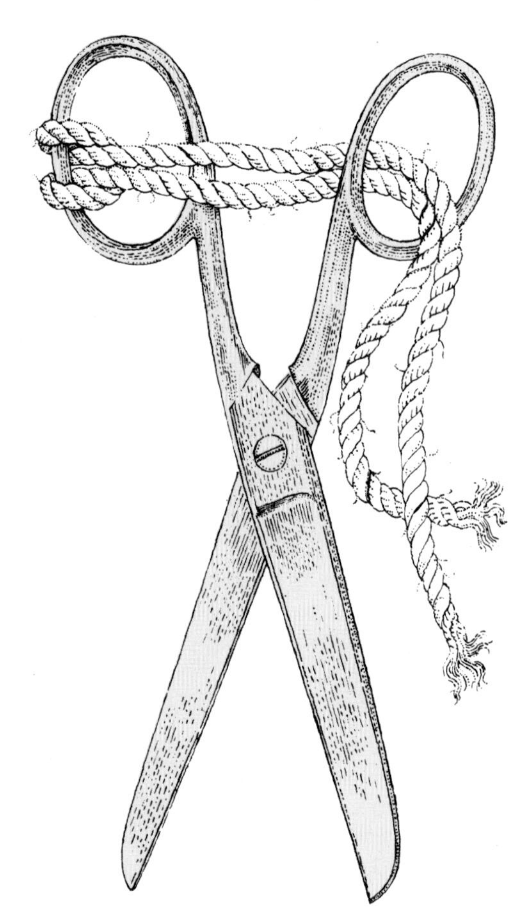

A pair of scissors threaded as above, with the ends of the cord tied to a chair, seems impossible to release without cutting the cord. But it can be done.

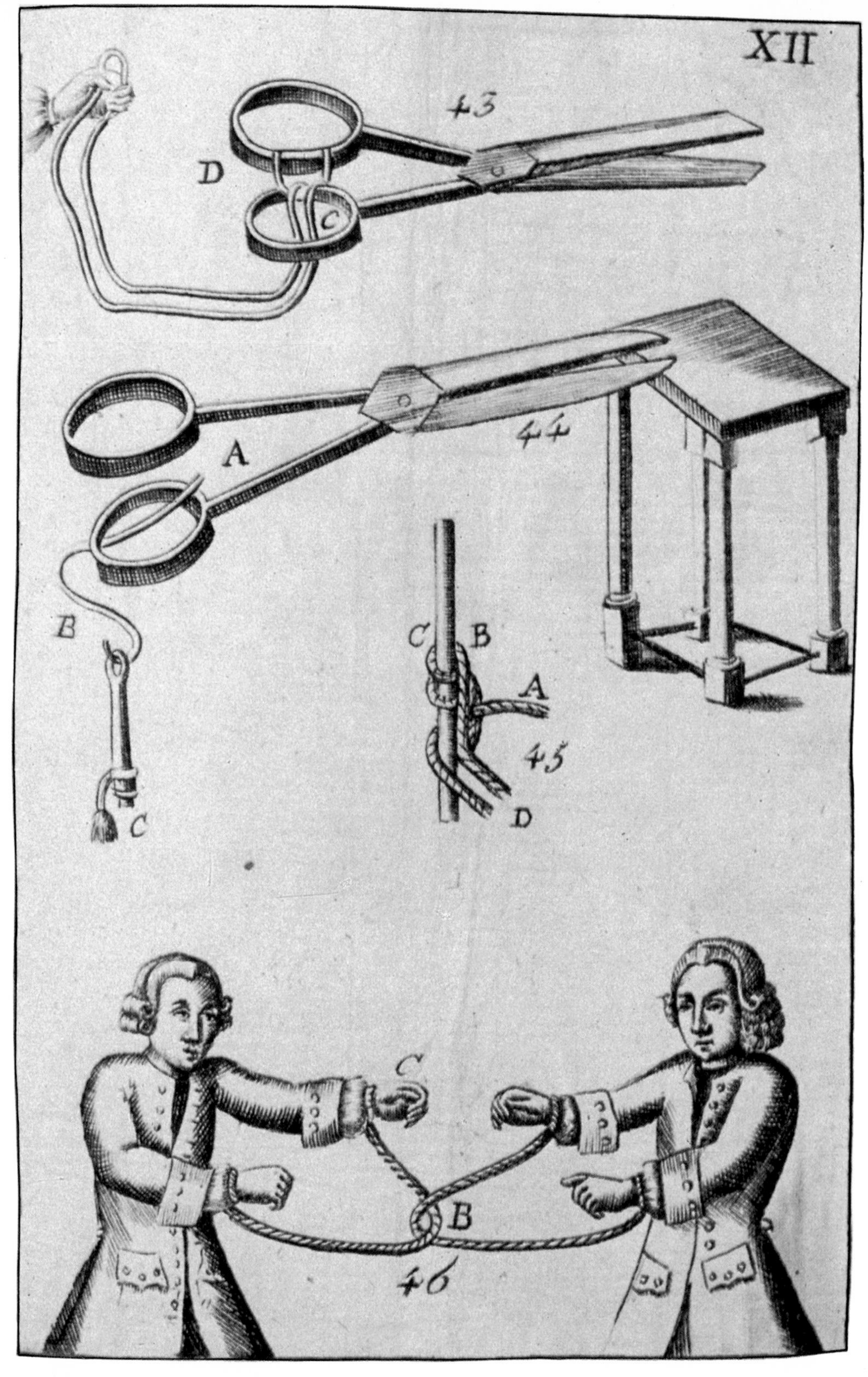

This engraving is from the classic Italian work on puzzles and tricks, *I giuochi numerici fatti arcani palesati* by G. A. Alberti. First published in 1747, it shows that even society gentlemen of the period could be entertained by string puzzles.

The Wrist Twist

The two gentlemen above are trying to solve the wrist-twist puzzle. Their problem is to separate themselves from one another. To duplicate their predicament, tie a piece of cord in loose loops around your wrists, and interlink it with another cord similarly tied around a friend's wrists. Then demonstrate the following escape. Make a loop of the middle part of your cord with your right hand, and pass it over your friend's left hand. Then draw the cord back through his wrist loop toward you and again over his hand. Let go of the cord, pull your hands apart, and you will be separated from your friend.

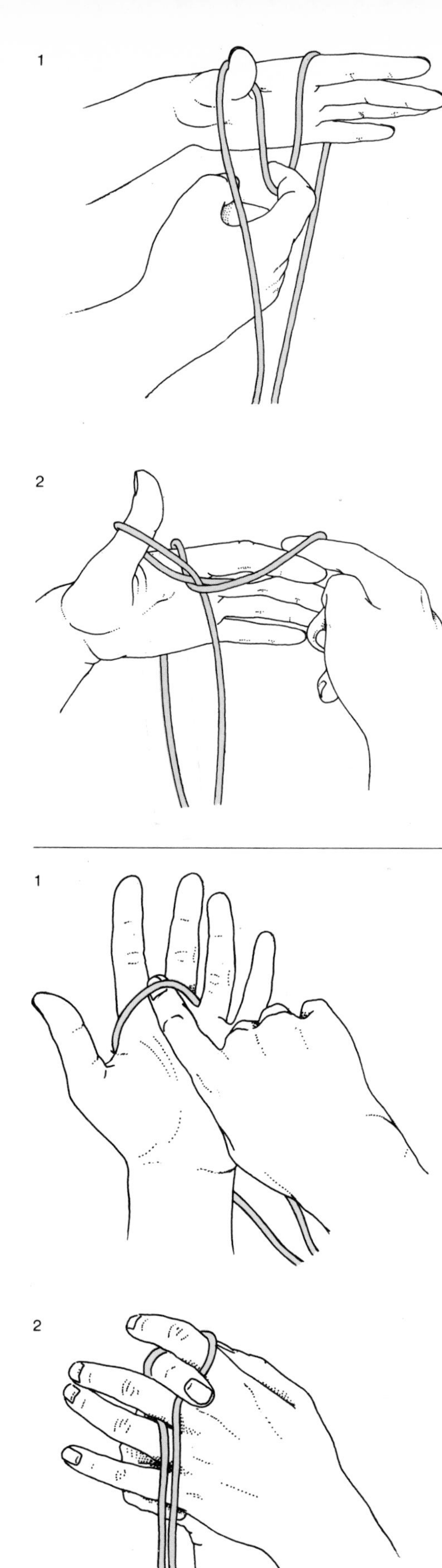

The Mouse

1. Holding your left-hand palm down in front of you, loop a 36" cord over the back of it. Pass your right hand through the loop, from behind. Now hook your right index finger over the cord between your left thumb and index finger and pull down a loop of cord.
2. Bring the loop around behind the hanging cord nearest you and turn your right-hand palm up, thus twisting the loop once. Pass the loop from your right index finger onto your left index finger. Then pass your right hand through the hanging loop again, as before. Put your right index finger between your left index and middle fingers, and hook it over the cord. Pull down a loop between these fingers, pass it around the hanging cord, and, turning your right-hand palm up, onto your left middle finger.
3. Repeat these moves in step 2, this time picking up the loop between the middle and ring fingers of your left hand and finally passing the loop onto your ring finger. Repeat step 2 to make a loop on your left little finger.
4. Slip the loop from your left thumb and hold it lightly between your left thumb and index finger. This is the mouse. Pull the right-hand hanging cord, and let the mouse disappear to release you.

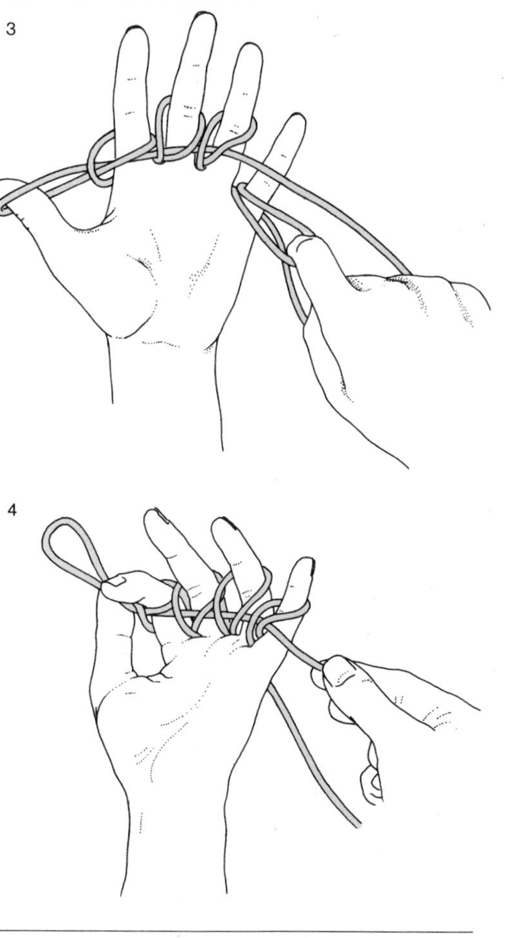

The Indian Rope Trick

Reputed to have originated in India, this puzzle is easy to learn and yet can baffle onlookers if carried out smoothly. You need a two-foot loop of cord.
1. Hold your left hand with your fingers and thumb pointing up and your palm facing you. Loop the cord around both your index finger and middle finger with the rest of the cord hanging down the back of your left hand.
2. From the palm side push your right index finger beneath the loop of cord between the index and middle fingers of your left hand.
3. Hook your right index finger over part of the hanging loop and pull all of it down under the section of cord between your left index and middle fingers. Pull the cord tight around your fingers.
4. Turn the palm of your left hand down so that the cord also hangs down. Make sure that the hanging loop is not twisted at this stage. Bend your left thumb toward your palm, passing it over the nearer side of the hanging loop and under the farther side. Bring the tips of your left thumb and left index finger into contact. Slip off the loop on your middle finger. Pull on the hanging loop and you will find that the cord is free of your fingers.

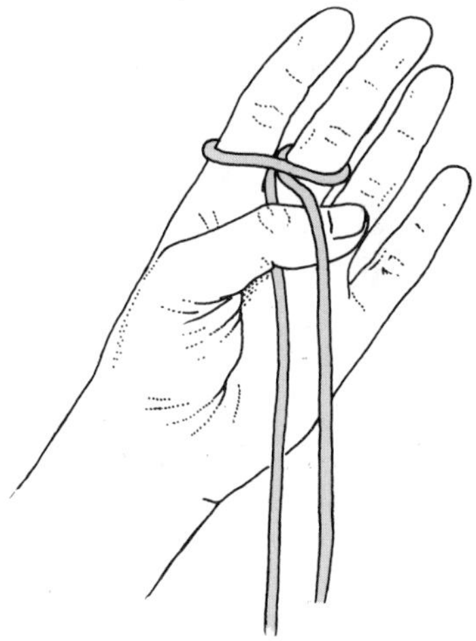

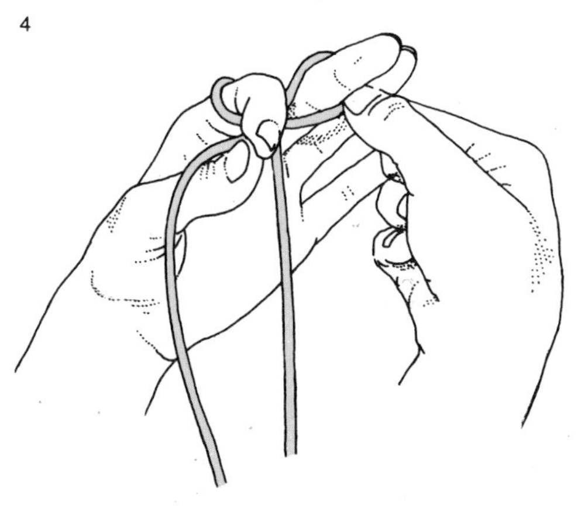

Freeing the Finger

1

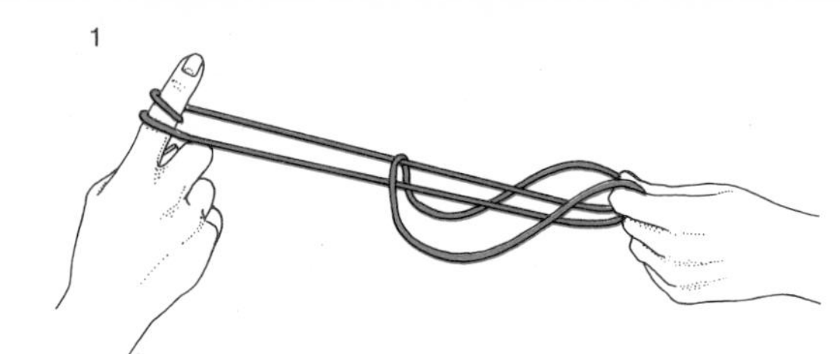

2

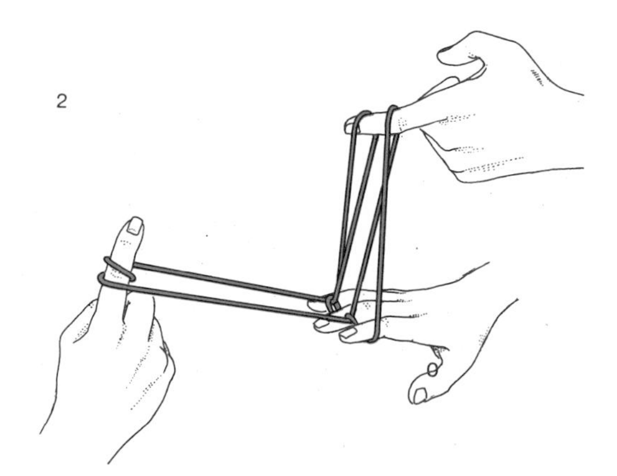

Ask an assistant to hold his index finger up in front of him. Make a loop from a 36" piece of cord and slip it over his finger. Then wind the section of cord on the right once around his finger.

1. Grasp the loop, with your left index finger above and left thumb beneath, about 12" from your assistant's hand. Keep the sides taut and parallel and flip the tail back over the parallel cords so that equal lengths are on each side.
2. Place your right hand underneath the parallel cords, palm down. Slip your right index finger through the left-hand hanging loop, bring your middle finger up between the parallel cords and over the cord crossing them, and slip your ring finger through the loop hanging on the right. Now raise your left hand directly above your right hand.
3. Move your left hand toward your assistant and turn it 90° counter-clockwise. With your index finger touching his, pass the first loop to him.
4. Twist the second loop on your index finger 180°, right cord over left, and slip this loop onto your assistant's finger. Let go of all the loops on your right hand except the one on your middle finger. Pull with this finger, and you will free your assistant.

3

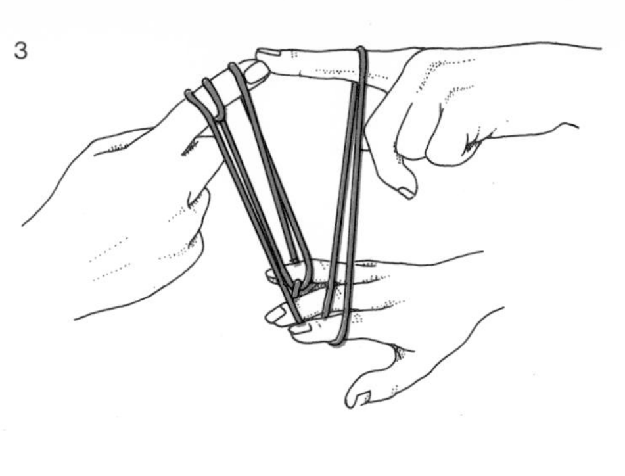

4

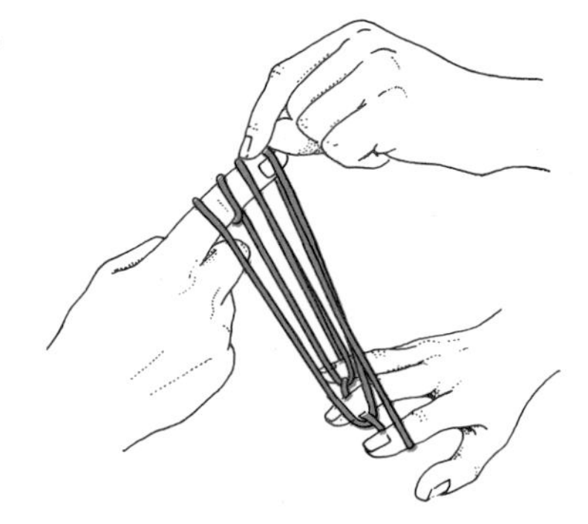

The Thumb Catch

1

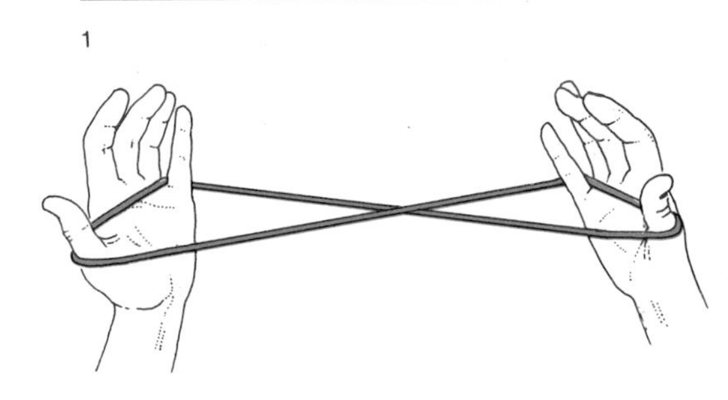

2

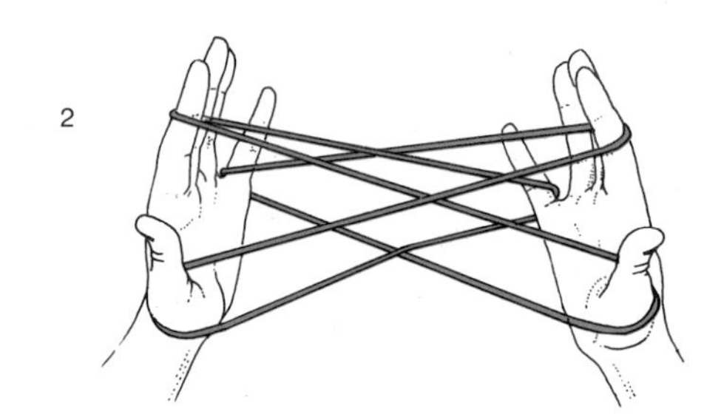

This ingenious puzzle has long been known in many different societies. It involves a series of steps that finally result in both thumbs being tied firmly together by a loop of cord. To try it, take a three-foot loop of cord, and follow these instructions.

1. Hold your hands apart and slip the cord loop over your thumbs and little fingers. The loop must cross itself in the middle, with the section that runs from the left thumb to the right little finger passing over the other section.
2. Pass the opposite index fingers beneath the sections of the loop that cross your palms and pull the cords across with the backs of your fingers. The left section should be picked up before the right.
3. Catch the loops on the index fingers with your thumbs by bending them over, away from you. Turn your hands so that your fingers and thumbs point downward, and, keeping your thumbs in place, let the loops slip free of the other fingers.
4. Keeping a firm hold on the cord with your thumbs, turn your hands so that your fingers point upward. Draw your hands apart and a noose will form around each of your thumbs.

3

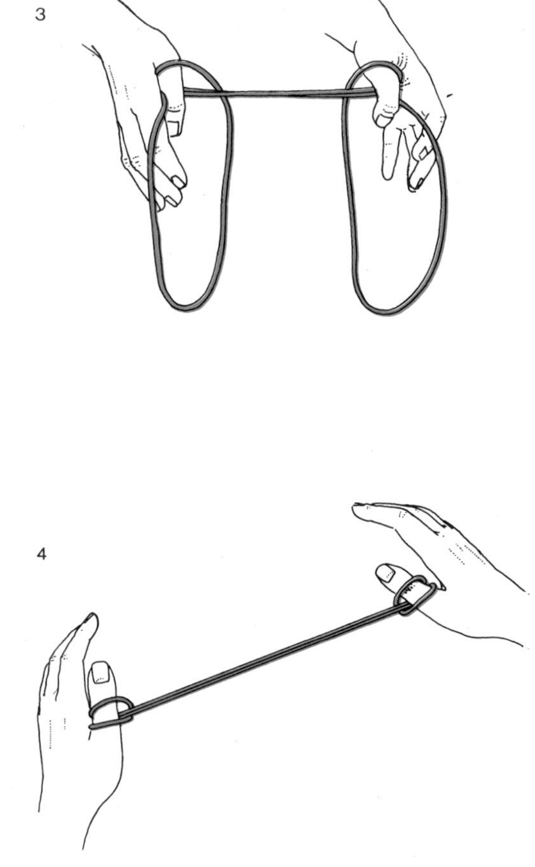

4

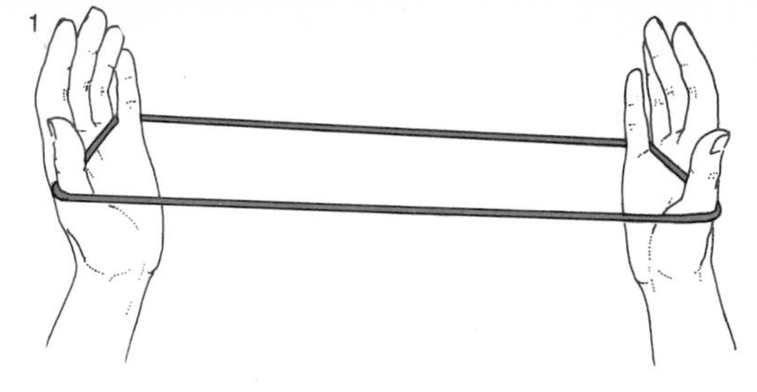

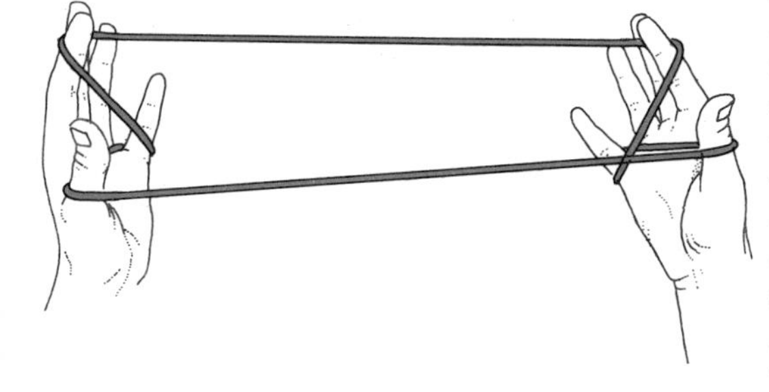

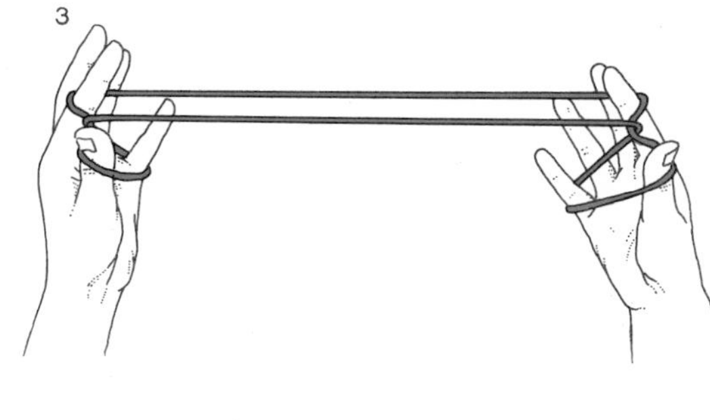

Losing the Yam

This string puzzle comes from the small islands of the Torres Straits off the Australian coast. A special loop, representing a yam, is made at each hand. The loops disappear, releasing the hands.

1. Take up the cord on your thumbs and little fingers as in the diagram.
2. Bend your index fingers, and hook them over the cord on the little fingers. Straighten them, catching the cord.
3. Move each thumb under the far little finger cord that now runs diagonally across each palm. Draw these loops under the thumb cord. Return your thumbs to the original position.
4. Bend your little fingers toward you, over the far cord and under the near cord that runs between your hands. Straighten your little fingers and return them to their original positions.
5. Move each thumb away from you, and take the near cord between your hands on the backs of your thumbs. Straighten your thumbs.
6. Take the loop from the left index finger, and hold it between your left thumb and index finger. This is the yam. Pull with your right hand, letting the left loop slide through your fingers and thus releasing your left hand. Make similar moves to free the right hand.

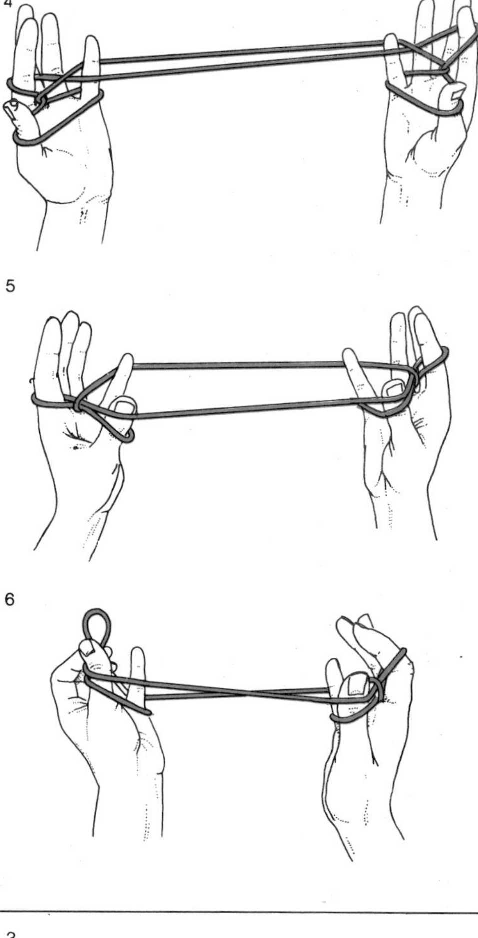

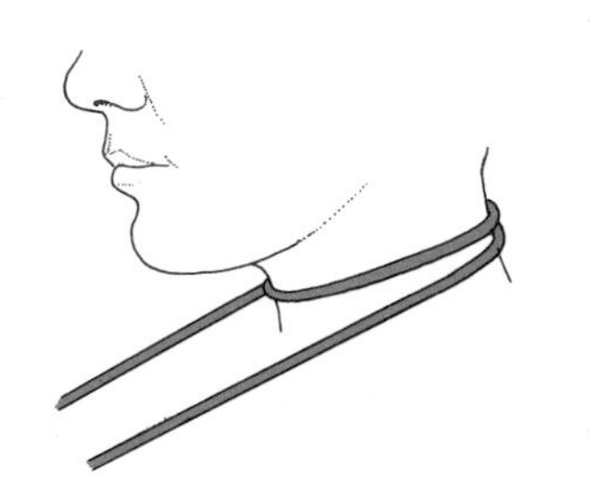

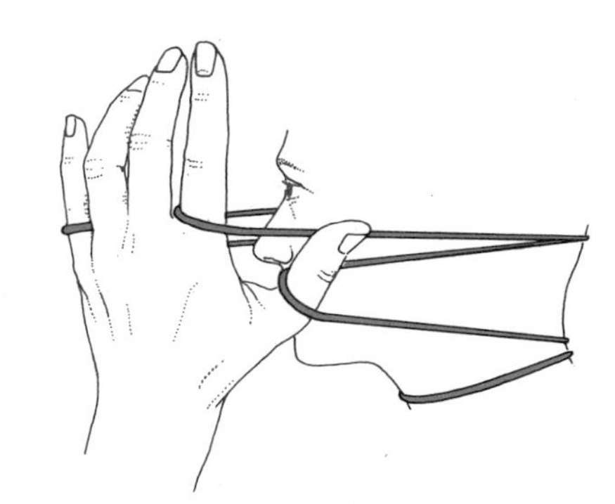

The Loose Noose

A seemingly impenetrable loop of cord is made to slip free from around your neck. The mystery of this is increased by the fact that at no time is a loop taken over your head from around your neck. For the loose noose puzzle use a loop made from about 12 feet of cord.

1. Loop the cord around your neck, and let it hang down in front of you. Take the right side of the loop and bring it around the left of your neck and over your head. Pull the excess to the front.
2. Take up each side of the long loop on your thumbs and little fingers. Pick up the cords which cross your palms, pushing first the right index finger under the left cord and then the left index finger under the right cord. Pull the hands apart.
3. Put your head upward through the loop that connects your index fingers. When you have pulled the loop over your head and it is around your neck, carefully take your hands away from all the loops. Now a single loop of cord will hang down in front of you.
4. Pull on any part of the long front loop, and the entire cord will fall free of your neck. Perhaps you should pull gently the first time — just in case you missed a step on the way.

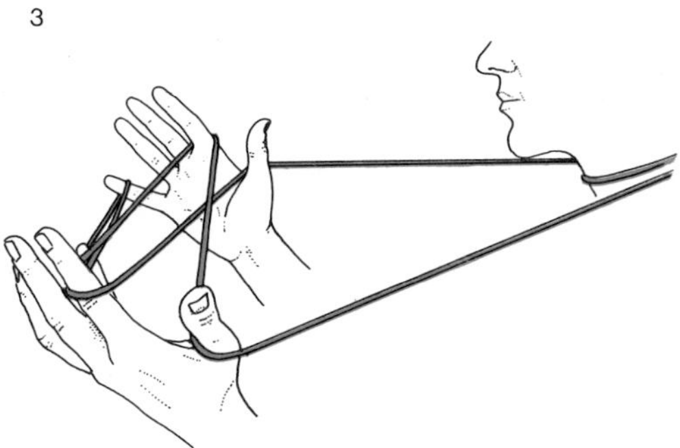

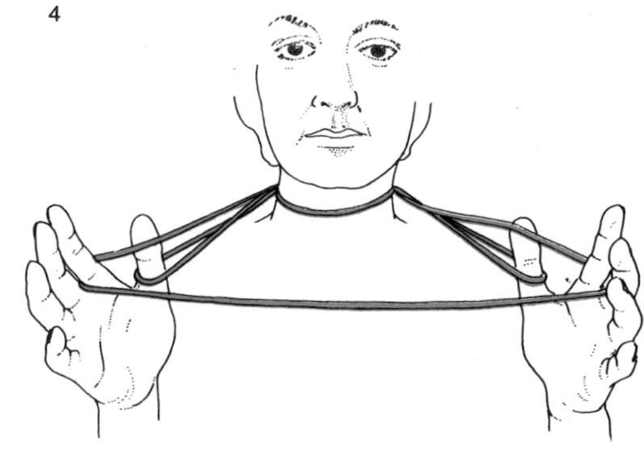

Plan of the Alkborough turf maze, seen below.

Mazes and Labyrinths

The labyrinth has been one of mankind's most potent and mysterious images for many thousands of years. Patterns of intricately winding paths have been cut into rock faces in the American desert and on Scandinavian cliffs, and drawn in sand on Pacific islands and in Zululand. Mazes have been cut in the turf of Wales and England from times so remote that their origins have long since been forgotten.

Monsters and giants have traditionally lived in labyrinthine lairs. And even Christian churches have drawn on the symbolism of the labyrinth, often used in mosaic mazes set into floors or walls.

For centuries, mazes have also been ways of having fun. The maze shown here, cut in the turf at Alkborough in England, is a winding path that youths would once try to run as fast as possible.

Today, we rarely think of the maze as anything but recreational. Typical of this type is the hedge maze at the Renaissance palace of Hampton Court, just outside London — a place in which to lose one's way on a fine afternoon.

Any intricately winding path can be called a labyrinth. The word "maze" is nowadays usually limited to the type of labyrinth that has branches leading wanderers into blind alleys or along time-wasting looped paths. The puzzler is, of course, interested in the maze proper, but other people have also been fascinated by winding unbranched paths like those in the Alkborough labyrinth, leading to a goal near the entrance, or even back to the start.

There is an amazing uniformity about the labyrinths found engraved on rock all over Europe. The carving (page 127) from Rocky Valley, in the Wicklow Mountains of Ireland, is typical. The pattern fills an overall circular area. Tracing the labyrinth from the outside, you at first head straight for the center. Then the path bends and leads you in spirals, going first inward, then outward, and after a few more reversals finally reaches the center. This carving is believed to date from 2000 B.C. Essentially the same design appears in Greece before 1000 B.C., in the Italian Alps around 300 B.C., and in a Pompeian graffito from the first century A.D. The turf and church mazes are very similar, and so are the Hopi rock engravings of Arizona, though these latter are made up of straight lines. Perhaps this labyrinth design is of such great, though

Julian's Bower, the turf maze at Alkborough in Lincolnshire, overlooks the valley of the River Trent. Until the last century it was used as a kind of running track for village festivities.

obscure, significance that it was independently evolved in Europe and America. But it is possible that it first appeared among the Indians after its introduction by the Spanish.

Modern mystics dream up complex symbolism for labyrinths found in ancient cultures or "primitive" ones of the present day. However, most of their speculation is without any foundation. But the living legends of the labyrinth-making peoples are sufficiently dramatic without any elaboration. Again and again the labyrinth is associated with some deeply important and dangerous journey.

Among the Pima Indians of Arizona, the children play a game in which the score is kept by moving stones around a whorl-shaped line in the sand. The game is called "The House of Tcuhu" — Tcuhu is the god who in legend led the Pima from the underworld along a spiral tunnel. Here a labyrinth is associated with the birth of a people. In other places it is associated with the death and rebirth of an individual. The people of Malekula, an island of the New Hebrides in the Pacific, draw a sand figure that they call the Path. They believe that each person's spirit meets this sand figure pattern again after this life, during the journey to the land of the dead. The guardian of that land draws the pattern in the sand and rubs out half of it. The spirit is able to find its way through the pattern only if it knows the complete design. The unfortunate spirit that fails to get through is eaten by the guardian, and thus is not reborn.

Among the Celts, too, the labyrinth seems to have been connected with death, for the spiral design and other meandering patterns occur on the walls of the ancient stone burial chambers in Ireland, Wales and Brittany.

But one of the most ancient examples of the labyrinth was not mystical or symbolic, but strictly practical. This was the meandering passage that led between stone walls or earthworks to the entrance of a fortress. Anyone entering was forced to travel a great distance while exposed to bombardment from the defenders. Perhaps it was in ancient battles that the labyrinth was first associated with danger and death.

Opposite page, top: Military labyrinths guarded the entrances to Maiden Castle, an ancient English hill-top fort. Though the site is 5000 years old, the earthworks reached their maximum size in the first century B.C. The ramparts towered 50 feet over the passageways along which attackers had to come.

Opposite page, bottom: A *tholos,* or rotunda, connected with the temple of Asclepius, god of healing, in the Greek town of Epidaurus. It has six concentric circular walls. Radial walls between the three innermost circles made a kind of labyrinth, which may have been used in rituals.

Left: The Hollywood Stone, nearly four feet across, found in the Wicklow Mountains of Ireland. The same design occurs at countless European sites (compare with the Cretan coins shown overleaf).

Below: It is 1921, and royal visitors make sport in a stone maze on St. Agnes, one of the Scilly Isles. Such mazes are also common in Scandinavia, and are often called Troy Town because of a supposed likeness to the legendary city's walls.

The Cretan Labyrinth

King Minos of Crete was a sorely tried man. His wife became infatuated with a white bull sent by Poseidon. The resulting offspring was the Minotaur who had a human body but a bull's head. Some time later, the king's son Androgeus was murdered while traveling.

The king's reaction to the murder was harsh. He ordered the people of Athens, whom he held responsible, to send him a tribute of seven youths and seven maidens every nine years. These were sent one by one into a vast and intricate labyrinth built by the master engineer Daedalus. While wandering, they would be slain by the Minotaur.

According to this story, one of the best known of the Greek myths, Theseus, son of the king of Athens, was able to end the practice of sending the tribute. He volunteered to be one of the youths selected for tribute, determined to find a way of slaying the Minotaur.

Theseus was in luck; Ariadne, the daughter of Minos, fell in love with him and gave him a "clew " or ball, of thread that he could unwind while he walked through the labyrinth, and retrace to find his way out. (This incident is the origin of "clue" in its modern sense.) The subsequent killing of the Minotaur has been celebrated by poets and painters through the centuries.

Labyrinthine patterns are found on coins from Crete for a period of hundreds of years, but they date from much later than any Minos who might actually have existed. Some of these are identical with the spiral labyrinths in carvings and paintings in Europe.

Such a labyrinth would not have given much trouble to Theseus, since it has no branches. The Minotaur's home must have been a true maze, for even its designer, the cunning Daedalus, couldn't find his way out when he was later imprisoned there with his son Icarus. But they solved the problem by making wings with which they flapped their way to freedom.

Above: A rock carving from Cornwall and a coin minted in Knossos a few centuries before Christ.

Right: A 15th-century painting shows Knossos as a Renaissance city and the Minotaur as a centaur. Note the thread entering the labyrinth, in which no one could get lost, since it is unbranched.

Scholars dismissed the labyrinth as myth until Sir Arthur Evans began excavating the Cretan site of Knossos in 1899. He discovered that an advanced civilization had reached its peak there around 1600 B.C. He called it the Minoan culture. A large palace with many rooms and winding corridors was uncovered. Maze patterns decorated the wall of a corridor. Frescoes depicted bull leaping — half sport, half ritual, in which young men would grab the horns of charging bulls and leap over their backs. Ritual double-headed axes were found everywhere — the name for them was *labrys*. Is it possible that the story of the Minotaur's labyrinth is a distorted memory of events in Knossos?

Above: Two coins from Knossos of a few centuries before Christ. The one on the left shows a simple meander pattern. The later one, on the right, shows the fully developed labyrinth. It is flanked by an arrowhead and a sheaf of thunderbolts.

Left: A sprightly Minotaur on a coin of Knossos. He might be engaging in the ancient sport of maze running, or perhaps he has Theseus at his heels.

Turf Mazes

At many places in Britain, spiral whorls can be seen cut into the turf of a village green or a remote field; probably they could once be seen all over Europe. These British "mizmazes" would have vanished long ago if they had not been periodically recut by local people who wish to preserve ancient things, even when their original use is forgotten.

The mazes range from about 40 feet to about 90 feet in diameter. Sometimes the path is formed by the trench, sometimes by the raised turf left untouched by the cutting. One theory of their origin suggests that the mazes were first made in Britain by occupying Roman soldiers about the time of Christ. Each army camp would have had one to use as a kind of running track. They were certainly used for running in later centuries.

The path of a turf maze is almost never branched, but spirals alternately in toward the center and out again, just like the Cretan labyrinth pattern that occurs so commonly in Europe. It is quite a challenge to try to run such a winding path to the center as fast as possible. It would have been even more so after a few ales at a country fair, where turf mazes were often an attraction. A common name for a turf maze is Shepherd's Race, and Welsh shepherd boys would while away their time in making and running them as they tended their flocks.

Shakespeare mentions mazes several times. In *A Midsummer Night's Dream* Titania, Queen of the Fairies, says that ". . . the quaint mazes in the wanton green, For lack of tread, are undistinguishable." These words became true of most of the mazes of Britain in the following centuries. By the mid-19th century the memory of games on the turf mazes had often faded. A writer in 1866 records his recollections of running Julian's Bower, the maze at Alkborough in Lincolnshire, 60 years before, where villagers would play "under an indefinite persuasion of something unseen and unknown cooperating with them."

The sport of running a turf labyrinth was called "threading" or "treading" the maze. Essentially the same thing was done through the mazes marked out with stones that are still widespread, especially on the coasts of Scandinavia. A common name for the stone mazes is Troy Castle, and mazes in Britain are often called Troy Town. Were they so named after the labyrinthine fortifications of the ancient city of Troy?

It has often been thought that the turf mazes were religious in origin, for some of them duplicate mosaic or carved mazes in nearby churches. But it is just as likely that in these cases the mazes in the churches are copies of turf mazes that existed previously. Many other turf mazes are found far from churches or any other habitation. But they are often close to some ancient site, such as a Bronze Age camp or burial mound. Perhaps they date from before Roman times. And perhaps, like other mazes, they first had magical uses such as warding off evil from people's houses.

The turf maze at Wing, Rutland, some 40 feet across (top left), still exists, while the one at Boughton Green, Northamptonshire (bottom left), no longer survives. The latter was 37 feet across and was popular in a June fair. The maze at Ripon, in Yorkshire, destroyed in 1827, was 60 feet across (above).

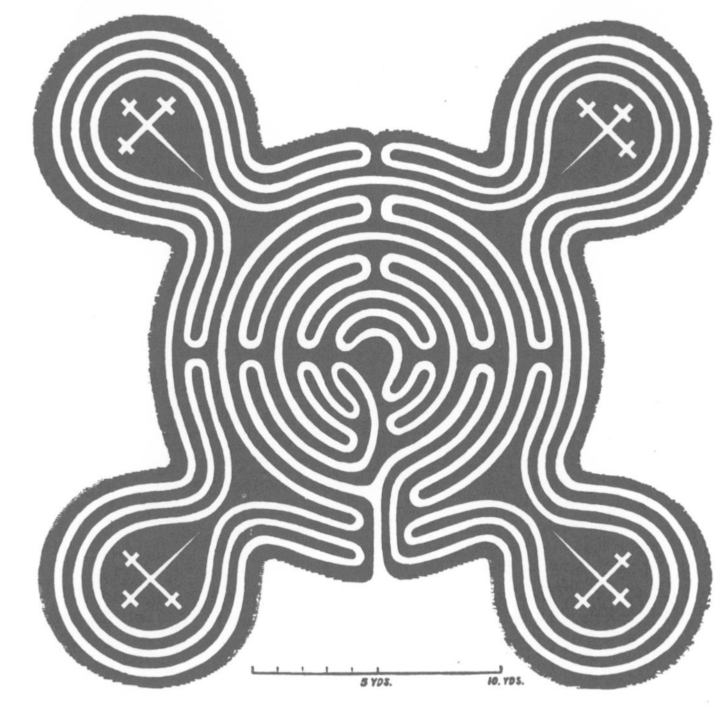

Above: The turf maze at Saffron Walden, Essex, is 138 feet from corner to corner (left). Shepherd's Race at Sneinton, Nottinghamshire (right), was ploughed up in 1797. It was supposedly cut by monks, who may have run around it for sport, or shuffled around it on their knees for a penance.

Below: Maze in full working order at Hilton, in Huntingdonshire. The pillar commemorates William Sparrow, who cut the maze in 1660, aged 19.

Church Labyrinths

As early as the fourth century A.D., a labyrinth was set into the floor of a Christian basilica in Algeria. They became a regular feature of churches, and most of the great European cathedrals can boast one. The largest are to be found in French cathedrals. At Chartres there is a labyrinth 40 feet across, made of blue and white stones set in the floor.

One of the smallest of the church mazes, shown at bottom right, is in Lucca cathedral in Italy. It is carved on a pier and measures only 20 inches across. Figures of Theseus and the Minotaur could once be seen at the center, but these have

Left: Labyrinth in the ruined abbey of St. Bertin at St.-Omer in France. It is apparently one of the many church labyrinths destroyed because churchgoers were too noisy in their enjoyment of them.

been erased by generations of tracers. A common French name for a church maze was *dédale*, recalling Daedalus, the designer of King Minos's labyrinth in the Greek legend.

Other French names for church mazes were *meandre* (meander) and *chemin de Jérusalem* (road to Jerusalem). The center of the maze was often called "Jerusalem" or "heaven." It is likely that the labyrinths were the paths of real journeys made by penitents on their knees in place of a pilgrimage to the Holy Land. The winding path was held to symbolize the twists and turns of the Christian's life as he avoids or succumbs to the temptations on the tortuous road to salvation. The maze presented an optimistic picture of the final outcome, for it was nearly always of the unbranched kind, without blind alleys.

Some of the younger worshipers managed to have fun with the mazes. At the cathedral of Rheims there was a fine maze. But it was ordered destroyed in 1779 because the noise of children running it interfered with services.

Below: The labyrinth at Chartres cathedral has been copied in this design on the lid of a wooden chest of the 19th century. The famous original is the largest surviving church maze, and is 40 feet across.

Bottom: A small labyrinth engraved on the wall of Lucca cathedral in Italy. It is less than two feet across. The figures of Theseus and the Minotaur, now badly worn, are carved at the center. The inscription reads: "This is the labyrinth that the Cretan Daedalus built, from which nobody who was inside could escape except Theseus; nor could he have done it if he had not been helped by Adriane, all for love." It is a pity that the stonemason spelled Ariadne wrongly.

The design of the turf maze at Alkborough, shown on pages 124 and 125, is reproduced in several other places in the village. It is cut into the stone floor of the church porch, it appears in a 19th-century stained-glass window in the church, and it figures here on a headstone in the village cemetery. The grave is that of a prominent man of the village who died in 1922. Having helped to keep the turf maze in good repair, he shared the village's justified pride.

Garden Mazes

When we think of mazes, we are almost certain to think of narrow shady paths between high hedges of yew, twisting now and then and offering baffling choices of turning. This is the recreational maze of today, with no deep symbolism and no need for deep meditation. Ideally it would be equipped with seats, a guide if necessary, and refreshments nearby.

When European nations became settled and aristocrats no longer needed to live in castles, the art of gardening came into its own. Professional gardeners and garden designers made their appearance and devised intricate and beautiful effects. Winding paths bordered by colorful flower beds became a part of all well-cared-for gardens. The patterns formed by such paths showed at their best when viewed from the raised terrace of the great house. To those who strolled in the garden they offered an organized promenade along a succession of varied blooms. The idea of a puzzle did not present itself in such a garden, since the pattern could be seen by the stroller.

But with the development of topiary art (that is, ornamental hedge-clipping), the puzzle maze of tall hedges became a favorite. The 17th-century labyrinth designs opposite are typical of hundreds that were published in gardening books. Doubtless more people designed mazes than actually made the effort to grow them, and that is possibly a good thing, because some of them are more entertaining to look at on paper than they would have been to walk through. But people found much delight in hedge mazes and they were grown in increasing numbers. In their heyday, every great garden had at least one maze.

Only the most magnificent labyrinth was good enough for the Palace of Versailles. At the end of the 17th century a network of paths was constructed there, winding through acres of woodland. Strollers could encounter 39 groups of "hydraulic statuary," elaborately sculptured fountains that represented scenes from Aesop's *Fables*. Fourteen water wheels drove more than 250 pumps. But after only a century, the charm must have faded, for the whole construction was destroyed.

In Italy the Villa Pisani at Stra possesses a hedge maze with four miles of winding paths. At the center is an observation tower that can be mounted by spiral stairs. But this maze has suffered from neglect and is now closed.

The taste for garden mazes declined in the 19th century. Sophisticated people viewed them as fit only for children. Skilled gardeners wished to exercise their talents on more interesting creations than corridors of evergreens that take years to grow, take a lot of space and block the view, and soon look shabby from the depredations of short-cutting maze threaders. New hedge mazes are rarely planted now. But many

Built in the early 1900s as a recreation area for the local residents of Groningen province, the Netherlands, this maze can still be visited today.

Designs for garden mazes from *Architectura Curiosa* by G. A. Boeckler, published in 1664. The last one shown is very reminiscent of the traditional "Cretan" labyrinth that has cropped up in so many places since ancient times. The rest, however, have paths that branch at some point, so that they are genuine puzzle mazes. They seem to include some very long walks without turnings or partings of the ways, so it would perhaps be more entertaining to mark them out with flower beds rather than hedges.

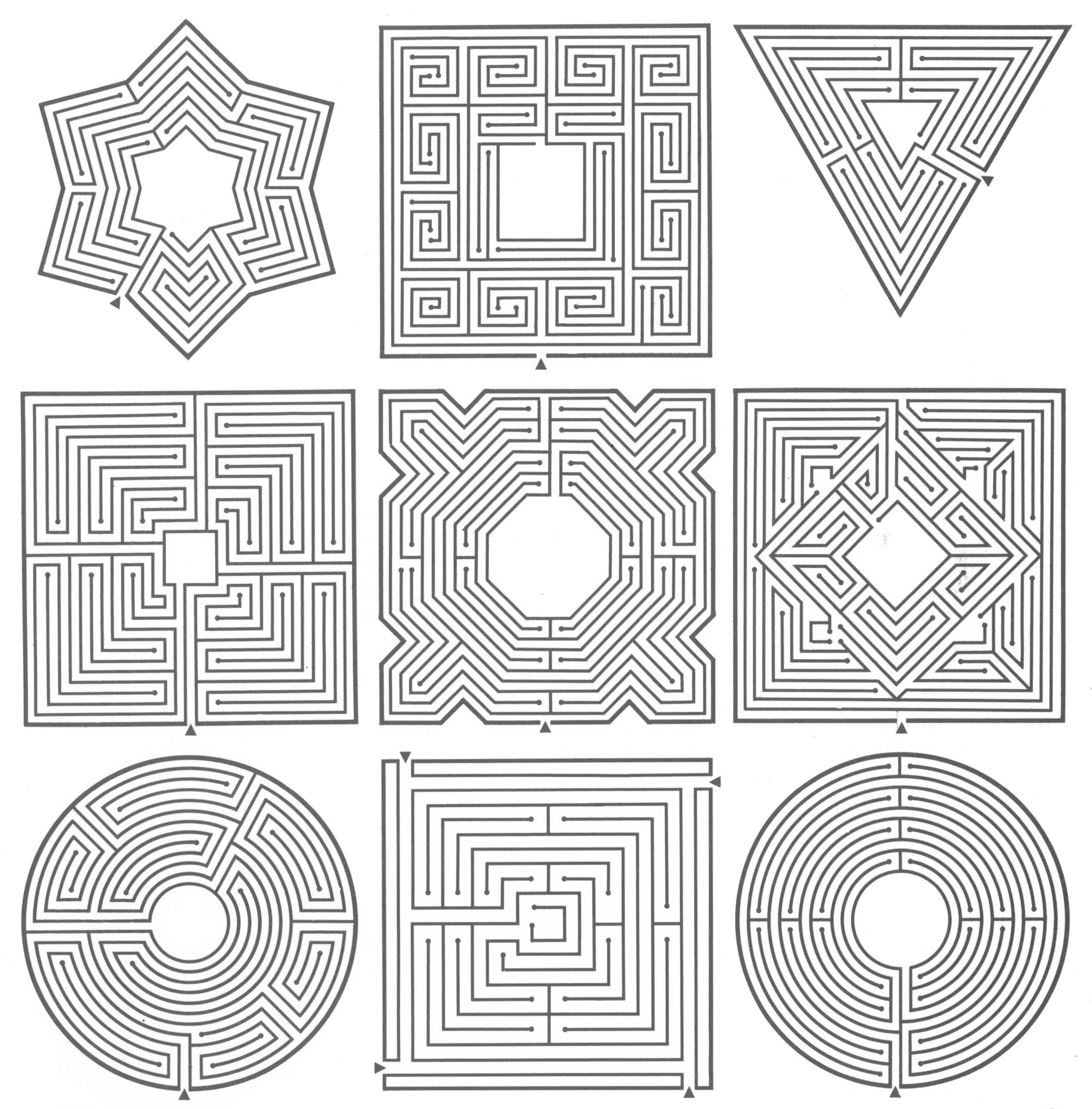

(See solution page 195)

of the old ones are still tended devotedly, and give pleasure to thousands.

The most famous of all hedge mazes was planted at Hampton Court in 1690, in the reign of William III. It is a simple design (shown on page 138) covering a quarter of an acre. It is the oldest surviving hedge maze in England, and it is showing signs of its age. Frustrated maze wanderers frequently crash through the hedge, and the original hornbeam has been patched with privet, yew, sycamore and even holly and hawthorn to deter these people.

Other English hedge mazes include the magnificent one with two entrances at Hatfield House (see page 138). Devoted puzzlers insist on leaving by a different entrance from one they used to enter.

There are some fine hedge mazes in the United States. One is a feature of the town of Williamsburg, Virginia, which

has been restored to its pre-Revolutionary condition. The maze stands on the grounds of the Governor's Palace. Its hedges are of holly, so they are not likely to be penetrated by visitors.

One of the few hedge mazes with symbolic significance was planted about 1820 at Harmonie, Indiana (now New Harmony). A religious sect, the Rappites, created it with a little temple "emblematical of Harmony" at its center. The maze represented the difficulty of arriving at harmony. The sect moved on, and the next settlers tore up the maze. A modern one replaces it.

Below left: This hedge maze of native American holly is in the city of Williamsburg, Virginia. The former colonial capital has now been restored to the glory of its pre-Revolutionary days. The maze, a major attraction for vacationers, stands in the stately surroundings of the grounds of the palace once used by the Governor of the Colonies.

Below: Plan of the Williamsburg maze. The route to the center is short; the blind alleys are very long.

Right: Painting by Bartolommeo Veneto of an early 16th-century gentleman. His tunic is emblazoned with a labyrinth and "Solomon's knot" designs.

Bottom: The delightful laurel hedge maze on the Glendurgan estate in Cornwall. It was planted in 1833 by the owner, Alfred Fox, and his wife, Sarah.

Below: Plan of the Glendurgan maze, whose paths curl back and forth in a charmingly irregular way.

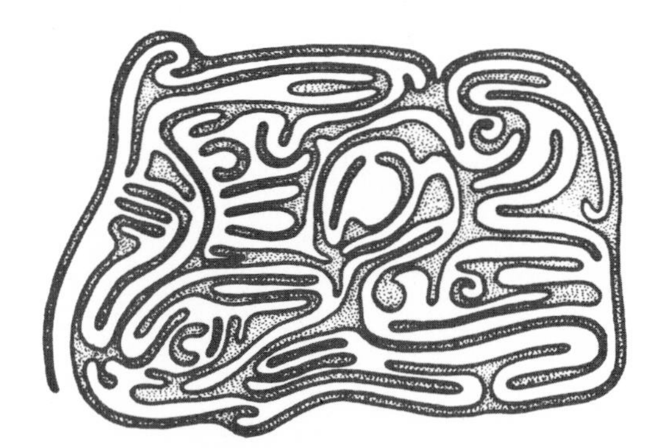

(See solution page 195)

How to Solve Mazes

Rats are able to find their way through mazes and remember their route. When they run the mazes again, they improve their efficiency, leaving out the blind alleys. Even ants can remember how to find their way through mazes with as many as ten points of choice. Robots have also been made that can learn their way through a maze and can then travel through another one of the same pattern without mistakes, though distances and angles may be different. But animals, like most human maze solvers, waste a lot of time at their first attempt, going over the same path repeatedly, missing turnings and getting confused. Are there rules we can use to find our way systematically through mazes without wasted effort?

When dealing with a fairly simple paper maze it is easy to make it still simpler. Just shade in the blind alleys. Then do the same to any loops that you can see. You will be left with a route to the goal, though it may branch. You can then choose the most direct of these paths.

However, you might not always find this method easy to apply. Look at the complex maze on the opposite page. There are no dead ends. The paths branch, but the loops and alternative routes are so long and winding that they cannot be picked out at a glance and eliminated. And this method cannot be used when you walk through a hedge maze (or hunt Minotaurs in a labyrinth), with no plan to study.

Since you have no idea at the beginning where the goal is, you need rules that guarantee that with perseverance every inch of the maze is explored. One method, which is simple but doesn't work for all mazes, is to go through the maze always keeping one hand — either the right or the left — in contact with the wall. Imagine you are doing it in the Hampton Court maze, or in the Hatfield House maze; their plans are at the right.

When will this method fail? Well, it will not work if there are two entrances to the maze and there is a route connecting them that doesn't pass through the goal. But even in the usual case where there is one entrance, the method will fail if there is a route that loops around the goal. On the far right is such a maze. The hand-on-the-wall method would lead you back to the entrance. The Hampton Court maze has a loop, but it does not pass around the goal.

Below: Plan of the Hampton Court maze. An 18th-century writer who decried garden mazes said that they were "a mere conceit" and that "sagacity affords no aid to tracing a labyrinth"; but anyone with the sagacity to walk through this maze with one hand constantly touching the hedge is guaranteed to reach the center. Below the plan is a key diagram showing the route as a straight line to the goal (at right), and blind alleys as branches.

Bottom left: Plan of the Hatfield House maze in Hertfordshire, with a key diagram next to it. The hand-on-the-hedge method will lead you to the goal and then out again by the alternative route.

Center right: This maze is trivial, but it cannot be threaded by the hand-on-the-wall method since some paths loop around the goal. Another method described in the text will succeed, however.

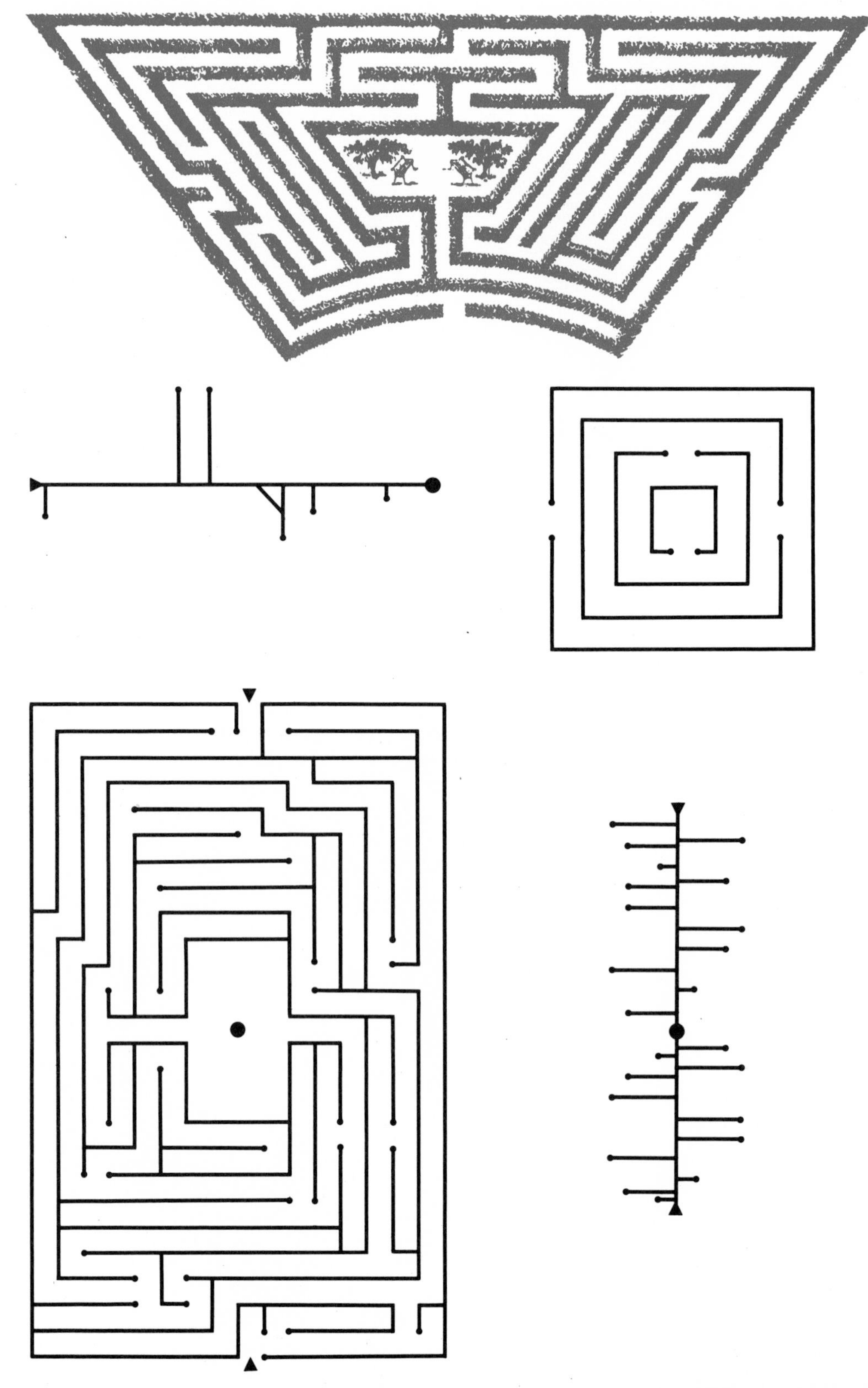

There is a general method that will work in any maze. These rules were given by the French mathematician Trémeaux:

1. Mark one side of the corridor — say the right-hand — as you pass through the maze. (In a hedge maze leave a marker on one side of the path at each junction.)

2. Whenever you reach a dead end, retrace your steps, still marking the right-hand wall. (This is the unmarked, previously left, wall.)

3. Whenever you reach a previously visited junction along a path that you are following for the *first* time, turn around and retrace your steps, still marking the right-hand wall.

4. When you reach a previously visited junction along a path that you have used before, take a *new* path if there is one available; otherwise take any previously used path from it (subject to the following rule).

5. Never enter a path that has been marked on both sides.

The method is infallible, but it may call for a weekend's work when applied to a maze like the one on the right.

When you have found your way through a maze, you may want to record your route in a handy key diagram. One way of doing this is shown in the key to the Hampton Court maze (opposite page). The route to the goal is drawn as a straight line. The blind alleys and alternative paths are drawn branching to left and right as appropriate. They can be drawn to scale in cases where you wish to compare the lengths of alternative routes. In very complicated mazes, you may find you have to mark each branch as you trace it with color or with letters.

But is this methodical and scientific way of solving mazes the right way to treat them? Perhaps one should merely wander, grateful for lucky turnings, and stoical about the wrong ones, all the while pondering on the unpredictability of life. Greg Bright, a notable modern maze enthusiast who designed the maze shown here, would insist on this. He even suggests that his mazes be traced by cutting a small hole in a piece of paper and sliding it over the pattern, so simulating the restricted vision of a person wandering in a labyrinth.

This extraordinary network is the brainchild of Greg Bright, a famous creator of mazes drawn, painted, built, and dug. The paths are to be taken as passing over and under each other. There are two directions in which you can thread the maze; one is very difficult, the other is colossally so. Going from the large blank area to the small one is the more difficult direction, because there are many choices of initial path, and many routes that lead back to the starting point. Only one path leads away from the small blank area, but it forks so frequently that tracing it in that direction is a giant task. Notice that there are no blind alleys. The solver who wants a slightly easier time can cover the page with tracing paper and mark his route in pencil. The enthusiast will trace his path with a matchstick and run the risk of covering the same ground twice, or even more times just as if he were a wanderer in a hedge maze.

(See solution page 195)

How to Make Mazes

Not many of us get the chance to grow a hedge maze. So we shall not bother to dwell on the importance of making sure that there are no long walks unrelieved by a turning, or that dead ends are not visible too soon in advance, or what kind of art object should delight the eye at the goal. There is more scope to dig a turf maze, if convenient ground can be found. But don't think it's easy. Greg Bright lived in a tent for months while digging the maze shown in the frontispiece. When he abandoned it with a third of the design still not dug, he had spent a year on it. While you plan a similar project, practice with mazes drawn on paper and the three-dimensional maze over the page.

If the maze is to be made up of straight lines, it is a good idea to rough it out on graph paper before copying it neatly. If you want it to be made up of circular paths, draw concentric circles with compasses and experiment with those. It is usually best to draw in the route to the goal first, and fit other paths around it. Of course, you will want to provide blind alleys that lead temptingly toward the goal to provide the maximum frustration for the solver. Maze makers claim that people are more likely to turn right than left, so make sure that plenty of false turns go to the right. And build in blind alleys that offer themselves to solvers who try to trace the maze back from the goal.

Of course, you don't have to restrict yourself to mazes with one goal in the center and one entrance. You can have both starting point and goal inside the maze. Or you can provide a number of goals that have to be reached in a specified order. You can also make it harder to go from point A to point B than from B to A. For example, if more paths pass through A than through B, the solver will be more likely to keep returning to the point A.

Then you can arrange the design to make it not only attractive, but fiendishly difficult. Look at the baffler on the right: many choices, with no hint of which might be correct; long paths to traverse before you know whether you're in a blind alley; and every chance of crossing a "wall" without realizing it. Legend has it that a Philadelphia salesman, trying to count the many possible routes through it, was driven to suicide — a high compliment to the skill of the maze designer.

Below: Maze motif in tiles on the wall of a London subway station. The maze is a punning reference to the "warren" of the station's name; Warren Street is in fact named after a 17th-century admiral's daughter. In the rush hour travelers have to wait two minutes for their trains, on an average. The designer has estimated that it will take most people three minutes to solve his maze.

Bottom: Your chances of getting through this fiendish maze are greater than you might think, for at each junction there is only one choice of path that will lead you astray. But you have to avoid the wrong choice at six different places. And, of course, there is the likelihood of crossing onto another path without noticing it. The great puzzler Henry Dudeney calculated that there are 640 ways of getting to the center without going over any path twice or taking any wrong turnings along the way.

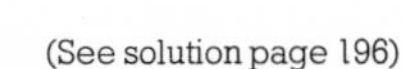
(See solution page 196)

A handsome ball-in-the-maze puzzle. Just tilt the maze to roll the ball through the molded passages. Sometimes the ball will take a path of its own choosing, adding a random element to the puzzle. Similar mazes have been made in which steel balls are guided with a magnet. Toys like this have been popular since the Pigs in Clover game was sold in the 1880s. That had three marbles to coax into the goal; and the toy was designed to ensure that, as you rolled one in, another one would roll out.

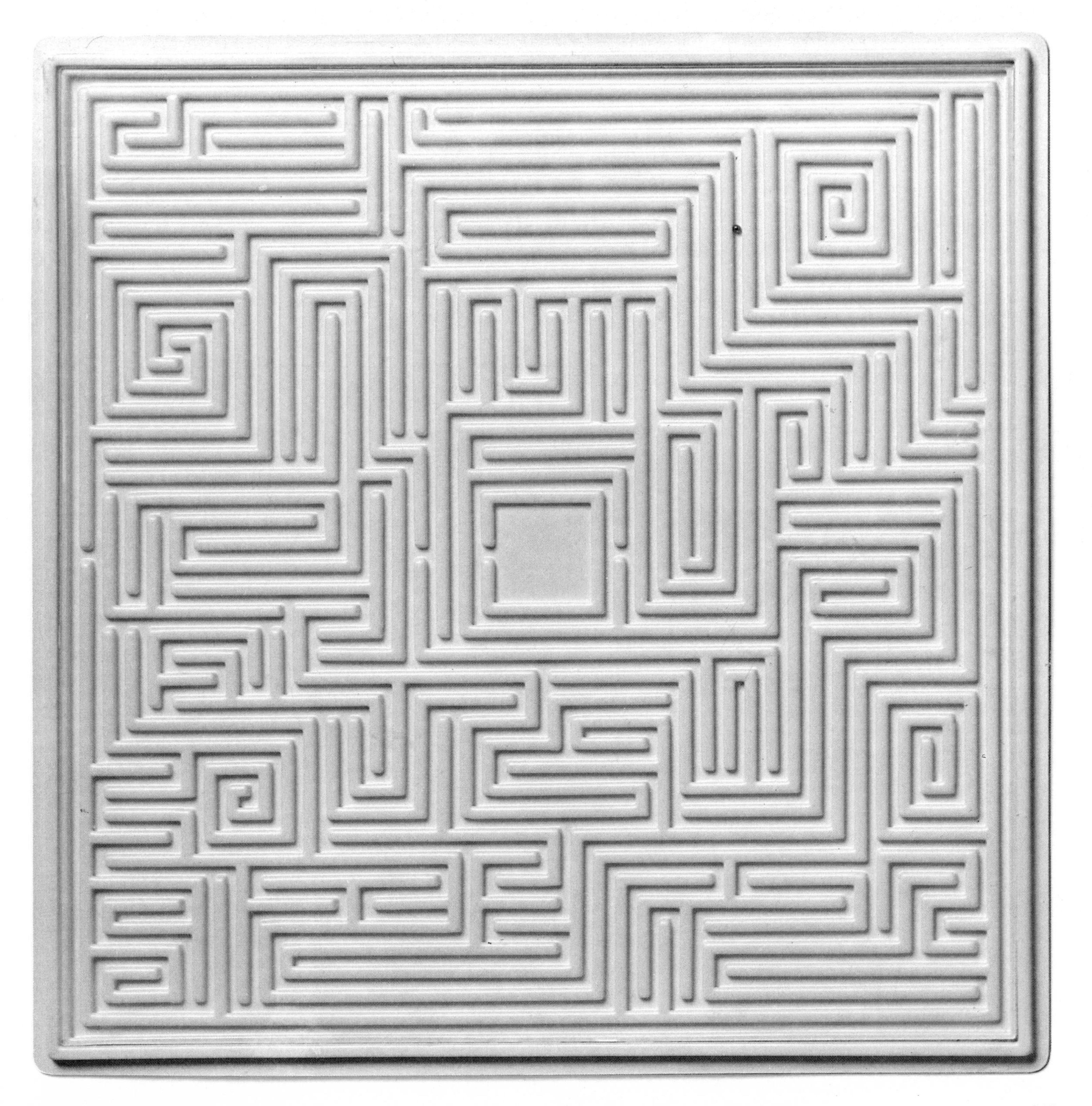

(See solution page 196)

Three-Dimensional Maze Puzzle

Mazes can be drawn as if they used all three dimensions, the paths crossing above and below each other. This adds a new level of complexity that maze makers often exploit. Some outdoor mazes are genuinely three-dimensional, with bridges and tunnels. And some of the old inns where smugglers hid were veritable mazes in three dimensions, with many staircases, trap doors, and rooms with connecting doors.

You can make a pleasing puzzle in the form of a warren of tunnels bored in a block of wood, through which a marble or a ball bearing can roll. The puzzle shown on the right is of this kind. Only one hole, B, appears on the outside of the block, but plugs at A, C, D, and E seal four other passages.

Systematic experiment will show the solver with a good visual imagination that the paths are arranged as in the diagram. It is then only a question of dexterity to coax the ball out of the box.

Materials

Block of larchwood, 2″ × 5″ × 6″
Piece of doweling, 1/2″ diameter and at least 1″ long
Piece of doweling, 1 1/4″ diameter and at least 1 1/2″ long
Wood glue
Ball bearing or marble, 1/3″ diameter

Tools

Electric drill or hand drill; 1/2″ bit for drilling metal (pointed) and 1 1/4″ bit for drilling wood; backsaw; round file; sandpaper; ruler and pencil.

How to Make the Puzzle

Mark three points, A, B, C, on the 2″ × 5″ face, on the centerline and 1 1/4″ from each other and from the ends of the block, as shown in the diagram. With the 1 1/4″ bit, drill holes 1 1/2″ deep centered on the two outer marks, A and C. The wood-drilling bit will give flat bottoms to these holes. Then drill into the centers of these holes with the 1/2″ bit. At A, drill to a depth of 5″ from the surface. At C, drill a hole 3 1/4″ deep.

Then, with the same bit, drill another hole centered on point B to a depth of 3 1/4″. (All these depths relate to the *sides* of the holes; the conical bases of the holes made by the metal-drilling bit will extend a little way farther.) If you do not have a depth guide that you can use with your drill, you can mark the desired depth with chalk on the bit.

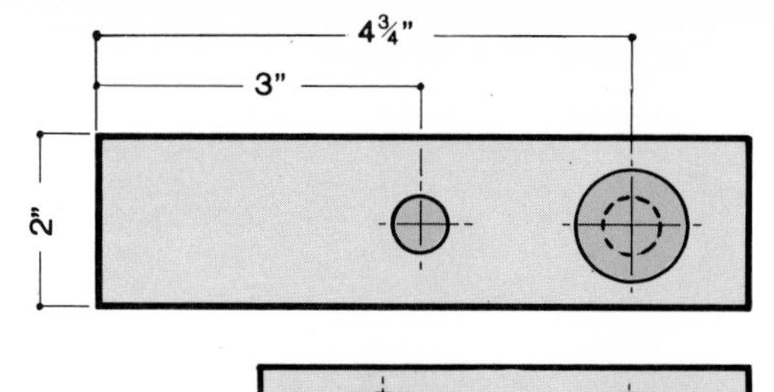

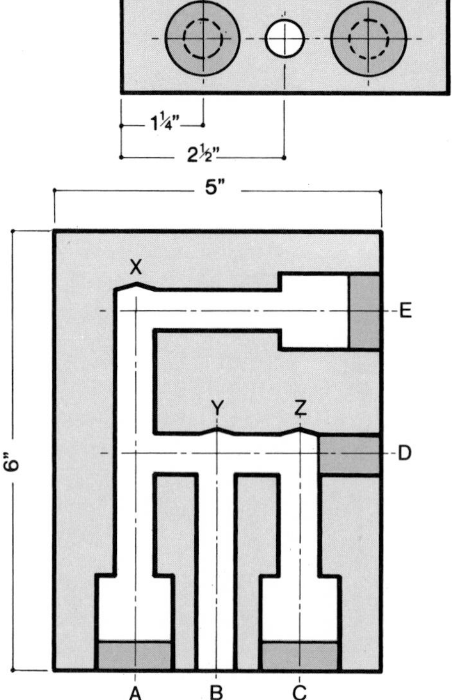

Following this guide diagram, drill out a few passages to make a simple labyrinth for a ball.

Now drill the crosswise holes. Mark points D and E on the 2″ × 6″ face; D is at the center, E is 1 1/4″ from the right-hand face. With the 1 1/4″ bit, drill 1 1/2″ deep at point E. Then, with the 1/2″ bit, drill into the center of this hole to a depth of 4″ (from the face of the block); you will then meet a drilled hole at X.

Finally drill the hole at D with the 1/2″ bit. Take it to a depth of 3 3/4″, where it will meet AX. There will be conical depressions remaining at X, Y and Z, but nowhere else if you have been careful in drilling the holes at D and E.

Smooth the edges where the passages meet, using the round file. Then make the plugs to seal the holes. Using the backsaw, cut three pieces of the 1 1/4″ dowel, each 1/2″ thick, and one piece of the 1/2″ dowel, 1″ long. Glue these respectively into the large holes and the smaller hole at D. You can apply teak oil to the block to enhance the grain if you wish. Now you only have to put in the ball, shake it about a bit, and challenge friends — and yourself — to get it out.

Only one hole appears on the outside of this puzzle, but the circular plugs mark other passages. Freeing the ball calls for logic and dexterity.

Wire Puzzles

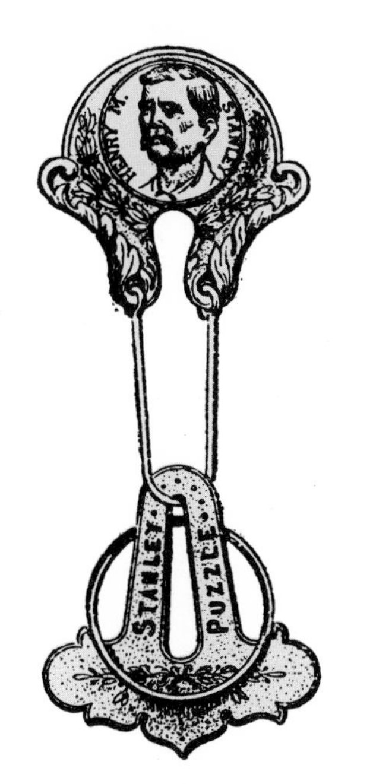

The Stanley puzzle, distributed early in this century by Perry and Co., bears the head of the famous explorer stamped on a brass medallion. Both ends of the puzzle are wider than the ring that encircles it, and that has to be removed by the puzzle solver.

Wire puzzles, where the object is to separate two seemingly interlocked parts from one another, have been in existence for many years. Some early examples, dating back to the mid-17th century, can still be seen in museums, while the simple "bent nail" puzzle which developed even before then is still played today. While many early puzzles were solely for amusement, some were incorporated into jewelry, such as the familiar Eastern puzzle rings. Put to practical use, coiled wires were often used to link chains together, making a connection as secure as expensive early locks, and presenting something of a puzzle to thieves.

The beginning of the 20th century saw a boom in wire puzzles, then considered as suitable family entertainment, and elaborate boxes of them were produced. At the same time it also became popular to offer them as gifts; the Stanley puzzle was issued by Perry and Co. of England as a sales premium. After being neglected for several years, recently there has been a rise in the popularity of wire puzzles, and now many are available in toy and games shops. While these puzzles are fun to do, and are an ideal first step into the world of wire puzzles, they tend to be similar to one another. So the following pages include a number of different types of puzzles, ranging from the simple key ring, based on the bent nails principle, to the more elaborate staircase puzzle. Many of these cannot be bought, but instructions for making them are on page 156.

In most of these wire puzzles the solution involves the removal of a metal ring or ellipse, or tied loop of cord, from the main component. The puzzles tend to fall into different groups. Some are so tortuous and confused that they appear impossible to solve, but are remarkably easy once you have the knack. Others appear simple; yet these demand a break from traditional thought patterns to release the trapped pieces.

Made in America in 1919, the various wire puzzles in this box, including the familiar bent nails, were clearly designed to entertain the whole family.

Keyrings

The interlocking loops of the key ring puzzle look impossible to separate without forcing or distorting the rings in some way. Yet by gentle manipulation you will find that the rings will suddenly separate. The main problem then is to put the puzzle back together again as smoothly as it came apart. If you tackle this puzzle in the correct manner, then the rings can be slid apart and back together again easily.

Two identical metal components, each with a brightly painted handle, make the key ring puzzle.

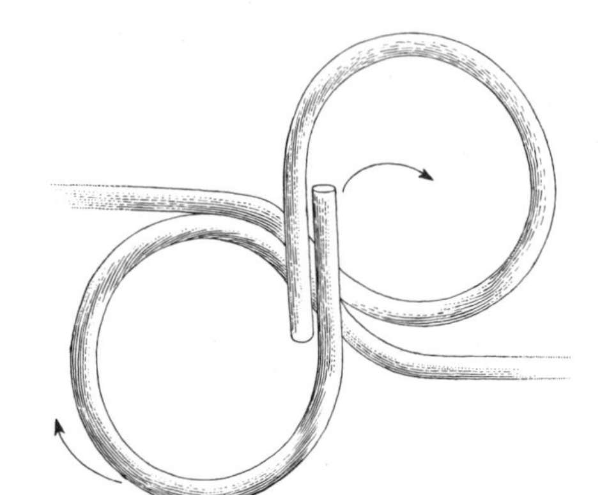

If you didn't solve this one, refer to the illustration above, which shows how to link the two loops together. Hold the rings as shown, then, keeping the left ring steady, give your right wrist an oblique twist to slide the rings together.

Simplex

The simplex puzzle really is as simple to do as its name implies. But at first glance its convoluted and interlocking forms belie this fact. The aim here is to separate this puzzle into its three constituent parts, again without bending or forcing any part of the puzzle. Just keep moving the three pieces until you see how, and in what order, they will separate from one another. The solution is given in the diagram below.

Twist the U-shaped piece of bent wire free of the ring and metal component to solve this problem.

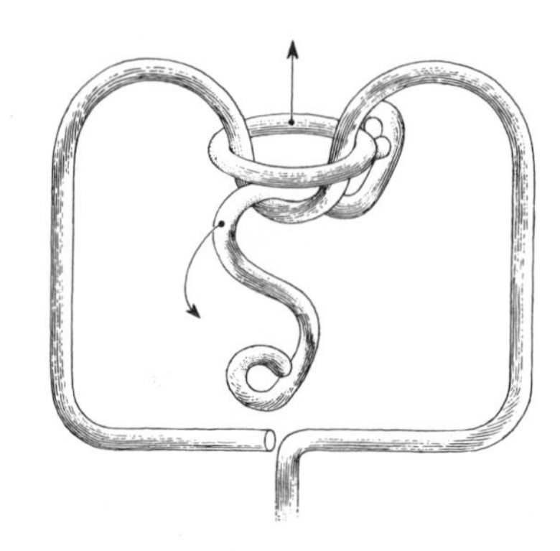

No luck with this puzzle? The diagram above shows how the three pieces of the puzzle must be arranged in order for them to separate easily. Make the same shape with your puzzle, then move each part in turn, according to the arrows.

The Imprisoned Heart

This puzzle involves the liberation of the imprisoned heart from the metal bars which hold it captive. As with the simplex puzzle, there are three movable pieces, all linked together in a special way. Using the same technique of patient manipulation, try to work out the moves which free the heart shape. It is no more difficult than the simplex puzzle, and it is the order in which the pieces are moved that is important.

The heart shape can be separated from the bar and rectangular part of the puzzle shown above.

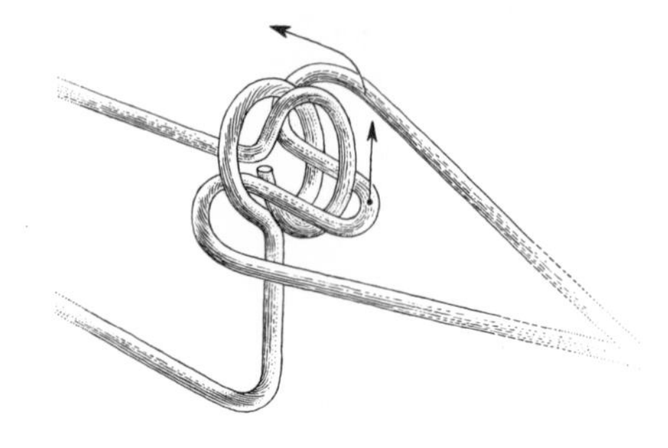

Did you fail to free the locked heart? If so, follow the diagram above. Push the loop of the heart shape through the right fixed ring before trying to work it around the ring at the end of the cross bar. Don't forget how to replace it all.

The Handcuff Puzzle

As with most wire puzzles, the aim in the handcuff puzzle is to free one part from the main component. In this case the ring that overlaps the openings of the handcuffs must be released, and clearly it cannot slide off the cuffs since they are far too wide. The nine circular parts that make up this puzzle are all involved in its solution. Since this is one of the more intricate wire puzzles shown in these pages, solving it will probably require a considerable amount of concentration, and some talent for manipulating the parts to find the proper positions. Don't give up too easily though — it's worth some time to see if you can solve it alone.

How to Solve the Puzzle

If your own methods have failed, then resort to the directions and diagrams below to discover the secret of the cuffs.

1. First hold the handcuffs taut between your hands with the ring over the circlets of the top cuff. Turn this top cuff about 15° to the left, away from you, and make the openings of the two handcuffs intersect.
2. Let the ring fall to encircle both left-hand metal circlets, before folding the top handcuff over toward you, as shown in figure 2, as far as it will go.
3. This leaves the ring between the two left circlets. Then lift the top of the ring over so that it is behind both circlets, as in figure 3. Now let the ring come to a central position for the next move.
4. Gently move the cuffs apart at the bottom, so that the ring is free to fall to the bottom of the cuffs. This can be seen in figure 4. Now it is a simple matter to slide the ring off the cuffs.

Replacing the ring can also be a puzzle, so if you cannot follow the directions in reverse, perhaps these hints will help. Hold the handcuffs vertically and make the same twist and fold movements as in figures 1 and 2. Slip the ring over the two right circlets and let it drop to the bottom. Part the cuffs slightly at the bottom, and slide the ring up the center until it can be manipulated over both of the left-hand circlets. Now open the puzzle out and the ring should once again form an integral part.

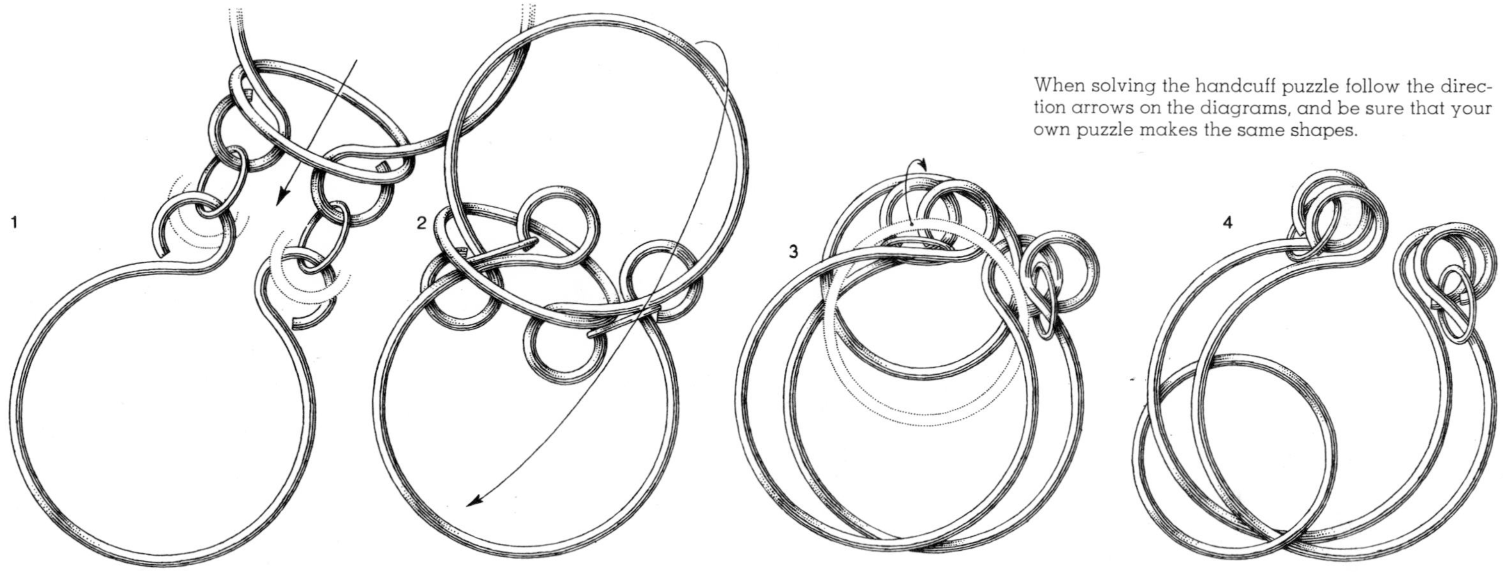

1 2 3 4

When solving the handcuff puzzle follow the direction arrows on the diagrams, and be sure that your own puzzle makes the same shapes.

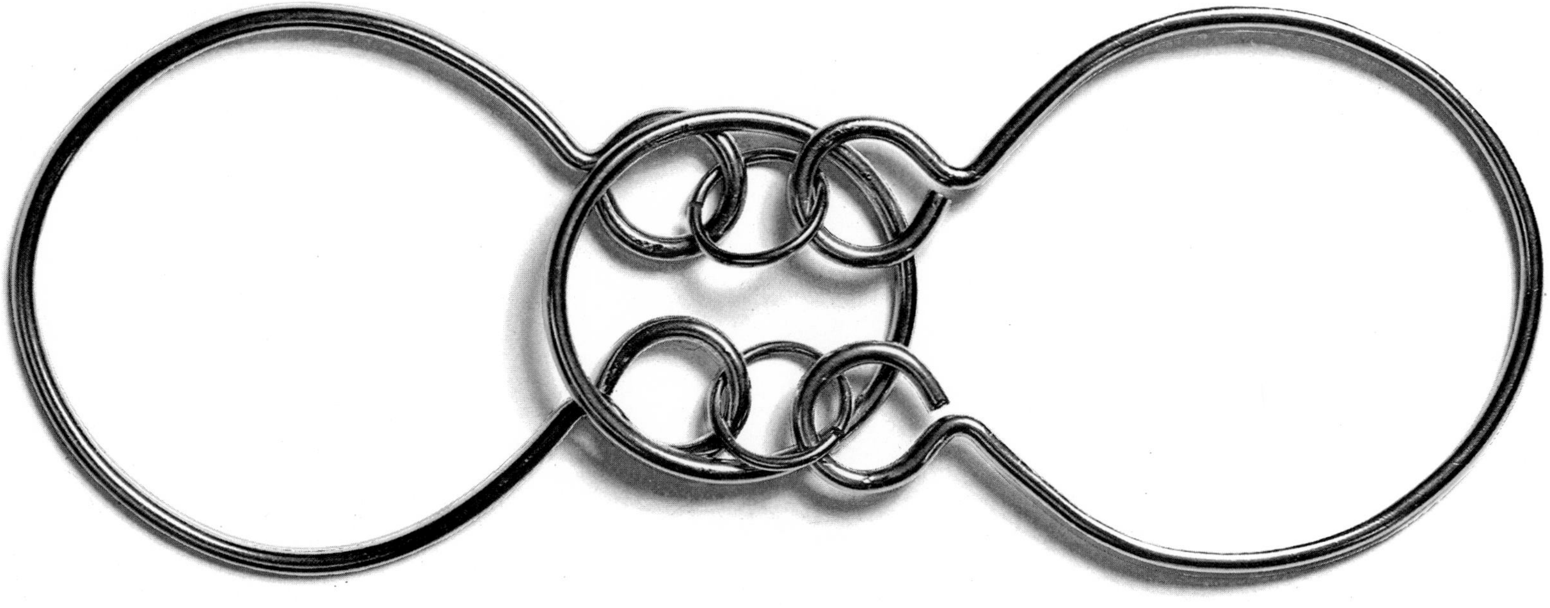

The nine silver rings that make up the handcuff puzzle may seem to be irrevocably intertwined. But a few deft moves in the right directions will result in the central ring coming free of the handcuffs.

The Gordian Knot Puzzle

According to Greek mythology, the Gordian knot was named after Gordius, king of Phrygia, who tied a cart yoke to a pole with an extremely complex knot. The oracle then proclaimed that whoever could discover the secret of the knot and untie it would become king of all Asia. Many tried, but all failed.

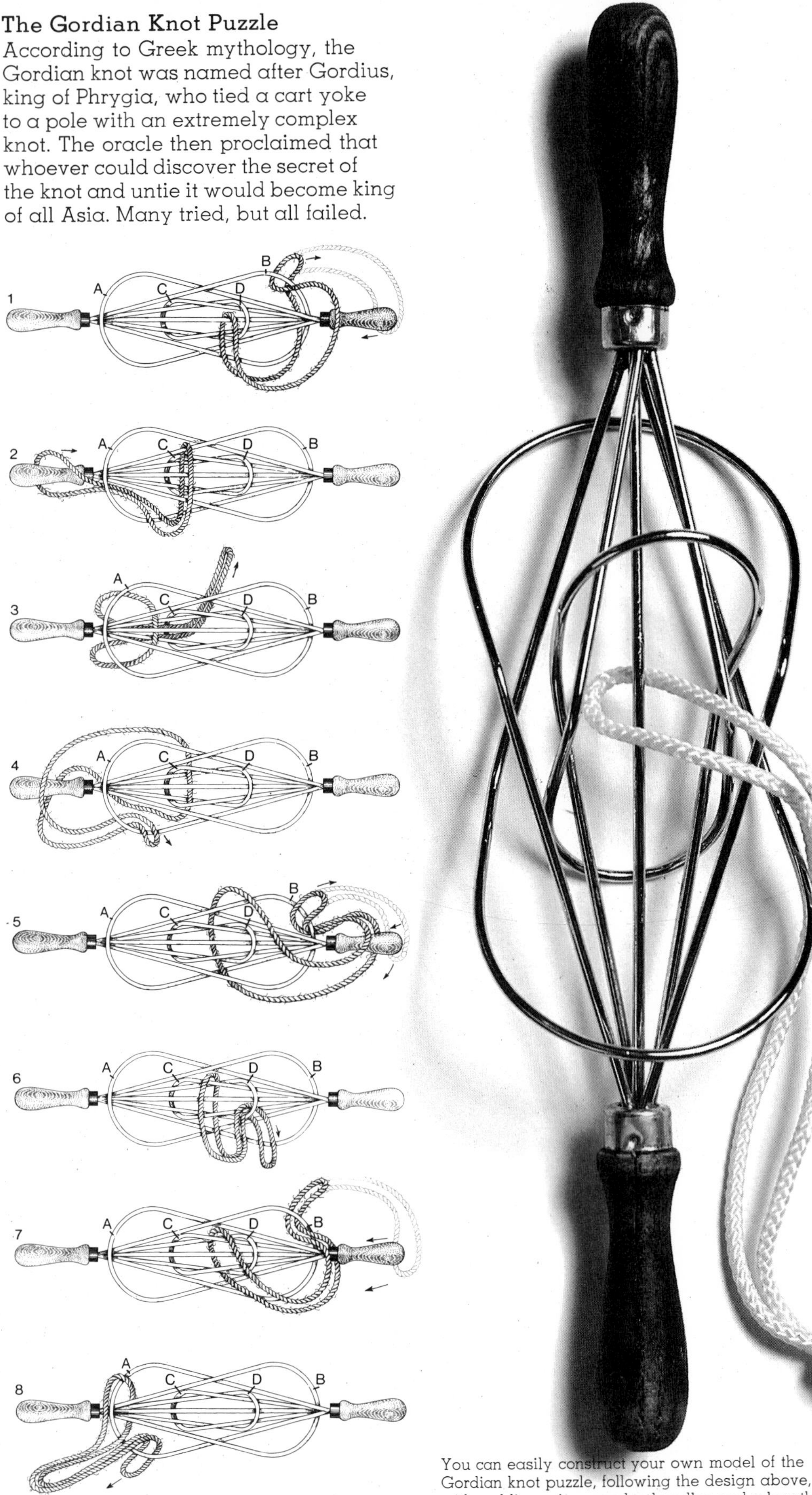

Keeping the metal component in the same position, move the cord according to the eight figures above.

You can easily construct your own model of the Gordian knot puzzle, following the design above, with welding wire, wooden handles and a length of cord. General directions and further details for making this puzzle are given on page 156.

For centuries the priests of Zeus guarded the knot zealously, until the arrival of Alexander the Great. Possibly frustrated by being unable to untangle the mystery, Alexander hacked the knot in two with his sword.

Please do not resort to this desperate measure when you try to unravel the Gordian knot puzzle on this page; there is a far more satisfactory solution to be found, which leaves the cord intact, but free of the metal component.

How to Solve the Puzzle

In order to simplify the explanation of the moves necessary to slip the tied loop from the wire component of the Gordian knot puzzle, sections of the metal component have been labeled A, B, C, and D in the diagrams and instructions. Furthermore, direction arrows and shadow drawings of the cord have been indicated where necessary, to avoid confusion. Throughout the working of the puzzle it is easiest to hold the knot of the cord loop, and it is never necessary to strain the puzzle. The correct moves enable the loop to slide easily around, and off, the metal parts.

Before starting, look closely at the photograph (left) and make sure that your own puzzle is in exactly the same position. Then go on to the diagrams.

1. Holding the cord by the knot, pass the loop over the right handle. The knot then goes through wire loop B, from the front toward the back, before the cord loop is brought over the right handle again, toward you. The result of these moves is that the cord now lies under wire loop B and the central bar.
2. Pass the knot under the bow of A, and then loop the cord over the left handle from front to back.
3. Pass the knot through the wire loop C, also from front to back.
4. Loop the cord back over the left handle toward you. The knot then passes under A again, so that the cord lies under B, C, and the central bar.
5. Now loop the cord over the right handle, and this time bring the knot through B from the back to the front, and again over the right handle.
6. Pass the knot through wire loop D, from left to right of the puzzle.
7. Loop the cord over the right handle, through B from front to back, and back over the right handle to the front.
8. Pass the knot under A and, believe it or not, the cord loop should slip free of the metal component.

Caught on the shanks of two of the three silver crosses, this ring can only move a few centimeters either way. Change the arrangement of the crosses and discover how to move, and free, the ring.

The Triple Cross

The aim of this puzzle, made up of three linked crosses and a metal ring, is to slip the ring free of the rest of the puzzle. It looks impossible! But in fact it can be accomplished in surprisingly few moves. If you fail to free it by trial and error, then take a look at the instructions and diagrams below to find the path that the silver ring must follow.

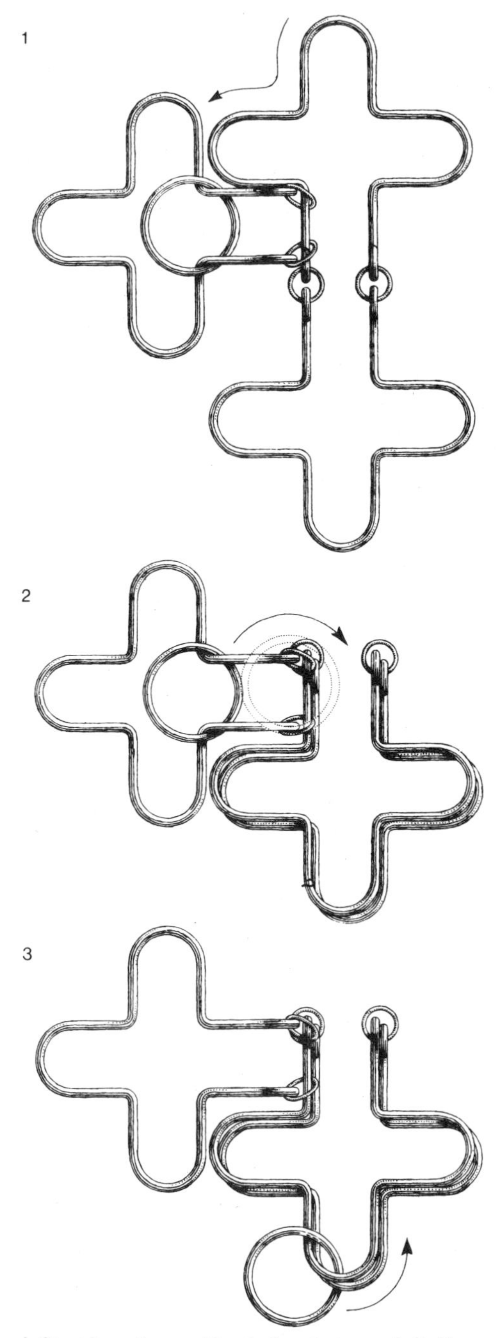

1. Start from the position in the photograph (left). Slide the ring onto the top cross, and following the arrow in figure 1, work the top cross to the left.
2. Holding the left and upper crosses, fold the puzzle over so that the upper cross now covers the lower one. The ring can then be worked up the shaft of the left cross, and over the joint that links the upper and lower crosses, as in figure 2.
3. Slide the ring around the two folded crosses, in the direction of the arrow, until it is free.

The Locked Ellipse

The wide convolutions on each "handle" of this puzzle totally prohibit the ellipse from sliding free of the main component. Or do they? With some subtle bends and twists, and careful manipulation of the four parts, you may find the trick of releasing the ellipse.

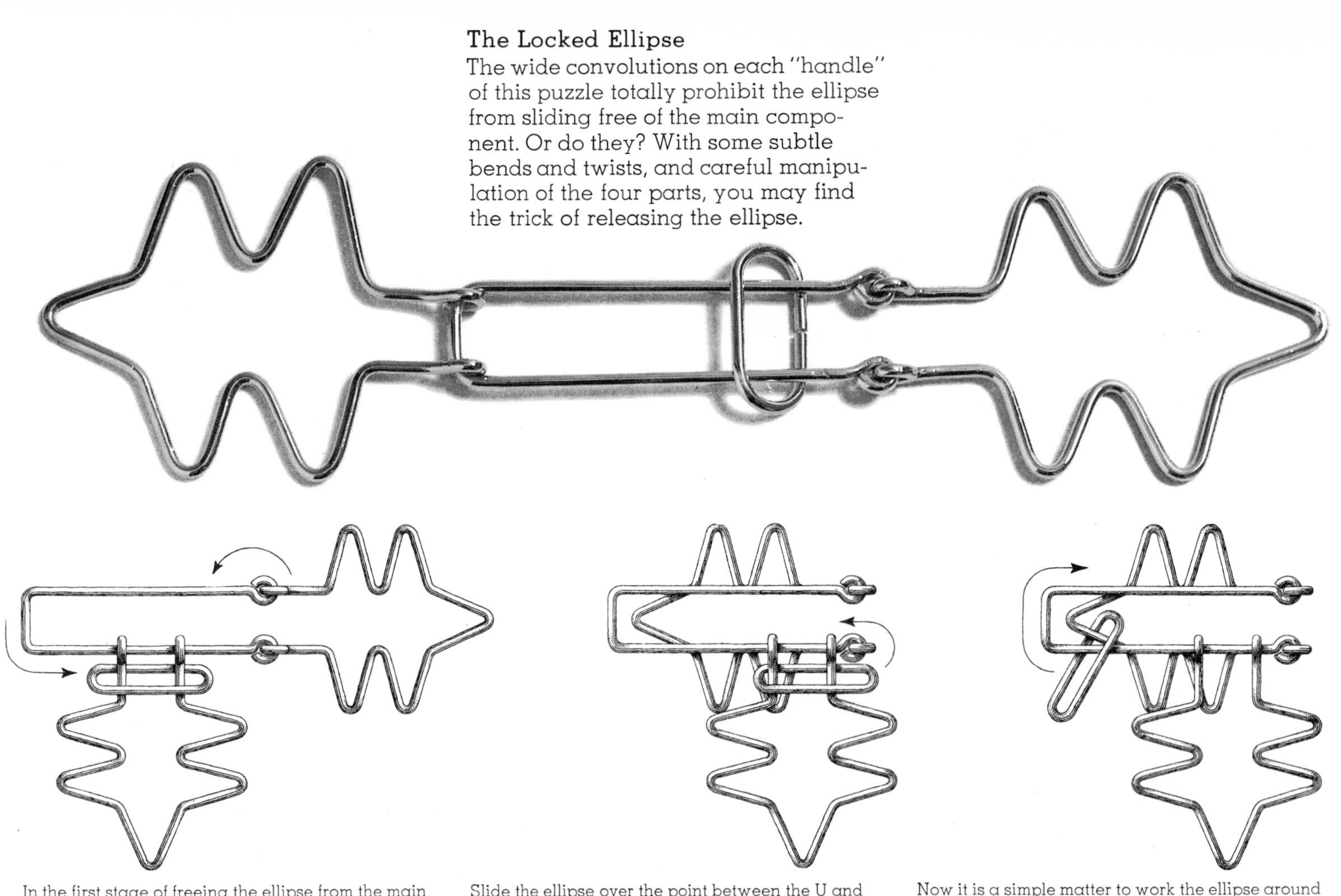

In the first stage of freeing the ellipse from the main component, the movable "handle," carrying the ellipse, is twisted to hang underneath the metal U. Then the puzzle is folded over toward the left.

Slide the ellipse over the point between the U and the left handle, as shown in the diagram above. In this way the ellipse passes off the right handle and comes to lie around the U and left handle.

Now it is a simple matter to work the ellipse around the U and left handle at the same time. Then, as with many of these wire problems, the ellipse is released from the puzzle at the joint.

Triangular Trickery

Each half of the main component of this puzzle is made of a single piece of wire bent into two triangular shapes. The two main parts are then linked together by means of small rings, resulting in a wide, starlike form. Hanging from one of the main parts is a small triangle attached by a narrow loop; it is thus unable to be passed to the other half of the puzzle. Free to be moved around, however, is the silver ring. The problem is to free this ring from the rest of the puzzle. Starting with the position shown in the photograph at the right, the small triangle hangs at the bottom right of the puzzle, with the silver ring looped around its narrow neck.

As with most wire puzzles, solving it may seem an impossibility. But follow the basic principles employed in all wire puzzles, and after some manipulation the ring should come free. If, after working at the puzzle, you give up, refer to the diagram and instructions (right) and move the ring as shown.

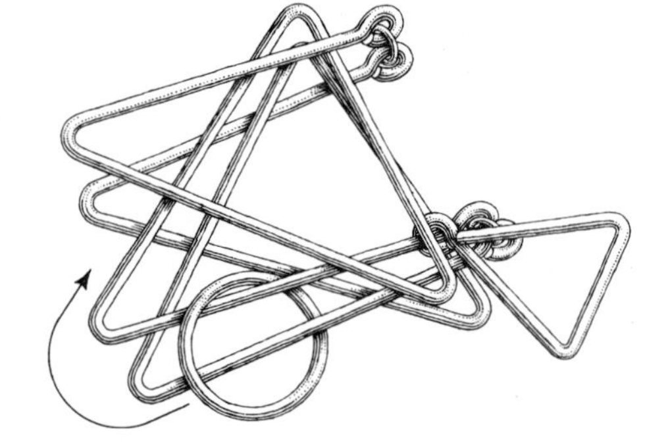

If you didn't manage alone, then the diagram and the directions below should give you some help. Hold the puzzle as shown in the photograph, with the right-hand joint at the back. Keeping the small triangle in place at bottom right, fold the top half-puzzle away from you, to lie behind the other components. Work the triangle up the right-hand side, and slip the ring over the joint. Now the ring can pass down the two vertical limbs at the right, free of the hanging triangle. Open the puzzle out slightly to manipulate the ring to the left joint. Work it past this point by opening the puzzle further, and then past the right joint as well. Fold the top of the puzzle toward you, and slide the ring around the triangle until it comes free of the puzzle at the left joint.

The symmetry of this elegant puzzle is deceptive; try solving it in an asymmetrical fashion.

Jack's Special

Neither ball in this puzzle can pass through the lower eye, but one is small enough to go through the upper eyes. Can you see how to release the cord?

The coil in this puzzle creates some confusion when you try to free the cord and attached balls.

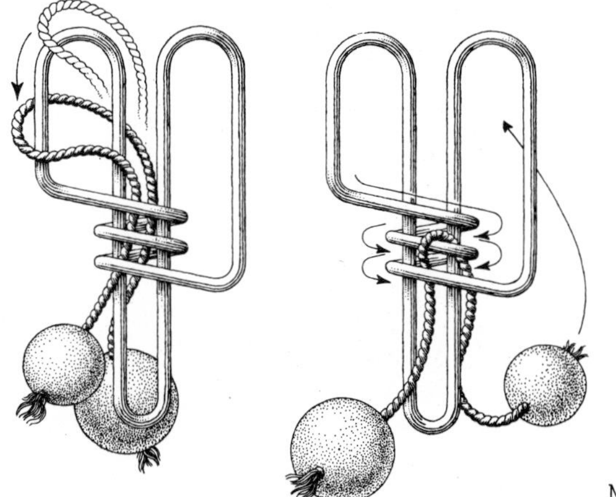

Pass the loop of cord up inside the metal coil, before looping it over the shorter of the large eyes. The cord will then drop onto the top of the coil, and can be manipulated around the spiral. Once at the bottom, the smaller ball is passed through the right eye, as in the second diagram, freeing the balls and the cord.

Chained Up

Removing the chain from this puzzle should pose no problems, even though it is too short to slide over the handle. But try replacing it — that's a puzzle!

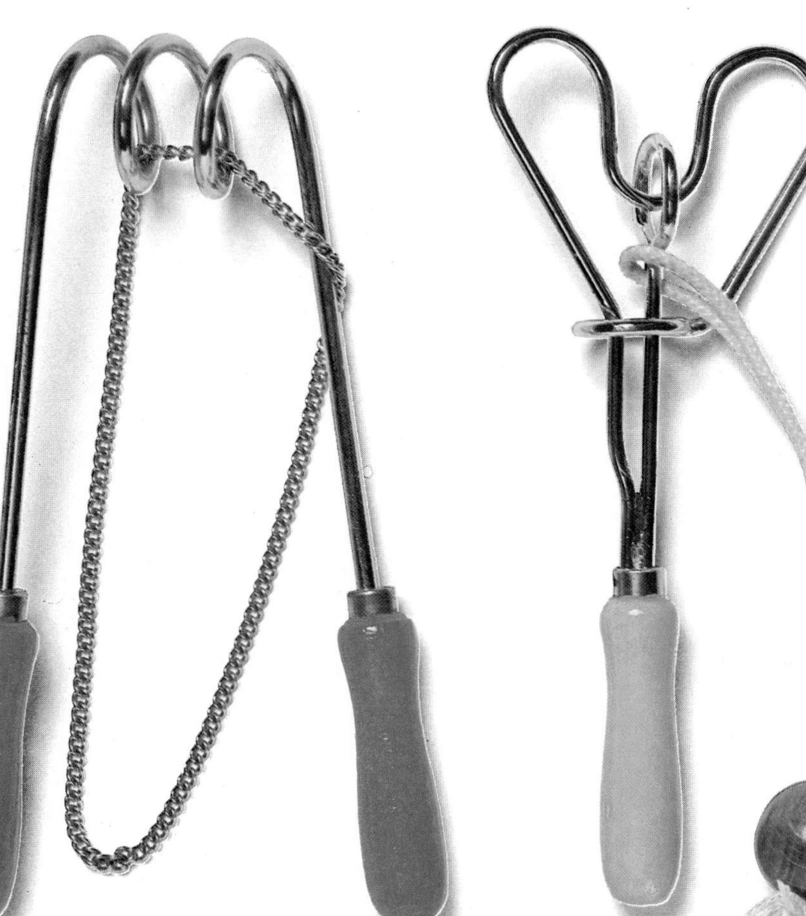

Be careful you don't get into tangles when trying to work the chain back onto this wire puzzle.

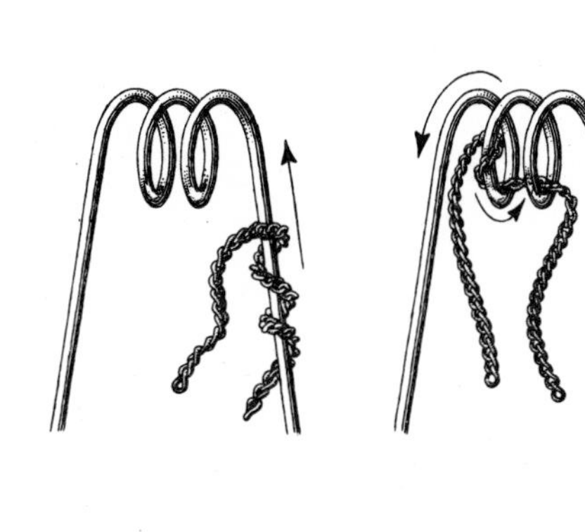

Move the chain loops around the spiral to one side and it will slide off the handle. But to replace it follow the directions and diagrams carefully. Wind the chain around the right bar, to make three coils with the leading edge of the chain over the bar, as in the figure. Slide the chain coils to the first turn of the wire spiral, and hold the last coil there. Move the other two coils onto the next turn, and hold the last of these in place while pushing the remaining coil onto the last turn. The chain is now back in position.

The Heart Lock

Just one wooden ball, too large to pass through either eye of the heart shape, complicates the task of freeing the cord from the metal component of this puzzle.

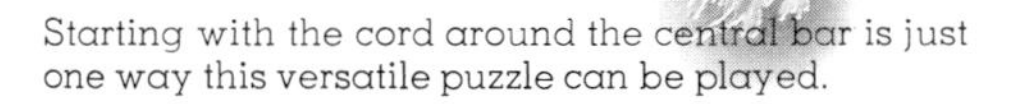

Starting with the cord around the central bar is just one way this versatile puzzle can be played.

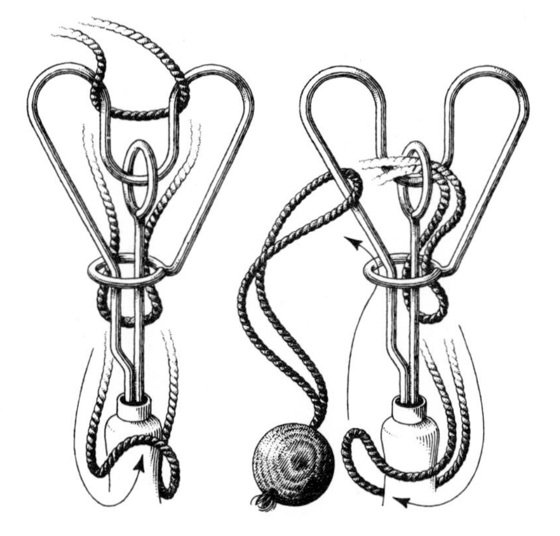

Follow the diagrams above to free the cord and ball. The procedure in the first figure results in the cord hanging from one limb of the heart. Pass the head of the loop through the circlets and along the path indicated by arrows. Now only a simple slip knot stands between the cord and freedom.

Loop the Loop

In this puzzle an unbroken loop of cord is wound around a double figure-eight made of wire. The seemingly impossible task set here is to free the cord circlet without damaging either part of the puzzle in any way. It it difficult to see how this can be done by studying the photograph alone — so why not try making it yourself? Instructions on how to make this elegantly curvaceous puzzle, along with full details of the materials necessary, are on page 156.

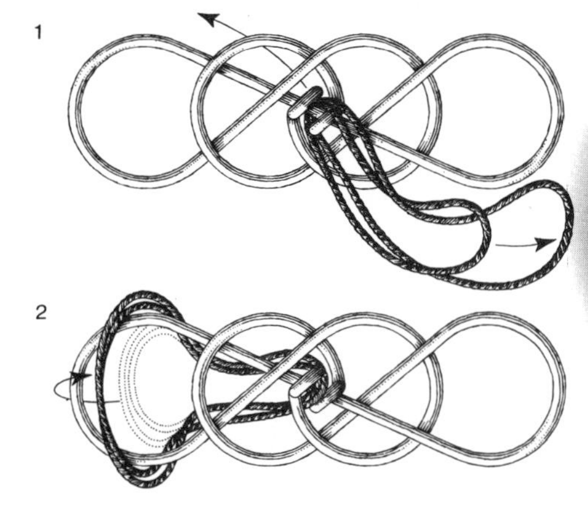

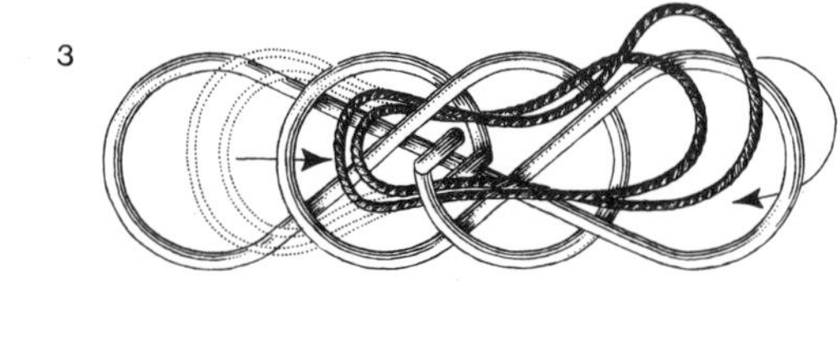

Follow the above sequence to free the cord.

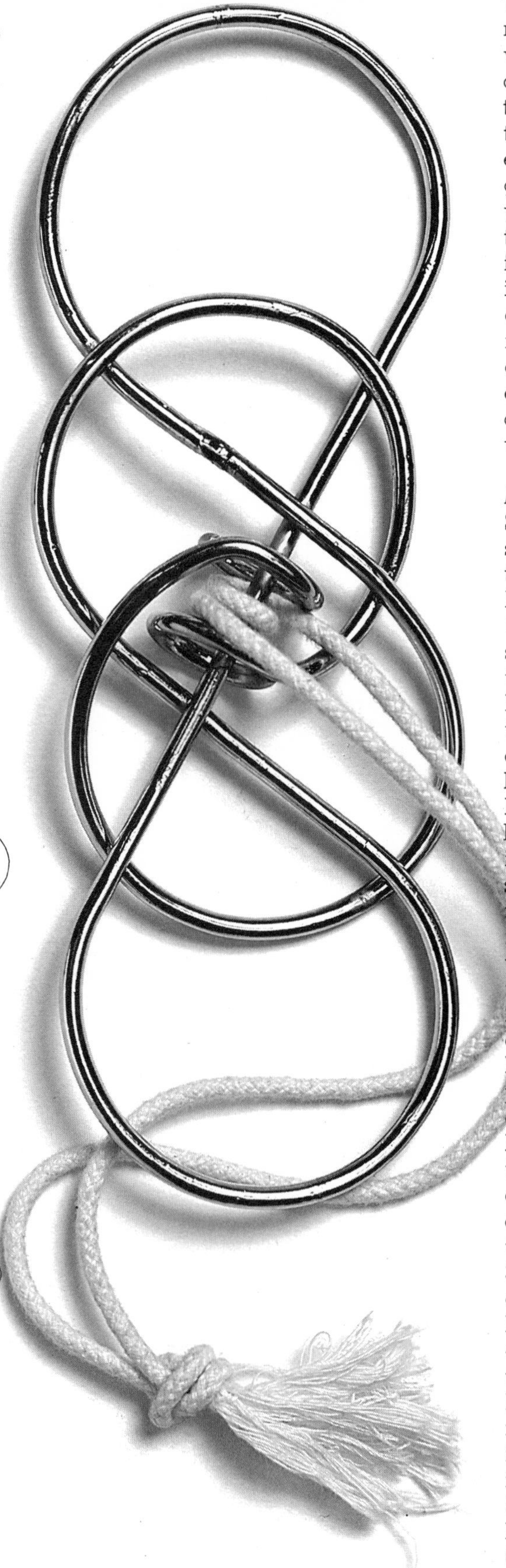

Loops of wire and cord intertwine to make this curvy problem. Wind yourself around these figure-eights and release the tied cord loop.

To solve this loop-the-loop puzzle and remove the continuous cord ring involves a few simple moves of the doubled cord loop. Yet the solution to this puzzle can be confusing to follow if the position of your own puzzle does not exactly match that shown in the diagrams (far left). Check carefully before you start, as well as at each stage of the solution, that you have the puzzle in front of you with the inner metal loops in the correct place with respect to the outer loops. The metal component remains in the same position throughout; only the cord needs to be moved. To ease the explanation of the diagrams, direction arrows have been included which refer to the cord moves.

How to Solve the Puzzle

Start with the puzzle in the position shown (left); the cord loop is wrapped twice around the central bar, and lies between the two small circlets.

1. Turn the puzzle through 90° to the left, so that the metal component is now in the position shown in this figure. In the beginning one loop of the cord is pulled taut, binding the other loop tightly around the central bar. Now draw this latter loop out, so that loops of equal length result. While solving this puzzle, keep these loops equal in length, holding and moving both together at each stage. With the metal component in your right hand, first pull the double loop from the back of the puzzle, away from you. If in doubt, follow the direction of the left arrow in figure 1.
2. You can see in this figure that the double cord is now brought over the left outer loop toward the front of the puzzle. Release the left side of the doubled cord and pick up the double loop from around the central bar. Pull this loop toward you, so that the double cord is drawn between the left inner and outer loops. Take care not to move the metal part of the puzzle at all.
3. Still holding the double cord, pass it over the right outer loop toward the back of the puzzle.
4. The double cord now goes between the right outer and inner metal loops. From there push the cord through the right inner loop to the back; if you are in doubt look at the direction arrows in the figure to see how this is done.
5. Bring the cord over the right outer loop toward you.
6. Arrange the cord as in figure 6, then a swift tug and the loop will come free of the metal component. Don't pull too hard though; if you missed one step you could have a knotty problem.

The Magic Spiral

Caught in the twists of this spiral is a closed silver ring. The ring is free to move up and down the spiral, but cannot escape from either end as the last twists are sealed. Without forcing the ends open, or breaking the ring, work out how to remove the ring — and, of course, how to put it back again. Try not to look at the solution too soon!

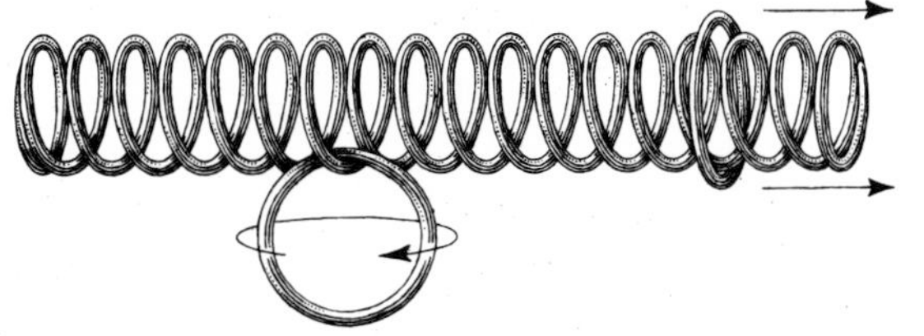

If your attempts to free the ring from the spiral have failed, take a look at the diagram above. Hold the spiral steady, and then give the ring a twist to the left. You will find that it is no longer caught up in the spiral, but encircles it, and can be slipped free.

The original puzzle (top) can be made more interesting by twisting the ring through several turns.

Triple-U Puzzle

The ring on the curved component of this serpentine puzzle lies between the two trapeze-like loops. Figure how to get the ring past these, and off the end of the puzzle, when wooden balls stop either loop from sliding off the main part.

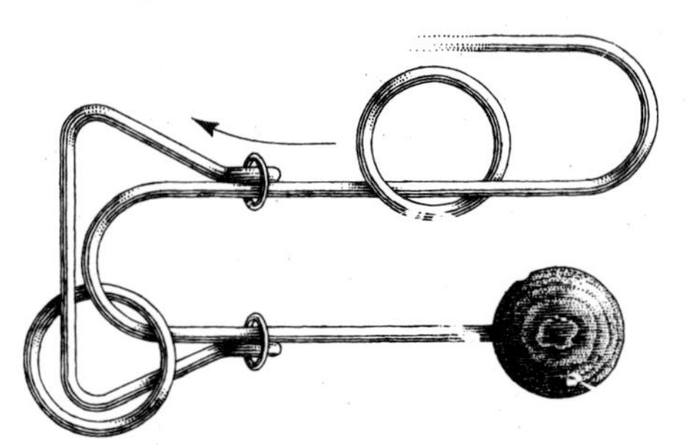

Once the ring is over the triangle, as above, pass it around the curves and over the wooden ball.

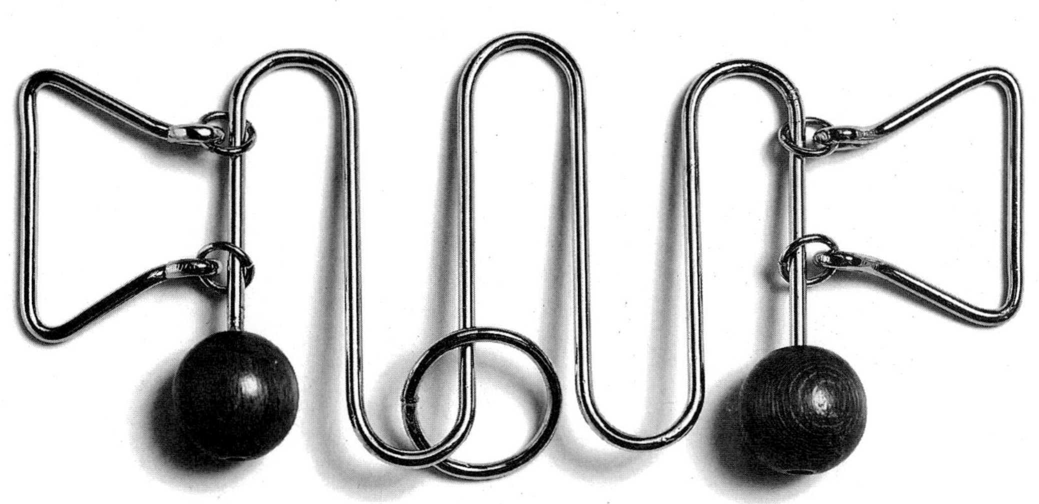

The symmetry of the triple-U puzzle offers a double chance of being able to solve it.

The Clover Leaf

This attractive puzzle well deserves a place on any coffee table, and will keep guests amused as they try to find out how to free the metal ring from the clover-leaf component. The loop that hangs from the main part is the barrier here, for it cannot be taken off.

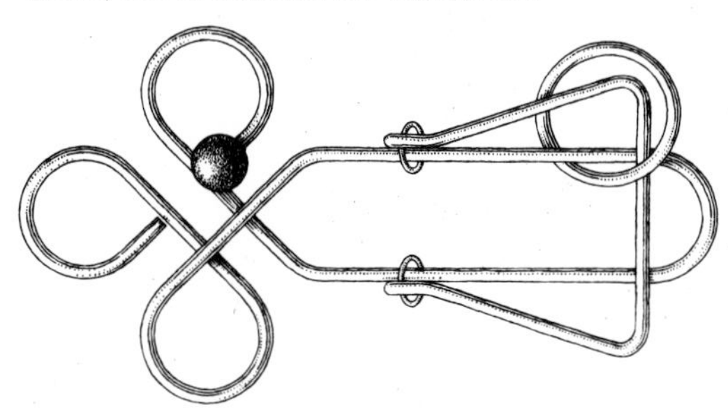

Bypass the loop that hangs from the puzzle, as in the diagram, in order to release the ring.

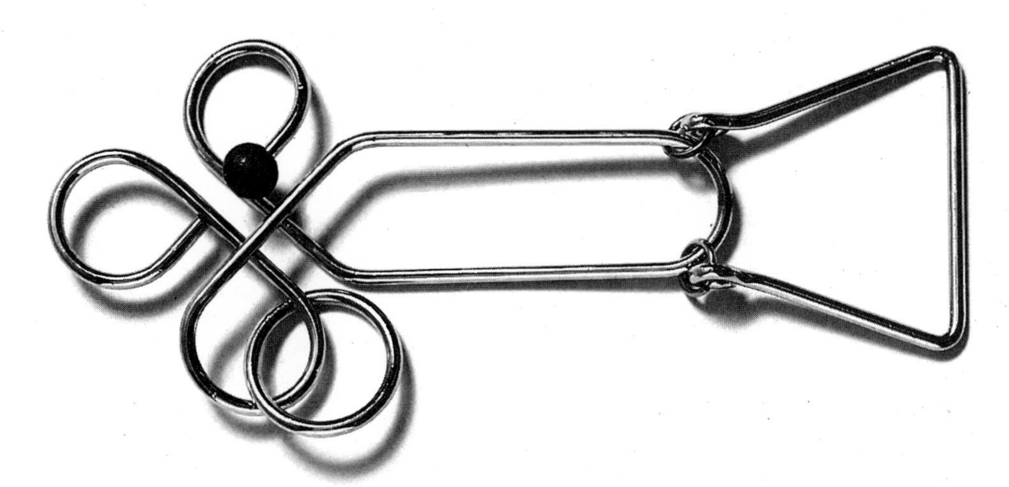

A small wooden bead at the free end of the wire provides the finishing touch to the clover leaf.

The Staircase

Tied around the shaft of the lowest circlet of the staircase is a loop of cord which must be removed from the puzzle. This task is complicated by the arrangement of shafts, such that each runs through the center of a preceding, lower circlet. One of the most interesting puzzles, this is also one of the more difficult, involving some thirty steps.

Ascending silvered circlets set in a larch block make up this elegant, free-standing puzzle.

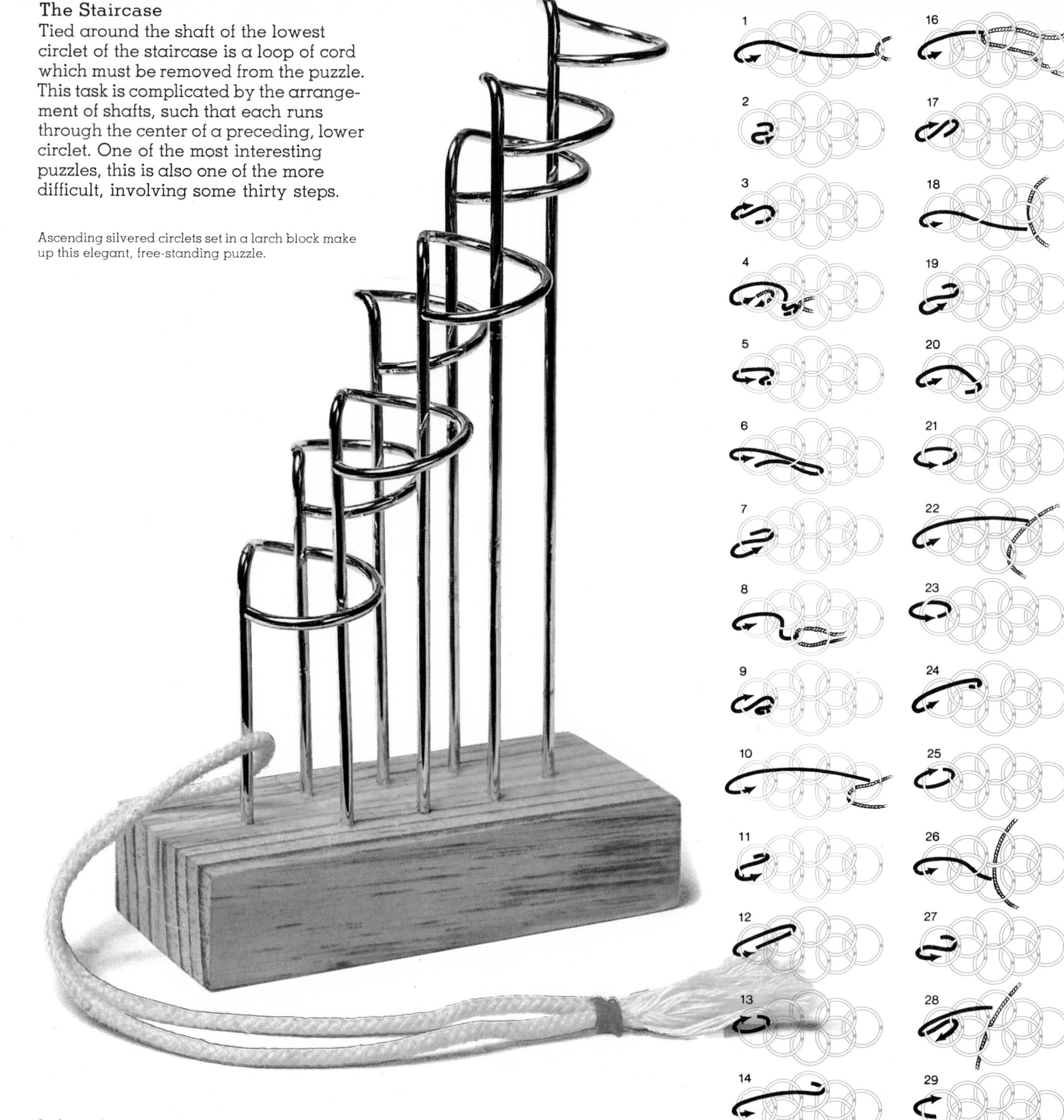

As the cord cannot be slipped free of the lowest shaft, the only way to approach this puzzle is to manipulate the cord so that it encircles all eight shafts, and will then fall free. Hold the head of the loop between your fingers, and lead it carefully along the path marked by the arrows. In the diagrams the puzzle is drawn as seen from above, with arrows threading through the top rings. Draw the head of the loop to the tail of the arrow before starting each move. When the loop reaches the last, tallest circlet it is always passed over, either from above or below, as indicated. Every few steps result in the inclusion of yet another shaft within the loop. Thus to bring the cord around the first two shafts requires nine steps; to encircle the third, a further eight moves; the fourth, four moves; the fifth, three steps; the sixth, two steps; and the seventh just one move. Then take the loop over the eighth shaft, from the seventh, in a single action. Segments of cord drawn in some diagrams give the position of the taut cord at that stage.

A Fishy Problem

A Russian book of pastimes for young pioneers by E. Minskin was the source of inspiration for this fishy puzzle. In the photograph below you can see that the fish is firmly hooked on a metal ellipse. This ellipse lies over the two lower bars of the fish, and is prevented from moving far by three equal-sized silver rings which are wrapped around the insides of the fish. These rings can only move a few centimeters, and they do not come free of the fish during the course of the puzzle. But there is a method of unhooking the fish and removing the ellipse completely. It looks difficult, but a little time and concentration may reveal the series of moves that must be made to solve the puzzle.

The fish body for this puzzle can be made quite simply, by following the directions and diagrams on page 156. Details of the materials and equipment that are needed are also given on pages 156-58. After making the puzzle, if you still fail to solve it, then follow the direction arrows on the solution diagrams and the instructions below.

Make this splendid fish from the instructions (page 156), and then try to free the silver ellipse without looking at the solutions below. When you've succeeded, why not pass it on to your friends to tackle?

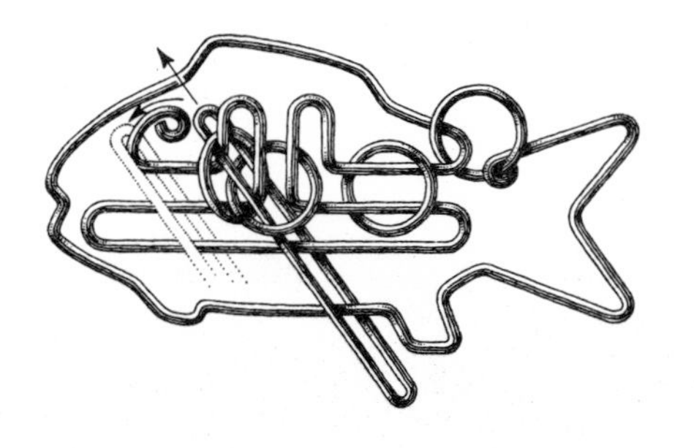

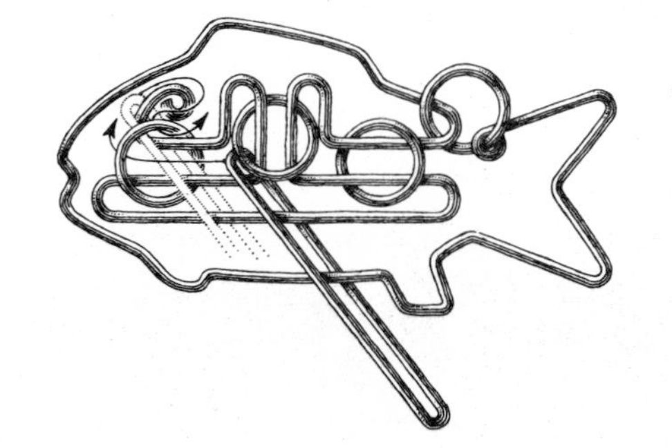

At the start of this puzzle the metal ellipse lies on the lower two bars of the fish, as in the photograph above. Start to solve the puzzle by pushing the ellipse through the central silver ring, before trying to manipulate it through the ring nearest the fish's head. Take a careful look at the first solution figure before making this move. After passing through the rings, the loop of the ellipse slots over the "eye."

Work the ellipse downward so that it comes back through the head-most ring. Once it is free of that one, slide the central ring away. The ellipse now lies over three bars of the fish, between the first and second rings. Lead the ellipse from the right, through the first ring, and then backwards over the "eye." Place the first ring flush with the body of the fish, and slide the ellipse over it, so it hangs from the frame.

Move the ellipse around the fish in the direction shown, and pass it through the ring which links the tail with the body of the fish. To finish the solution, it may be easier to lay the puzzle flat on the table, so that the rings fall flush with the fish. One by one, slide the rings through the ellipse as it passes toward the head. Once it is over the leading silver ring, the ellipse will separate from the rest.

The Ball and Ring Puzzle

How do you get the closed silver ring free from this arrangement of cord and twisted metal, when its diameter is smaller than that of the wooden ball? That is the problem posed in this puzzle. Try not to resort to looking at the solution given below unless you feel totally defeated by the problem.

This is one of the easier wire puzzles to make.

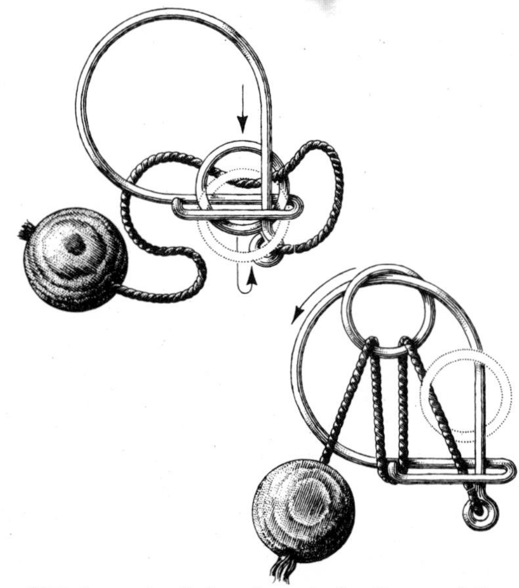

With the cord coiled as shown in the diagram, follow the direction arrows to release the ring. Finally pass the ring through the metal loop at the base of the puzzle again, and you should be able to solve this one without tying yourself in knots.

Shoot the Shuttle

In this problem it is the elliptical shuttle and not the ring that must be freed from the other components. Without changing the shape or form of any of the pieces, it is possible to remove the shuttle intact. As with other wire puzzles, the simplicity of the solution is amazing — when you've succeeded!

The bizarre shapes in this puzzle seem to be locked.

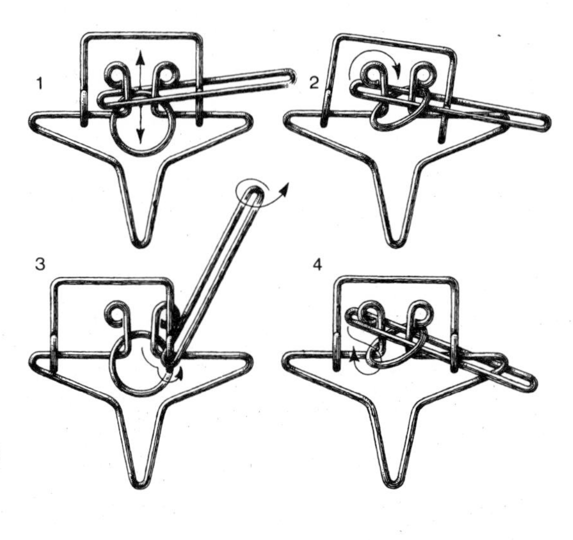

Follow these diagrams very closely, making sure that your puzzle exactly mimics them at every stage. Then the shuttle will come free without any trouble. Direction arrows help simplify the vital moves.

The Loony Loop

This loony loop puzzle was stumbled upon by the great American puzzler, Stewart T. Coffin. The aim of this puzzle is to free the tied cord from the figure-eight metal loop, without breaking or untying the cord. But — beware — the simplicity of the wire loop and intertwined cord may be deceptive.

Problems with this one? Then look below for help.

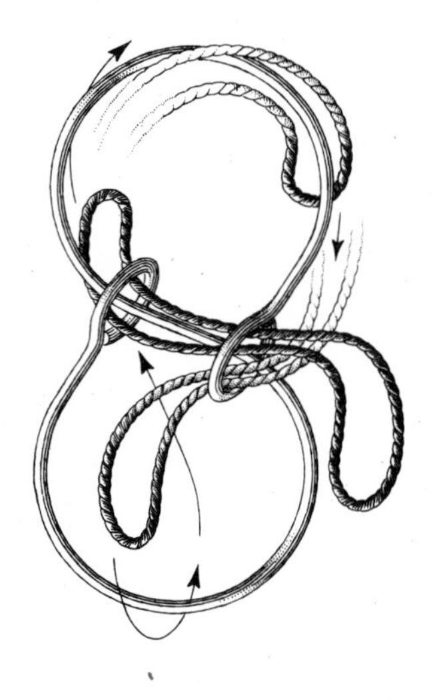

Follow the direction arrows on the diagram: pass the cord loop through the left eye; over the top loop; through the right eye; and around the bottom loop. Now the cord should come free — or should it? After all, no one has proved it impossible!

Squaring Off

The shape of this puzzle is deceptively simple; if you manage to solve this one without consulting the solution below, you are really a master of wire puzzles.

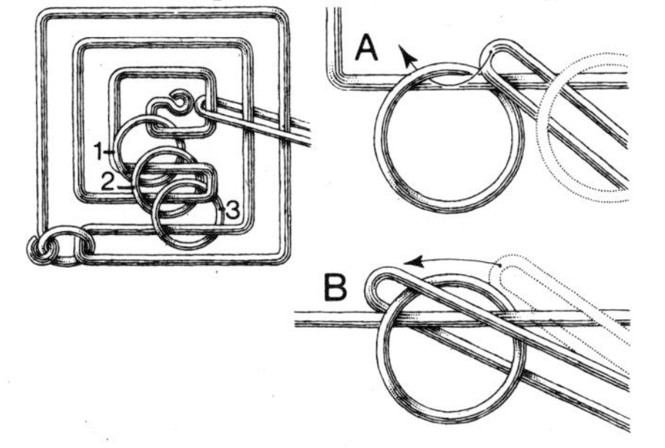

Lead the head of the ellipse through ring 1. Now slot the ellipse over the eye, from right to left. Pull the ellipse back out of ring 1. Put the head of the ellipse through the top of ring 2, then slot the ellipse over the eye, inner frame and ring 1 together, moving to the left. Pull the ellipse out of ring 2, to the right.
Slide the ellipse over ring 3 (see diagram B), then back through ring 3, from left to right. As it passes through ring 3, turn the ellipse so that it will also go through ring 2, from right to left. When it is moving through both rings, maneuver it so that it passes over the inner frame and ring 1. Drop the ellipse down, out of rings 2 and 3. Slide the ellipse right over the whole of the inner frame system and rings, so that it then hangs from the outer frame of the square only. Push the head of the ellipse through the lock ring from left to right; and from underneath. As it goes through, lead it along the bottom edge of the frame until it can slide over the bottom right-hand corner of the inner frame. Pass the ellipse over the entire inner frame toward the left and allow the ellipse to drop through the lock ring.

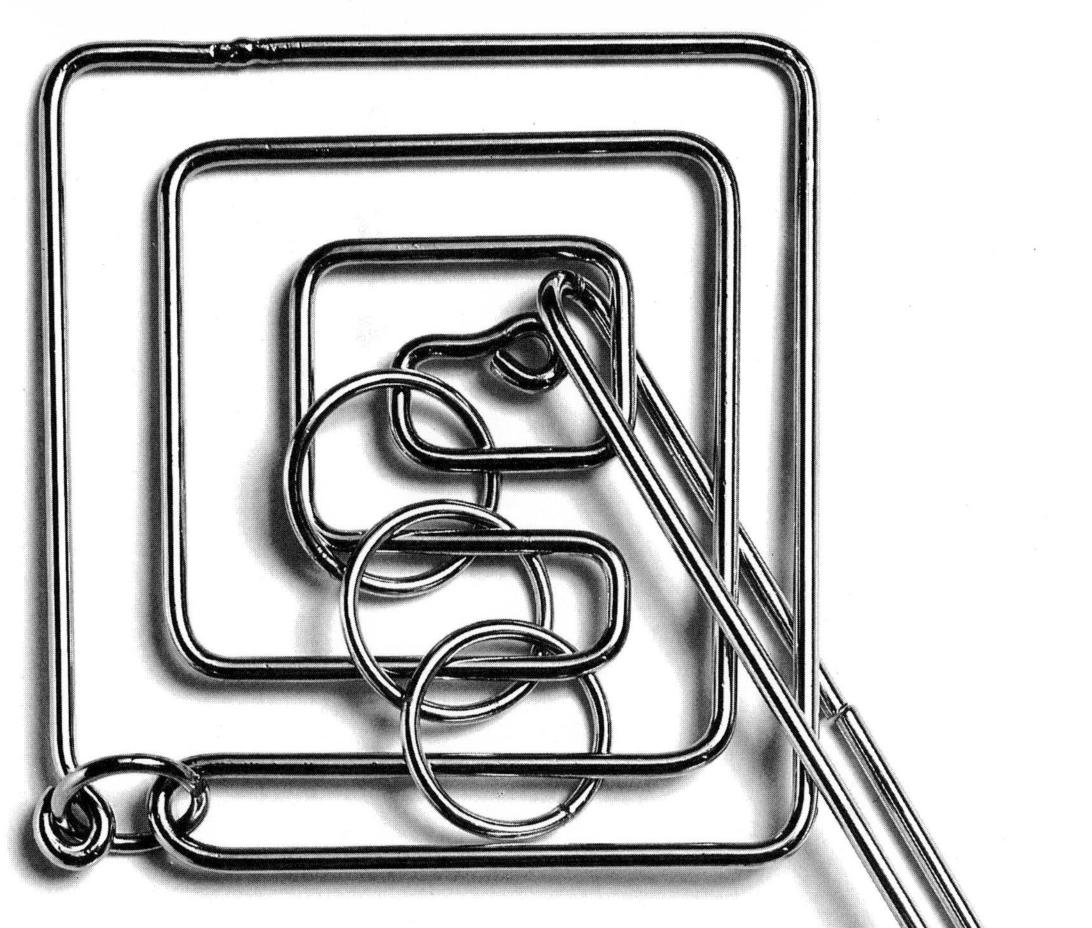

Try not to get trapped in blind alleys when you work your way around this maze-style wire puzzle.

The Triangular Spiral

The ellipse in this puzzle is looped onto a triangular, spiral component, and while the ellipse is free to move around the spiral, it will not come off. The tantalizing problem here is to find a way of removing the ellipse from the main component — it is possible — without bending or breaking any part.

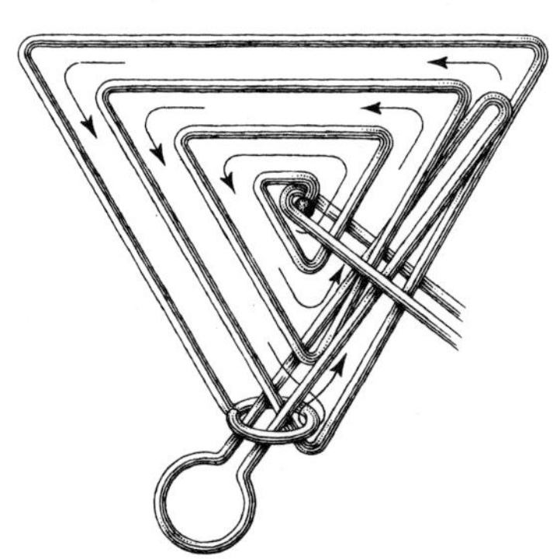

Hold the puzzle with the circlet of the main part on the right, and the wide end of the ellipse outside the puzzle. Holding this end, move the ellipse around the twists of the spiral, as shown in the diagram, and bring it to the apex of the triangle, nearest the circlet. Now push the narrow end of the ellipse through the circlet to the left. Once around the triangle and the ellipse is free.

The ellipse looped around the triangular spiral puzzle has one end wider than the other — thus increasing the difficulty, and fun, in solving it.

Materials
Welding wire, from 1 to 5 mm. thick
Thick-walled steel pipes with various outer diameters

Tools
Combination pliers
Engineer's pliers
Soldering iron, or soldering torch (gas tank and torch) if using wire with a diameter greater than 2 mm.
Bench vise
A fine, double-cut file
A small hammer
A wire-bending form
Sandpaper

How to Make the Puzzles
The following general directions apply to bending acetylene-welding wire of at least 2 mm. thickness. Often, if the wire is thinner, less elaborate preparation will suffice, since thin wire can simply be bent around a wire-bending form with pliers. Wire-bending forms, which house various shapes and molds, are available from tool and hobby shops.

Before starting to bend the wire to make any of these puzzles, first draw up the pattern of the puzzle on a grid, and enlarge this to the required size. This size will be dependent on the thickness of the wire you wish to use; the thicker the wire, the larger the puzzle that can be made. Wire is generally available in 1, 2, 3, 4, and 5 mm. thicknesses, and in 1 yard/meter lengths. Take care before you start that you have a long enough piece of wire for the entire puzzle, bearing in mind that the thicker the wire, the greater its length should be. In, for instance, the "squaring-off" puzzle the wire bends around a number of corners, so to make it from one piece may necessitate using quite thin wire. In this and other puzzles it is possible to weld two pieces of wire to get the desired length; however, this section assumes that you have a wire long enough.

To make large puzzles with thick wire, a bench vise and gas torch are essential in order to shape the wire. To bend, for example, a thick wire into a round shape with an inner diameter of an inch, you will need a steel tube with an outer diameter of an inch, clamped in the vise. Heat the wire with the gas torch until it is bright red, then, using the engineer's pliers, hold the wire firmly against the steel pipe and bend the free end around it. The wire can only be bent when it is red hot and, as it will rapidly lose heat to the pipe and vise, it will be necessary to reheat it several times to accomplish the final shape. Before starting to make any specific wire shape with the thick wire, it is a good idea to make it first in thin wire, bending it only with pliers. By doing this you can find out how the puzzle works and where the difficulties will arise when bending the final shape.

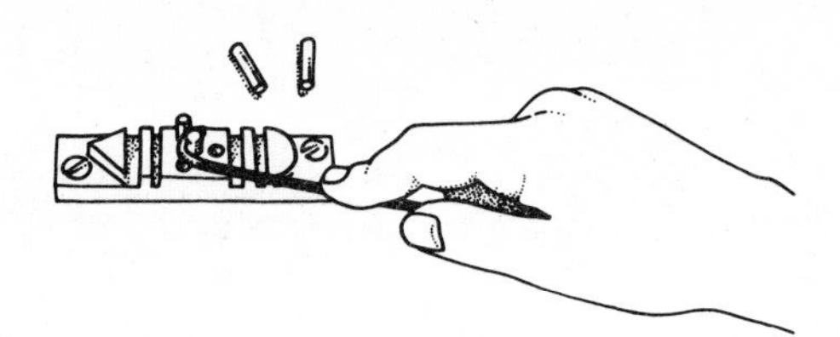

The versatile wire-bending form offers many possibilities for manually bending wire thinner than 3 mm. into a variety of curves, arcs, and angles without the aid of heat or a hammer.

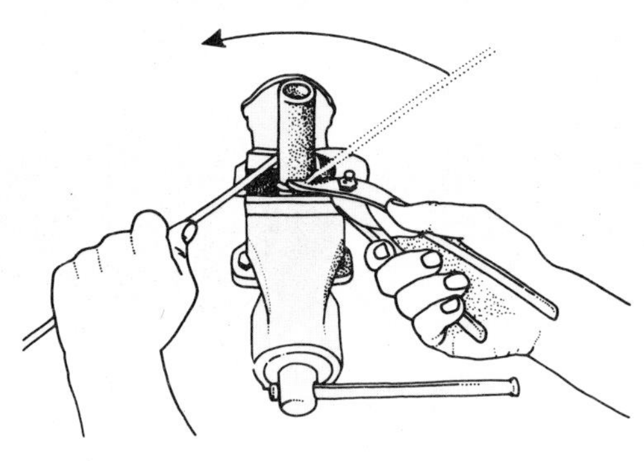

The heated end section of the wire must be clamped to the underside of the pipe with the engineer's pliers. Then gradually, by hand, work the wire around the steel pipe to make the circular form.

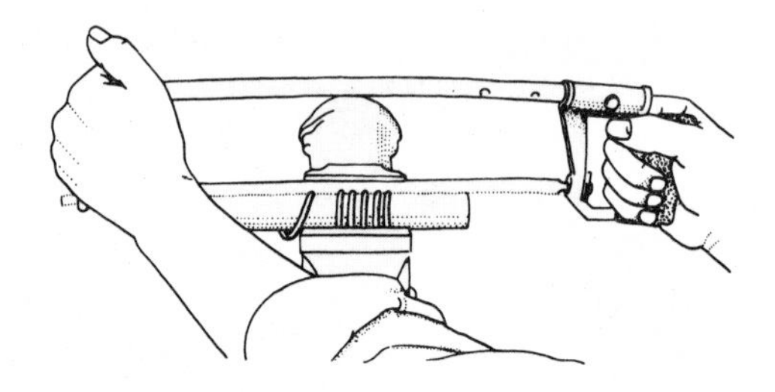

Having wound the wire around a steel pipe in a spiral, clamp it lengthwise in the vise in order to saw the spiral into rings. With thicker wire a tight fit on the pipe will not be possible.

How to Make Wire Rings
For this you need wire, steel pipe with an outer diameter equal to the inner diameter of the rings you want to make, the bench vise, metal saw, and the engineer's pliers. With the pipe clamped in the vise, wind the wire several times around it, holding one end against the pipe with the pliers. Release the pipe from the vise, and then replace it so that the spiral is horizontal. Cut the spiral lengthwise with the metal saw. File down the free ends of each ring before bending them together as closely as possible. Even with thick wire it is possible to spiral the wire around the pipe without applying heat. However, in doing this remember that the rings will be larger than the diameter of the pipe.

Finishing Off
Before adding any finishing touches to your wire puzzle, first file and sandpaper away all the scars left by the pliers. Then the wire is ready to be chrome-plated. Most small chroming companies will be glad to help you, usually for a very low charge, since they can chrome a puzzle between their larger jobs. After that some puzzles need wooden handles. Drill a hole of the same diameter as the wire into the handle, then glue the wire in place.

Hints on Individual Puzzles

The Handcuff
The rings connecting the two handcuffs can be of thinner wire than the rest.

The Gordian Knot
Be sure to follow the model extremely carefully when assembling this puzzle, and solder the parts together before chroming or adding the handles to it.

Jack's Special
Start bending a length of wire in the middle to make one "ear" and the "nose." Put the "nose" into a steel pipe, and wind the wire around the pipe to make the central spiral. This can be done without applying heat, as the diameter is not too important. Then bend the free wire to make the other "ear."

The Heart Lock
Solder the two ends together before chroming or adding the handle.

Loop the Loop
This puzzle is almost impossible to bend from a single piece of wire, as the loops lie on top of one another. So it is better to make two identical half-puzzles, and then weld them together.

The Magic Spiral
For this puzzle it is better to buy a wire spiral of the size you require, and fit a ring that just slides over the top.

The Staircase
The only tip for this puzzle is to mimic exactly the position and shape of each of the standing forms in the block.

The Ball and Ring
Take care that the ring fits through the flat loop bent in the main wire.

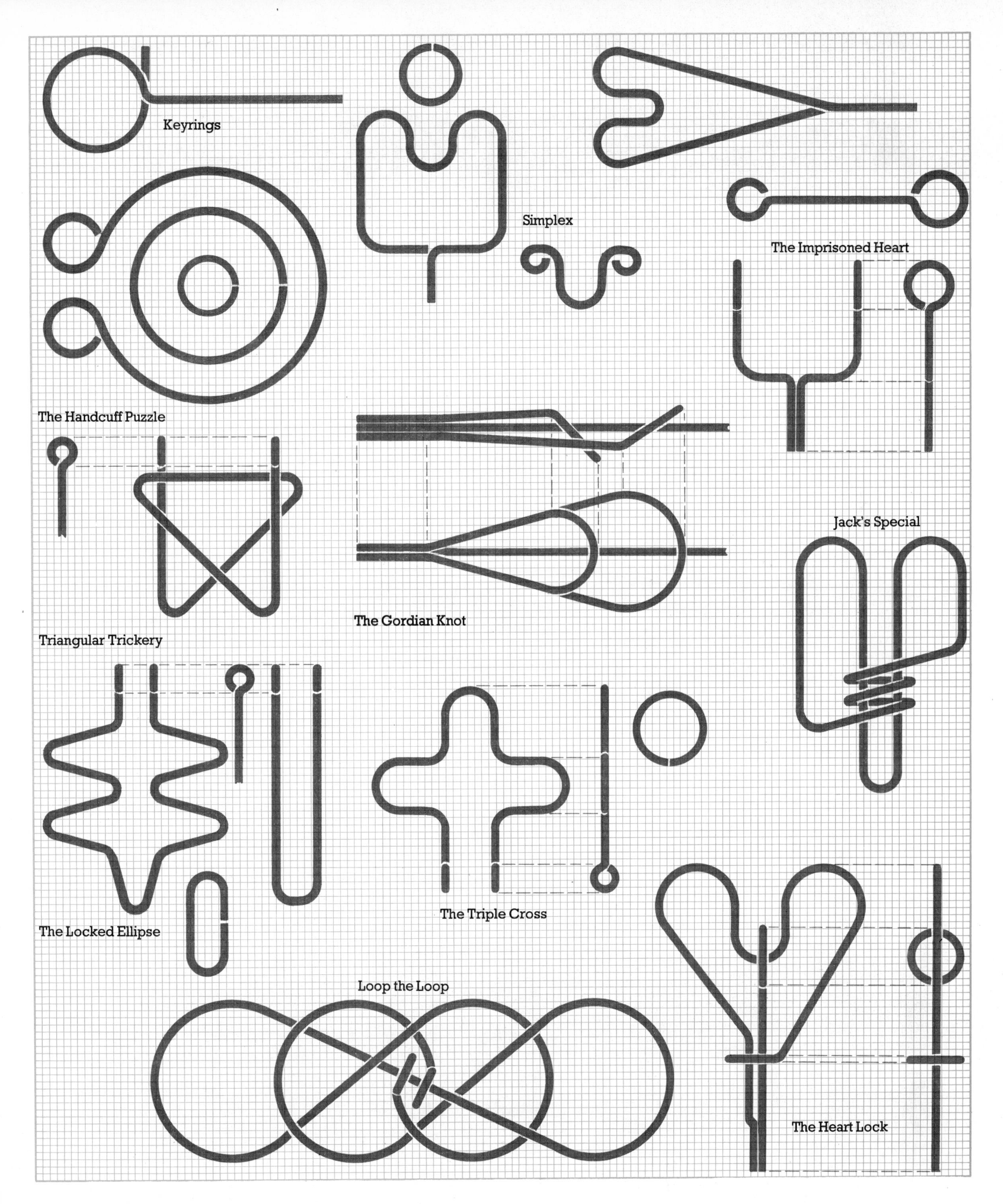
Keyrings
Simplex
The Imprisoned Heart
The Handcuff Puzzle
Jack's Special
The Gordian Knot
Triangular Trickery
The Triple Cross
The Locked Ellipse
Loop the Loop
The Heart Lock

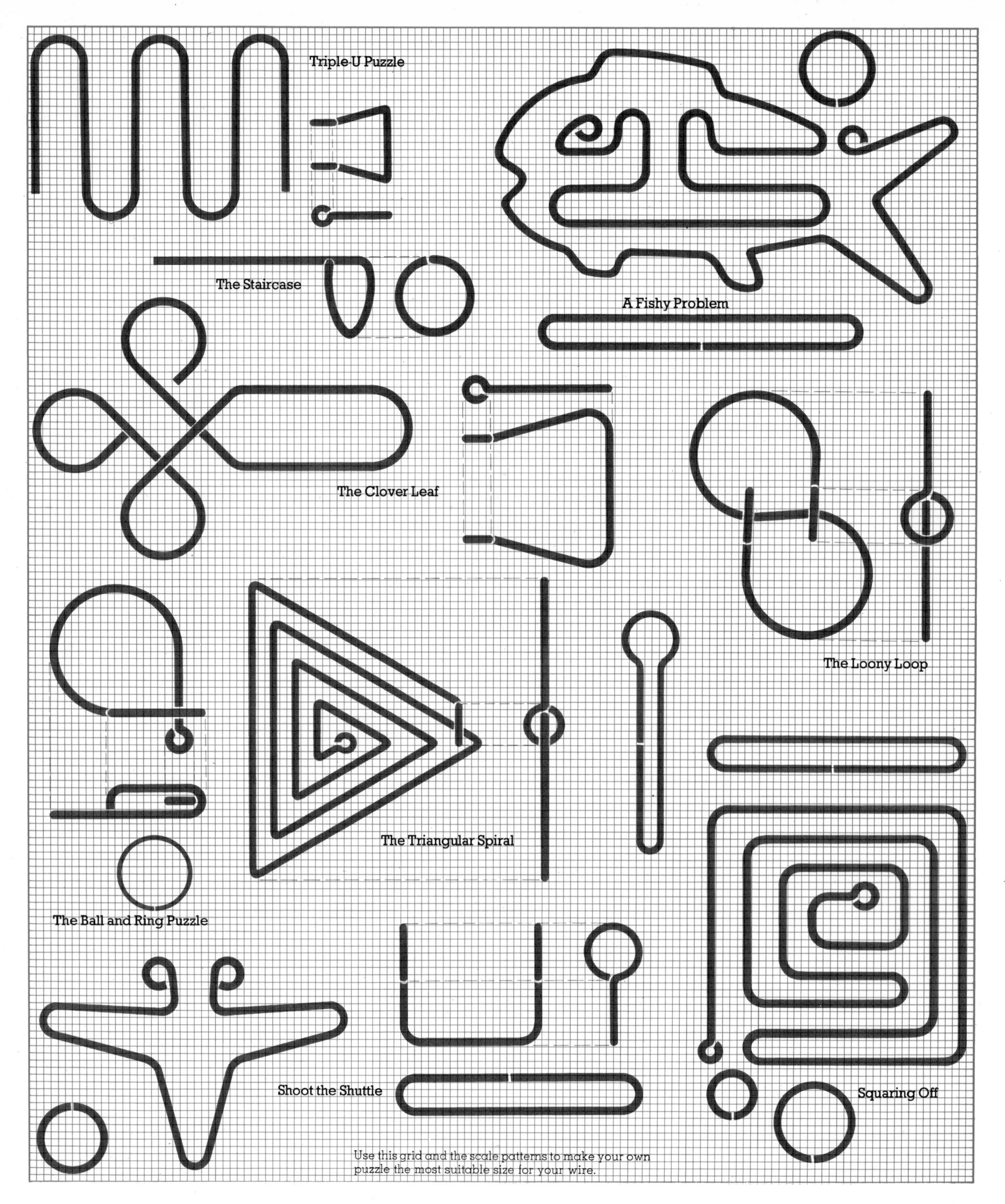
Triple-U Puzzle
The Staircase
A Fishy Problem
The Clover Leaf
The Loony Loop
The Triangular Spiral
The Ball and Ring Puzzle
Shoot the Shuttle
Squaring Off
Use this grid and the scale patterns to make your own puzzle the most suitable size for your wire.

Number and Logic Puzzles

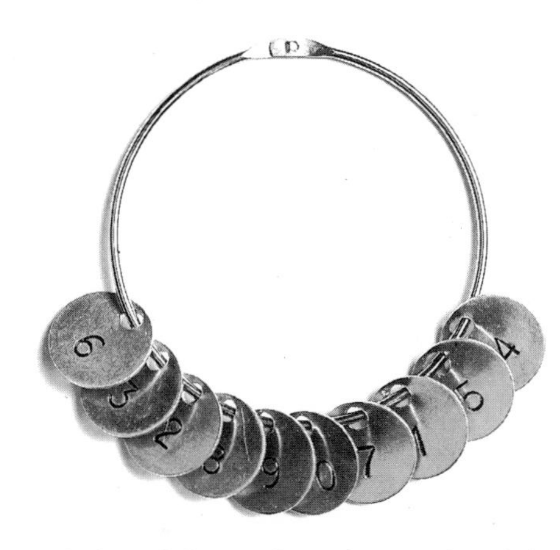

Divide these disks into three groups — imagining you are sliding them around the ring if necessary — in such a way that the number formed by the third group equals the result of multiplying the numbers formed by the first two groups. An unsuccessful grouping would be: 890, 71, 54632.

Use the information that Tommy's parents have provided to help him in calculating their ages.

To some people numbers are old friends, each with its own personality. When they see the number 1369 for example, they remember — or calculate — that it equals 37 multiplied by itself. When they meet the number 293, they know immediately that it is a prime — that is, it cannot be divided by a whole number, except itself and 1, without leaving a remainder. Not many people are that familiar with numbers, but anyone can have fun with them. Few puzzles in this chapter need mathematics more advanced than multiplication. Some problems in pure logic are also presented and even include the instructions for making a simple logical "computer." This chapter touches as well on binary notation — a system in which all numbers are written with the digits 0 and 1 alone.

Finding the Ages

Young Tommy was eager to know how old his parents were. They would not tell him directly, because they wanted him to practice his arithmetic. So they told him some facts that would enable him to work out their ages. They began with the fact that his father is six times as old as Tommy. Since Tommy could not remember his own age to the nearest month, they added the information that if the ages of Tommy, his father, and his mother were added together, they would total 70 years. And many years from now, when Tommy is half as old as his father, the total of their three ages will be exactly twice what it is now. This problem fascinated Tommy, but it was too difficult for him to work out the ages. Can you do it for him, and work out his age also?

(See solution page 196)

The Number Frame

Place one digit, from 1 through 8, in each circle in the pattern below.
Do it in such a way that numbers that differ only by 1 (such as 3 and 4) do not lie in circles directly connected by a straight line. For example, if you put 1 in circle A, you may not put 2 in B, C, or D, but you may put it in E, F, G, or H. This puzzle seems complicated at first, but there is a systematic approach that leads to the solution.

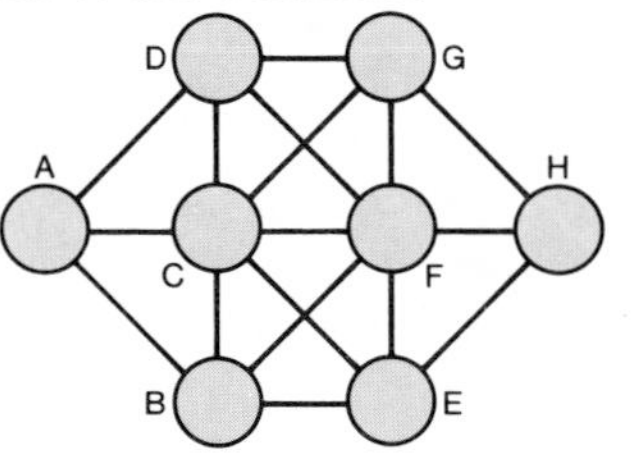

The Stopped Clock

Mr. Smith is a man of almost excessively regular habits. He particularly likes to have his clock set at exactly the right time. He was very distressed, therefore, when he discovered one day that it had stopped. He could not reset it because it was the only timepiece he owned. That evening he walked over to the house of his friend Mr. Jones for their weekly chess game. Mr. Smith always walked at the same unvarying pace, but he had never taken note of how long this journey took him. His friend kept a very reliable grandfather clock in his hall. After playing several games, Mr. Smith returned home, walking at the same steady pace. When he got home, he immediately set his clock to the correct time. How did he know the time?

Sharing the Apples

Mary was given some apples by a kind neighbor, and she shared them with three friends. To the first friend she gave half of the apples, plus half an apple. To the second she gave half of what was left plus half an apple. To the third she gave half of the remainder plus half an apple. She was left with one. How many was she first given?

The same neighbor shared 32 apples among eight children. She gave one apple to Ann, two to Betty, three to Cathy, and four to Dee. Each girl had a brother. Ed got as many as his sister, Frank got twice as many as his sister, George got three times as many as his sister, Harry got four times as many as his. Which boy is each girl's brother?

Salvation by Numbers

A sailing ship was sinking in a storm. The captain and crew made a hasty escape in one of the lifeboats, leaving the other lifeboat for the passengers. The remaining lifeboat could hold only ten of the 20 passengers on board. Ten of these passengers happened to be mathematicians and one of them suggested that in order to select those to be saved, the passengers should stand in a circle and, beginning with himself, count clockwise. Every seventh passenger would climb into the boat and not be counted again. The mathematicians unobtrusively claimed the positions they wanted in the circle, and soon they were rowing away while the other passengers were left. Where had the mathematicians stood?

The Magic Chain

Ask a friend to do the following calculations while your back is turned. First he writes down a number of at least six digits. Then he scrambles the digits to make a new number, and subtracts the smaller six-digit number from the larger. Then he adds the digits of the result, and if the number consists of two digits, he adds these to get a final one-digit number. Now tell him that you will count, left to right, along the chain of symbols below, beginning with the black square. When you reach the end, continue from the left. You predict, correctly, that you will reach his number on the star. How do you do it?

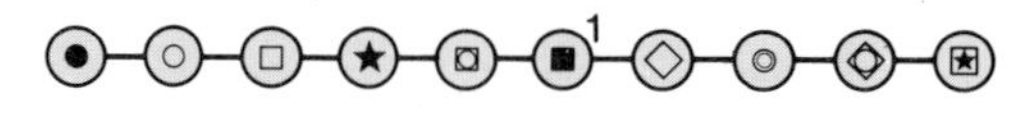

The Bookworm's Puzzle

The nine volumes of a scholarly encyclopedia are seen here. They are in this peculiar order because their owner, who loves arithmetic puzzles, has noticed that the volume numbers can then be read as the fraction 6729/13458, which equals $\frac{1}{2}$. Can you show him how to arrange the volumes so that they make fractions equal to $\frac{1}{3}$, $\frac{1}{4}$, $\frac{1}{5}$, $\frac{1}{6}$, $\frac{1}{7}$, $\frac{1}{8}$, and $\frac{1}{9}$?

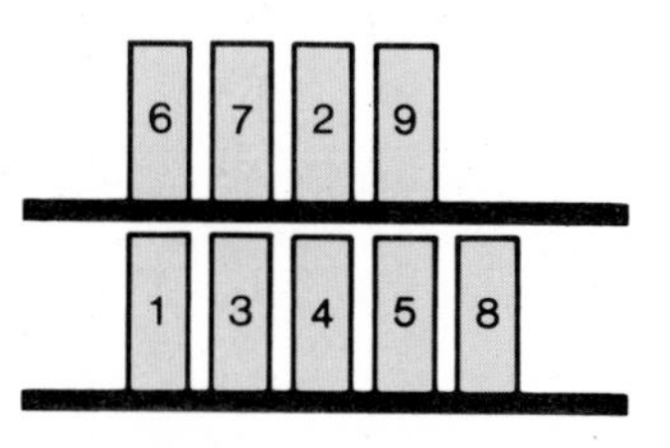

Balancing the Scales

How many triangles would balance the circle on the fourth set of scales?

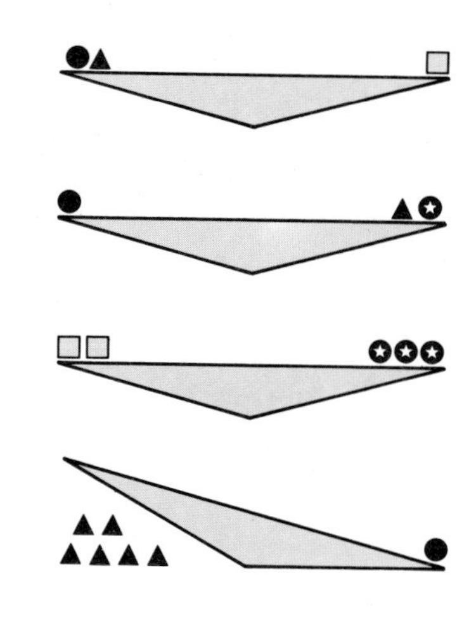

A Mystic Number

Have a friend write down a number of three digits, without disclosing it to you; the first and last digits must be different. Suppose he writes 246. Now, with a great show of mind reading, write down a number and seal it in an envelope. Tell your friend to reverse the order of the digits of his number, and subtract the smaller of the two numbers that he now has from the larger. In this case he would get 396. (A subtraction with different numbers might give him 0 as the first digit; if so, he must write it in.) Now he must add his result to the number obtained by reversing its three digits — that is, 693. This gives him 1089. You now open the envelope and reveal your prediction — 1089. How did you arrive at this?

Feeding the Cattle

You may be familiar with arithmetic problems that are of this kind: if three men can mow a meadow in three days, how long would it take one man? The usual answer would be nine days, but this ignores the effect of the growth of new grass, which could be considerable over a longer period of time. So try this more sophisticated problem, in which enough information is given to enable you to allow for new growth.
A ten-acre field can support 12 cows for 16 weeks. At the end of that time the cows have cropped the grass to its roots. The same field can support 18 cows for eight weeks. How many cows can be supported by a 40-acre field for six weeks? Assume an equal amount of grass per acre and equal growth.

(See solution page 196)

Cryptarithms

Many number puzzles consist of a calculation in which some or all of the digits are replaced by letters or dots. The aim of the puzzle is to work out what the digits must be to make the calculation correct. Such a puzzle is called a *cryptarithm*, which means "hidden number." Cryptarithms can nearly always be solved systematically with only the most basic knowledge of the properties of numbers — for example, the last digit of any multiple of 5 is either 0 or 5. A reminder of some terms used in the solutions might be useful. In the division 6 ÷ 2 = 3, the *divisor* is 2, the *dividend* is 6, and the *quotient* is 3. In the long-division puzzles here, all three of these quantities appear in one line to save space.

The Archeologist

This calculation (left) from the royal archives of an ancient civilization is carved on a weather-beaten rock in the jungles of the Amazon. Most of the numerals, such as the first two figures of the divisor, have been worn away. However, the archeologist can restore the complete quotient from the surviving figures. Can you see how to do it?

A Blot on the Copybook

A student saw that an addition had every digit from 0 through 9. She accidentally spilled ink on her book and only three digits remained legible. Can you reconstruct the addition?

```
  28.
+ ..4
 ....
```

Don't Repeat Yourself

When filling in the missing figures of the calculation below, do not repeat any digit from 1 through 9. The calculation has two parts: first a two-digit number is multiplied by a one-digit number with a two-digit result. Then a two-digit number is added to give a two-digit result. In the answer 0 does not appear. A little logic will enable you to put limits on the values of some of the digits immediately, but much trial and error is also required to arrive at a complete solution.

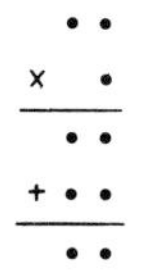

A Blank Division

There are no letters or digits as clues in this remarkable problem. Yet it is one of the easier cryptarithms on this page. Do not overlook the decimal point that appears after the fourth digit of the quotient. You must assume that any of the ten digits (0 through 9) may occur in the calculation.

```
        .... ....
.../......
    ...
     ...
     ...
      ...
      ...
       ...
       ...
        ....
        ....
```

The Clerk's Problem

A bank clerk is worried. He has lost his note of a calculation involving thousands of dollars. He remembers that two numbers, each with two digits, were multiplied to give a four-digit result. Then a three-digit number beginning with 1 was added. The final total had five digits. While trying to remember the numbers, he realizes that he can figure them out. Can you also find the missing numbers?

```
     ..
   x ..
    ...
   ...
   ....
  +1..
  .....
```

Deciphering the Division

This is a long division problem performed by a mathematician with bad handwriting; he often cannot read it himself. The day after he did the calculation below he found he could not recognize the figures except the 8 that appears in the third place of the quotient. Yet without very much difficulty he could work out what the whole calculation must have been. Can you do the same?

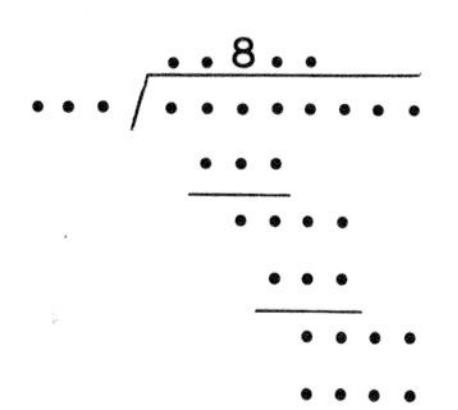

The Storekeeper's Accounts

The village storekeeper was always careful to keep his account books up-to-date. But he was sometimes careless about where he put them. One day he left them out in the rain and later found that one page was badly blurred. The multiplication below was on that page, and only the figures shown were legible. He found, nevertheless, that he could restore the missing figures. Can you do the same? It is possible that 4, 5, and 6 also occur among them.

```
    6..
  x...
    ...
  ....
 .5.5
..5.4.
```

A Coded Calculation

When the Transylvanian Intelligence Service succeeded in catching a dangerous foreign spy, they found that his papers were in code. This division calculation was among them. By carefully studying it, an agent was able to break the spy's number code. The only assumptions the agent made were that different letters stood for different digits and that the spy's arithmetic was correct. Can you equal the feat?

```
     ABJ
ECA/FDBHJ
    CGG
    AGAH
    AAEA
     KDDJ
     KDBH
       AJ
```

(See solution pages 196-197)

The Binary System

If, like most people, you occasionally have difficulty in doing arithmetic, you may at times have wished that there were fewer numerals (number symbols) to deal with. Our usual number system, the decimal system, uses ten numerals, from 0 through 9. In order to calculate efficiently, the results of adding or multiplying every pair of these must be learned. Calculation would be much simpler if the binary system of notation were used, for it utilizes only two symbols, 0 and 1. The binary system is used in computers and pocket calculators. There are amusing puzzles and tricks based on it, and some of these are presented in this chapter.

In the decimal system the numbers from 0 to 9 are represented by the corresponding numerals, standing alone. But the ten numerals also have place-value — they represent different values according to their position in a number. A numeral in the second place from the right represents a specific number of tens. Thus 23 represents the number that is the sum of two tens and three units. The largest number that can be written using two numerals is 99 — nine tens plus nine units. The next number is 100 — the third "place-value" is one hundred. Subsequent place-values are 1000, 10,000 and so forth.

In the binary system the numerals 0 and 1 standing alone have their usual meaning but the values of the positions in a number are, successively, 1, 2, 4, 8, 16, 32, and so forth. Two is represented by 10, three is represented by 11 (meaning 2 + 1). Four is written as 100, five as 101 (4 + 2), seven as 111 (4 + 2 + 1).

The table on the right gives the binary representations of numbers. As is evident, the binary system, though simple, is cumbersome. For example, six digits are needed to write the decimal-system number 60. However, the binary system is very convenient for computers, because many electronic components have two states — on and off — each of which can represent a binary digit. For example, a switch can be open to represent 0 and closed to represent 1.

Complex logical problems can be solved by means of calculations in binary notation. The digits 0 and 1 represent the falsehood and truth, respectively, of statements. Using the same principle, you can make a "logic computer" from a set of punched cards.

	32	16	8	4	2	1						
0						0						
1						1						1
2					1	0					2	
3					1	1					3	3
4				1	0	0				4		
5				1	0	1				5		5
6				1	1	0				6	6	
7				1	1	1				7	7	7
8			1	0	0	0			8			
9			1	0	0	1			9			9
10			1	0	1	0			10		10	
11			1	0	1	1			11		11	11
12			1	1	0	0			12	12		
13			1	1	0	1			13	13		13
14			1	1	1	0			14	14	14	
15			1	1	1	1			15	15	15	15
16		1	0	0	0	0		16				
17		1	0	0	0	1		17				17
18		1	0	0	1	0		18			18	
19		1	0	0	1	1		19			19	19
20		1	0	1	0	0		20		20		
21		1	0	1	0	1		21		21		21
22		1	0	1	1	0		22		22	22	
23		1	0	1	1	1		23		23	23	23
24		1	1	0	0	0		24	24			
25		1	1	0	0	1		25	25			25
26		1	1	0	1	0		26	26		26	
27		1	1	0	1	1		27	27		27	27
28		1	1	1	0	0		28	28	28		
29		1	1	1	0	1		29	29	29		29
30		1	1	1	1	0		30	30	30	30	
31		1	1	1	1	1		31	31	31	31	31
32	1	0	0	0	0	0	32					
33	1	0	0	0	0	1	33					33
34	1	0	0	0	1	0	34				34	
35	1	0	0	0	1	1	35				35	35
36	1	0	0	1	0	0	36			36		
37	1	0	0	1	0	1	37			37		37
38	1	0	0	1	1	0	38			38	38	
39	1	0	0	1	1	1	39			39	39	39
40	1	0	1	0	0	0	40		40			
41	1	0	1	0	0	1	41		41			41
42	1	0	1	0	1	0	42		42		42	
43	1	0	1	0	1	1	43		43		43	43
44	1	0	1	1	0	0	44		44	44		
45	1	0	1	1	0	1	45		45	45		45
46	1	0	1	1	1	0	46		46	46	46	
47	1	0	1	1	1	1	47		47	47	47	47
48	1	1	0	0	0	0	48	48				
49	1	1	0	0	0	1	49	49				49
50	1	1	0	0	1	0	50	50			50	
51	1	1	0	0	1	1	51	51			51	51
52	1	1	0	1	0	0	52	52		52		
53	1	1	0	1	0	1	53	53		53		53
54	1	1	0	1	1	0	54	54		54	54	
55	1	1	0	1	1	1	55	55		55	55	55
56	1	1	1	0	0	0	56	56	56			
57	1	1	1	0	0	1	57	57	57			57
58	1	1	1	0	1	0	58	58	58		58	
59	1	1	1	0	1	1	59	59	59		59	59
60	1	1	1	1	0	0	60	60	60	60		

Left: Numbers from 0 to 60 in binary notation.
Right: The binary digits are a guide in making mind-reading cards, described on page 164.

Materials
32 file cards, 3" × 4"

Tools
Hole puncher; utility knife; steel straightedge; pencil.

How to Make a Logic Computer
Punch a row of five evenly spaced holes at the top of each card. Use the first card you prepare as a guide in making the others, to ensure that the holes of all cards align exactly. Cut off the top right-hand corners so that you can readily detect a card that is the wrong way up. The cards will represent numbers in five-digit binary notation from 00000 to 11111 — that is, in decimal notation, from 0 to 31.

Next cut notches in the cards, as in the diagram on the opposite page. Every card has a different pattern of holes and notches. When a hole is read as 0, and a notch as 1, each pattern represents a number in binary notation. For easy reference write the number in decimal form on each card.

Place the cards in any order into a pack, making sure that the cut corners are at top right. Push a wooden match through, say, the second hole from the left, and lift. You will pull out all the cards that represent numbers with 0 in the second place (half the pack).

Problem Solving with the Computer
The fact that cards can be labeled in a certain way and then easily separated from other cards enables the pack to be used to solve certain types of logic puzzles rapidly. To use them for this purpose, label the holes and notches from left to right with the letters from A to E. A notch (binary digit 1) at, say, the fourth position from the left will represent a statement labeled "D." A hole (binary digit 0) in the same position will represent the statement "D is false," or "not-D." This is abbreviated as d. Let us see how a logic problem is solved with the cards. Here are five assertions:

1. If Arnold is watching TV, so is Betty.
2. Either Dave or Emily (or both of them) is watching TV.
3. Either Betty or Cleo (but not both of them) is watching TV.
4. Cleo and Dave are either both watching or both not watching TV.
5. If Emily is watching TV, then Arnold and Dave are also watching.

Who is watching TV? In order to sort this out, label the possibilities with letters. Thus, A can represent the statement "Arnold is watching TV." Then a (not-A) is the statement "Arnold is not watching TV." Likewise, B labels the statement "Betty is watching TV," b labels the opposite statement, and so on. Abbreviate "Both Arnold and Betty are watching TV" by AB. Then Cd, for example, will mean "Cleo is watching TV, but Dave is not."

The punched cards represent all the possible situations. For example, the card that has five holes but no notches (binary digits 00000) corresponds to abcde — the assertion that none of the five people is watching TV. Card number 9 (binary digits 01001) represents aBcdE — the assertion that only Betty and Emily are watching TV. It is now necessary to remove all the cards in the pack that correspond to situations ruled out by statements 1 to 5 above.

Statement 1 rules out Ab — it excludes the possibility that Arnold is watching TV while Betty is not. (Notice that it says nothing about what Betty is doing if Arnold is *not* watching TV; so far as this statement is concerned, both aB and ab are equally possible.) So it is necessary to reject the cards representing Ab. To do this, push a match through the holes in the A position and lift. The cards that are *not* lifted by this action are those with a notch in the A position, representing the assertion A. Take these cards, push the match through the holes in the B position, and lift it. The cards that are *raised* have a hole in the B position in addition to the notch in the A position. These cards represent Ab and must be laid aside. Form all of the other cards into a pack again.

Statement 2 rules out the possibility de. It is therefore necessary to reject those cards in the remaining pack that have holes in the D and E positions. First push the match through the cards at the D position and lift it. Take the cards that are pulled out by this action, push the match through them at the E position and lift it again. The cards that are pulled out on the second move are put with the previously rejected cards. The remainder of the pack is squared up. Statement 3 rules out BC and bc. So remove from the pack those cards that have holes in both the B and C positions, or notches in both positions. Statement 4 rules out Cd and cD; remove the corresponding cards from the pack. And statement 5 rules out aE and dE. (Again, be careful; the statement says nothing about what Arnold or Dave is doing if Emily is *not* watching TV.) When the corresponding cards have been removed from the pack, just one card is left — card number 6, representing the assertion abCDe. Thus the only situation consistent with statements 1 to 5 is that Cleo and Dave are watching TV, and Arnold, Betty, and Emily are not.

Several logic problems are posed on the next page. They can all be solved with the aid of the punched cards. In every example, remove all cards representing situations that are excluded by the conditions of the problem. Several of the problems are concerned with the truth or falsehood of only four statements. You can solve these by ignoring the E positions. This simply means that if the solution is, say, ABcd, it will be represented by two cards — one corresponding to ABcdE, the other to ABcde. One of the puzzles involves only three statements; in this case, work only with the A, B, and C positions.

It is possible to solve the logic problems without using the punched cards — but success is not likely to be achieved so speedily or so certainly.

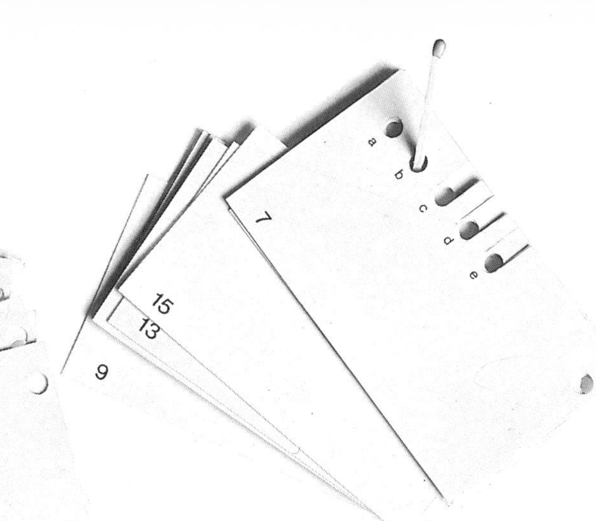

Logic problems can be rapidly solved by sorting cards in which holes and notches have been cut as shown below. A notch at position C, for example, means statement C is true; a hole means C is false.

The Battle of Baffleburg

The *Baffleburg Tribune*'s contest for the best new puzzle is not judged entirely on merit. Albright and Branebender are cousins of the *Tribune*'s owner, so at least one of them must get a prize. Branebender or Catchfinder — but not both of them because they were joint winners last year — must certainly win something. Dodgeley or Egghead or perhaps both will get a prize. In fact, if Egghead gets a prize, Dodgeley must also get one, to keep the peace. Catchfinder copied Dodgeley's puzzle, so either both get a prize or neither does. Albright will refuse a prize if Egghead gets one. Who will get a prize?

Murder at the Manor

Sir Harold Hound, the famous amateur detective, had assembled servants and house guests in the drawing room of the manor. He was about to reveal who was responsible for the murder of the squire two days before. After a complicated summary of the case, he concluded: "Clearly, if the admiral is telling the truth, then so is the butler. However, the butler and the count cannot both be telling the truth. But the count and the deacon are not both lying. And if the deacon is telling the truth, then the butler is lying." There are two people whose truthfulness — or lack of it — you can deduce. Who are they?

The Bad, the Sad, and the Mad

The parents could hear a disturbance from the rumpus room. "I don't know why there has to be so much trouble whenever Annie, Benny, and Connie meet," said Annie's Pa. "Well," said Benny's Ma, "when Benny is bad, Connie gets sad, and Annie gets mad." "In fact, Connie always gets sad when Annie's mad," replied Annie's Pa. "The trouble is," continued Benny's Ma, "if Annie didn't get mad, Benny would immediately start being bad." So what happens when Annie, Benny, and Connie get together? Is it inevitable that Annie must get mad or that Benny must be bad or that Connie must get sad?

Directions and Misdirections

When a driver asked some inhabitants of Wyburg about the shortest route to Zeeton, he got some confusing replies. The first resident told him to go through both Ashville and Beefburg. Yet the second told him to avoid Beefburg and go through Cowtown. Then a third told him to avoid Cowtown and Dragville, while a fourth told him to go through Dragville and avoid Beefburg. After looking at a map, the driver worked out his best route, and he saw that none of his advisers had given him directions that were completely correct. Can you tell whether his route took him through Ashville and Beefburg?

The Children's Ages

Mrs. Rackbrain's memory is not always reliable. For example, although she never forgets the birthdays of her niece and two nephews, she often forgets how old the children are. She remembers, however, certain facts about their ages. She is completely certain that if Bill is not the youngest, then Alice is. She also remembers that if Charles is not the youngest, then Alice is the oldest. She is correct on these points. Although her memory works in strange ways, there is nothing wrong with her powers of logic. She finds that she can work out which of the children is the oldest and which the youngest. Can you?

Keeping the Peace

A United Nations resolution declares that an international peace-keeping force must be sent to Zerovia. However, it is difficult to select a force that will satisfy all interested parties. If Abria sends a contingent, Bemblia will withdraw. Detria or Espria, or both, must be included. Bemblia and Costlia will either both participate or both refuse to, and Detria will likewise do whatever Costlia does. If Espria sends a contingent, Abria and Detria will insist on being included. The diplomats eventually succeed in finding a composition for the force that is acceptable to everyone. Which countries provide contingents?

Mind-Reading Cards

Mystify your friends with a telepathic feat. Number six cards in the way shown here. Ask a friend to think of any number from 1 through 60 and to hand you the cards on which the number appears. You can immediately tell him what number he chose. The method: add the first numbers of the selected cards.

You can even increase the mystery. Lay out the cards in an order that you have memorized, and then stand where you can see them but not read them. Ask your friend to turn over the cards on which his number appears. You can determine which cards they are because you can see their position. Or make the cards of different colors.

It is easy to extend the set of cards. Their first numbers successively double; thus the next cards begin with 64 and 128, respectively. Since, for example, 100 is the sum of 64, 32, and 4, it must appear on the cards with these in first place.

1	15	29	43	57
3	17	31	45	59
5	19	33	47	
7	21	35	49	
9	23	37	51	
11	25	39	53	
13	27	41	55	

2	15	30	43	58
3	18	31	46	59
6	19	34	47	
7	22	35	50	
10	23	38	51	
11	26	39	54	
14	27	42	55	

4	15	30	45	60
5	20	31	46	
6	21	36	47	
7	22	37	52	
12	23	38	53	
13	28	39	54	
14	29	44	55	

8	15	30	45	60
9	24	31	46	
10	25	40	47	
11	26	41	56	
12	27	42	57	
13	28	43	58	
14	29	44	59	

16	23	30	53	60
17	24	31	54	
18	25	48	55	
19	26	49	56	
20	27	50	57	
21	28	51	58	
22	29	52	59	

32	39	46	53	60
33	40	47	54	
34	41	48	55	
35	42	49	56	
36	43	50	57	
37	44	51	58	
38	45	52	59	

Six cards with the numbers indicated can be used in a simple yet effective mind-reading stunt.

(See solution pages 197-198)

The Colormatch Square

The binary system, described on the preceding pages, is the basis of an intriguing and entirely new color-matching puzzle. It employs 16 square tiles, made of cardboard, plastic, or other stiff material. Each tile is divided into four squares, colored light or dark as in the figure below. The aim of the puzzle is to arrange the tiles into a pattern called a colormatch square.

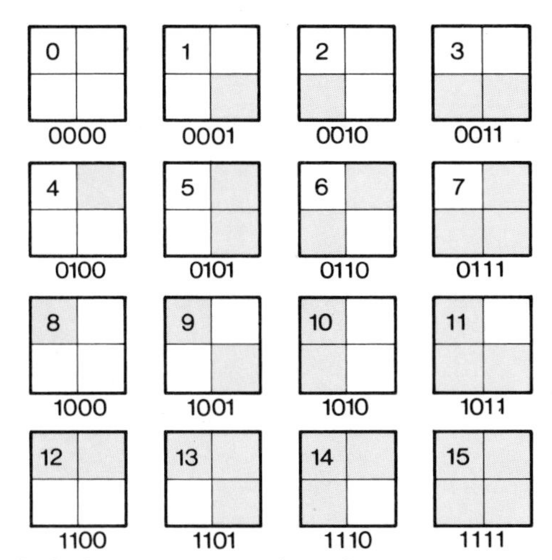

Each tile represents a number in binary notation: a light square equals 0; a dark square equals 1.

A colormatch square — 16 specially patterned tiles arranged in such a way that where tiles touch, they match each other in color.

A four-by-four square made from the tiles is shown above right. It is an example of a colormatch square. You will notice that where tiles meet, they match in color. For example, the 0 tile, whose four cells are all light in color, is bordered on the right by the 1 square, the left-hand cells of which are light. It may at first appear easy to form a colormatch square, but a little experience with the tiles will reveal that the number of tile arrangements is enormous compared with the number of colormatch squares. The puzzle's inventor, the leading computer scientist and puzzle enthusiast C. J. Bouwkamp, has found that there are only 50 colormatch squares that are essentially different from each other. Yet from each of these, related solutions can be derived in various ways — for example, by exchanging light and dark colors throughout the colormatch pattern. As you try to make a colormatch square you form an endless variety of patterns. A few of the patterns found in colormatch squares are shown in the series of diagrams at the foot of this page.

The relation between the colormatch puzzle and the binary system can be seen when you study the diagram at top left. Each light square on a tile represents the digit 0, and each dark square represents the digit 1. The squares on each tile are to be read in the following order: top left, top right, bottom left, bottom right. The whole tile represents the number, written in binary notation, that appears below it. The number, in its usual decimal form, appears in the tile's top left-hand corner.

Materials
Stiff cardboard or acrylic, 4" × 4"
Paint or colored paper or plastic tape

Tools
Utility knife (for cardboard); fretsaw (for acrylic); straightedge; sandpaper.

How to Make the Puzzle
If you are using acrylic, rule a grid of 64 squares, ½" on each side, on paper and stick it onto the acrylic as a guide. If you are using cardboard, rule the grid onto it directly. Cut the material into 16 tiles, each 1" on a side. If the pieces are of acrylic, sandpaper their edges. Color the tiles as they appear in the diagram at top left; colored paper or tape can be stuck onto acrylic. Add the decimal numerals, writing them on or using press-on type.

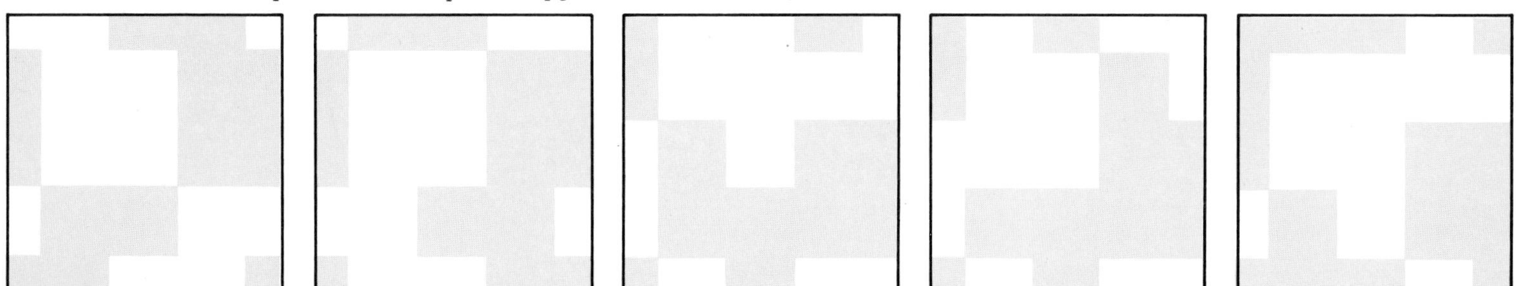

Five patterns formed by the contrasting light and dark squares of tiles in colormatch squares. There are 50 basic patterns altogether.

(See solution page 198)

Positioning Puzzles

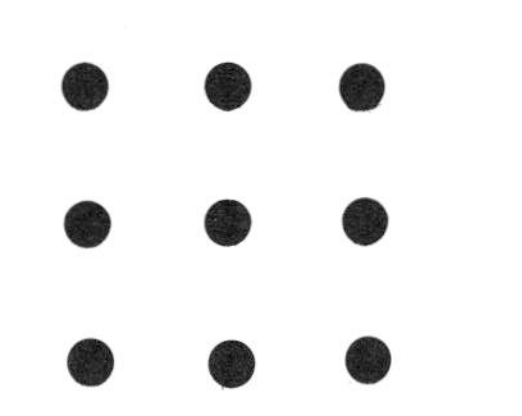

An old line-and-point problem, which seems simple yet is strangely tricky. Without lifting your pencil from the paper, draw four straight lines that join up all nine of the dots.

Railroads, bus companies, airlines, and shipping lines are faced with the problems presented in moving vast numbers of people and great quantities of freight from one place to another with a limited number of vehicles. Traffic planners might see the problems of their daily life reflected in the small-scale movement puzzles presented in this chapter. River-crossing puzzles and railroad-shunting puzzles are clear analogies to the real-life problems that originally suggested them. Even the sliding-block problem shown on the left, involving Donald Duck and some of his friends, is reminiscent of driving through city traffic in the rush hour. Not all problems in this chapter have a direct relationship to everyday life — although some of them provide good practice in playing games such as checkers. Yet all are concerned with positioning in a broad sense. Many can be tackled with pencil and paper.

The Moving Peg Puzzle

This puzzle, a type of peg solitaire, was widely sold in Victorian England. An array of holes is drilled in a board in the pattern shown in the picture below. White pegs are placed in the upper half of the board, and black pegs are placed in the lower half. The center hole is left vacant. The object of the game is to transfer the white pegs to the lower half of the board and the black pegs to the upper half. A peg may be moved in two ways: from one square to an adjacent vacant square, or it may be jumped over one neighboring peg into a vacant square. Moves may be made forward or backward, but only parallel to the sides of the squares. You can play with counters on the grid in the picture or on a copy of it. When you have solved the puzzle, try to improve your solution by reducing the number of moves. One solution consisting of 46 moves is given in the solutions section.

A sliding block puzzle featuring some famous stars of the motion pictures. The aim is to get Donald, who is at his own goal at the top of the square, down to the bottom (where Pluto is) where he can score.

The board for the moving peg puzzle, carved by a seaman on one of his voyages. He has given it an ornamental boatlike shape. You can try the puzzle using counters on this picture or on a larger copy. If you want to make a wooden board, adapt the instructions on page 174 for a peg solitaire board, using this picture as a guide.

(See solution page 198)

The Cross and the Dots

There are 25 dots in this square array. Draw a cross made up of straight lines connecting 12 dots in such a way that there are five dots inside the cross and eight outside it. The cross must be completely symmetrical.

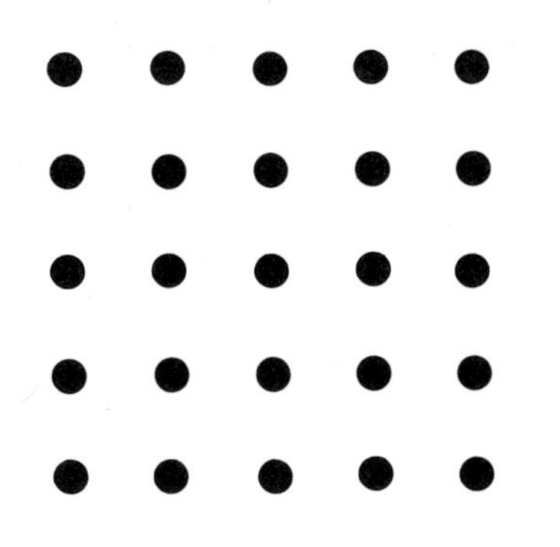

The Sixteen Dots

In the dot-and-line problem below, you must draw six straight lines that connect all 16 dots. Try the nine-dot problem at the top of the opposite page first, to get an idea of how to do this.

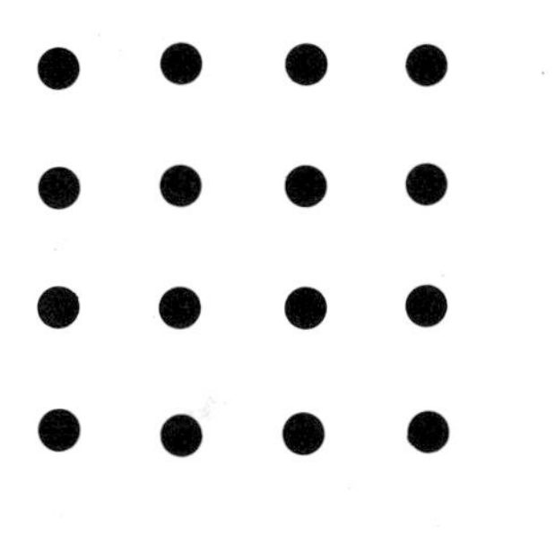

The Shortest Route

The 12 houses below have to be joined by a telephone cable. In order to save money, the telephone company wants to use the shortest possible length of cable. What is the shortest route that it can take through all of the houses? The cable can begin at any house, and it does not return to its starting point.

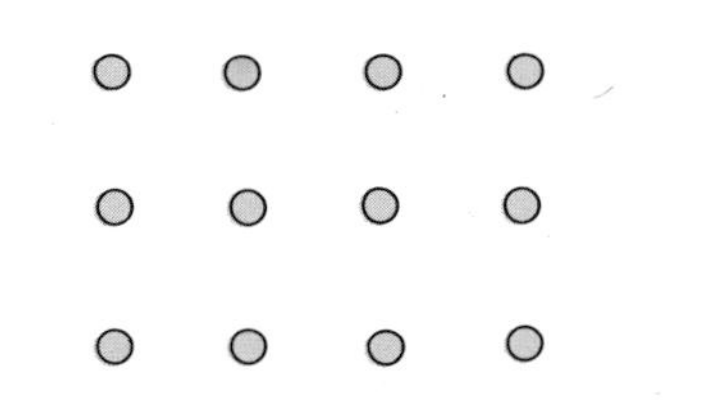

The Plantation

Can you subtract 27 from 7 × 7 so as to leave 21 × 4? You may think this would require a miracle, but in fact only trial and error and patience are necessary. Below is the map of a plantation where there are 49 trees growing in neat rows. As trees grow to maturity they are cut down. The puzzle you are presented with is the following: how can you cut down 27 trees so that the 22 remaining stand in 21 rows of four? In this new layout each tree is counted as belonging to several rows. No row contains more than four trees.

Changing the Checkers

This problem, like the one above, at first may seem to require magical powers. Take eight black and eight white checkers — or, if you prefer, 16 coins. Arrange them as shown in the diagram below, with colors alternating in each row and column (or heads alternating with tails). Now rearrange them so that the checkers in each column are all of the same color (or coins in each column are all heads or all tails). The magic part is that you must do it by touching *only* pieces 1 and 2.

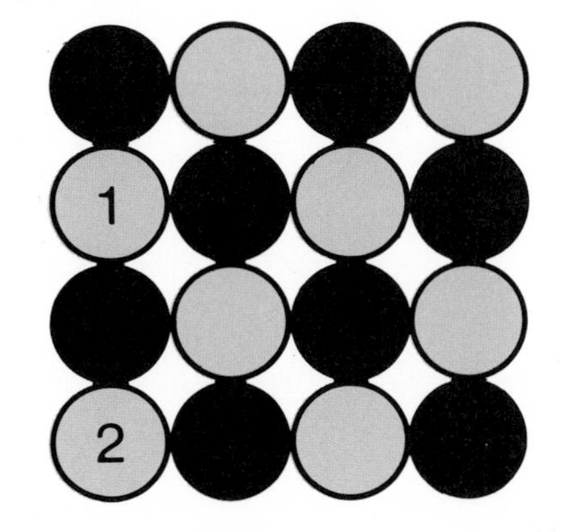

Thirty Trios

Draw a large copy of the network below. Take 21 counters and place each counter on a point where lines intersect. Arrange the counters to form 30 groups of three, the members of each group being linked by a line. Each counter must belong to at least one of the groups.

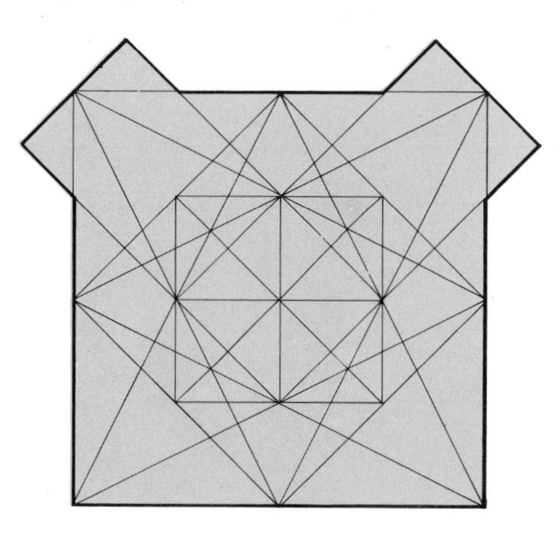

A Rising Readership

The eight offices of Tooth and Claw, Inc., are arranged along four corridors around a central courtyard, as shown in the diagram below. Twelve people work in each office. Not all of them take a copy of the new company magazine when it is brought around. In the first month three people in each office take a copy, indicated by the dots in the diagram. Interest in the magazine varies. In each office more people take copies when there is news about that department. In the second month only 20 people take copies. In the third month 28 take a copy, 32 in the fourth month, and 36 in the fifth. The employee who takes the magazine around notices that through all of these fluctuations the number of copies distributed in each corridor is constant — nine copies. (Remember that each corner office lies on two corridors.) How many copies are taken in each office in each month?

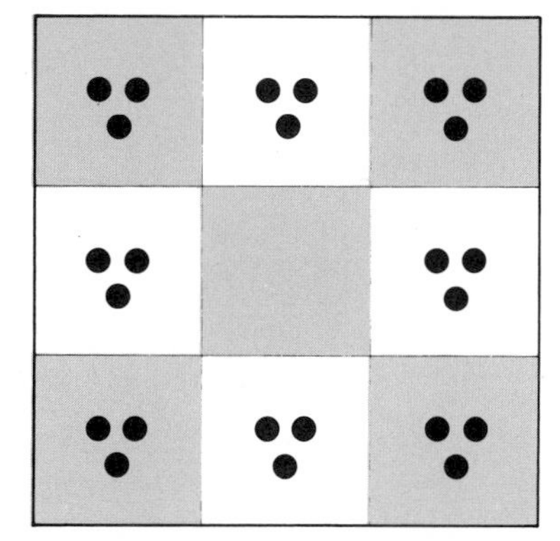

(See solution page 198)

Crossing the Water Puzzles

Puzzlers have long been interested in problems involving river crossings. In the 8th century, Alcuin, a great churchman and schoolteacher, proposed puzzles similar to the problem of ferrying a dog, a goat, and some cabbages, which appears on this page. In the 18th century the citizens of Königsberg, then in East Prussia, asked themselves whether it was possible to walk across all of the bridges of their city without retracing their steps. Leonhard Euler, one of the greatest mathematicians, analyzed the problem. He proved that the proposed tour was impossible, and he thereby founded a new branch of mathematics called topology. On these two pages is a selection of problems in which, in imagination, you must cross the water — or even go under it.

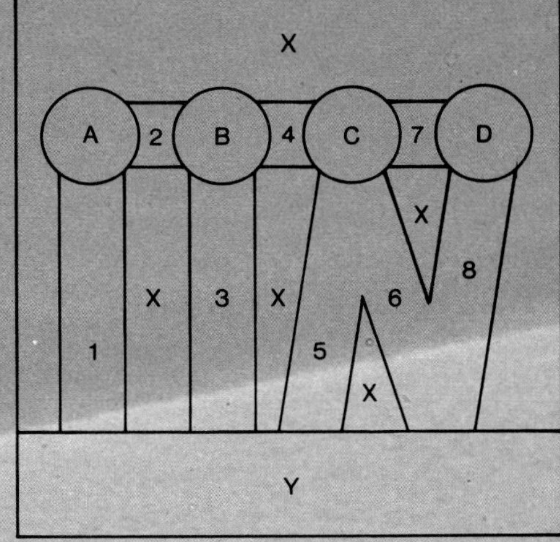

The Four Couples

The four pairs of young people seen here are engaged to be married. Ann is engaged to Arnold, Betty to Bill, Carrie to Charles, and Debbie to Dave. They have set out on a picnic, and they want to eat on the far side of the river. They have been able to borrow a rowboat, but it can hold only two people at a time. They then come up against a problem that is likely to beset them throughout their married lives. The men all suffer from extreme jealousy of an old-fashioned kind. None of them will permit his fiancée to be in the company of any of the other men, even if other people are there, unless he himself is present. Thus Arnold will not countenance Anne's being with Bill in Arnold's absence, even if others are present. The women are not so unreasonable. The party would never have been able to get across the river but for the lucky coincidence that there is an island on which people can be left temporarily during the ferrying.

The couples' problem: how can they cross the river in the smallest number of trips? Traveling from shore to island or from island to shore counts as one trip, as does crossing from shore to shore. All of the men and women can row well. There is a restriction that the men's jealousy imposes on them: no man may set out alone in the boat when a girl other than his fiancée is alone on either the island or the far shore — even if his immediate destination is not the spot where she is alone. It is possible to transport the whole party across with as few as 17 trips.

The Four Islands

In this map X marks areas of sea, and Y marks the shore. The offshore islands A, B, C, and D are connected to each other and to the mainland by the eight bridges shown. Is it possible to walk from island B over each of the bridges just once, finishing one's journey on the shore, without retracing one's steps? And can you perform the same feat if you start from island C?

The Dog, the Goat, and the Cabbages

A farmer has to cross a river in a boat big enough to carry only him and either his dog, his goat, or his cabbages. The cabbages will be eaten if they are left alone with the goat, and the goat will be eaten if left alone with the dog. How does the farmer take the dog, the goat, and the cabbages safely across?

(See solution page 198)

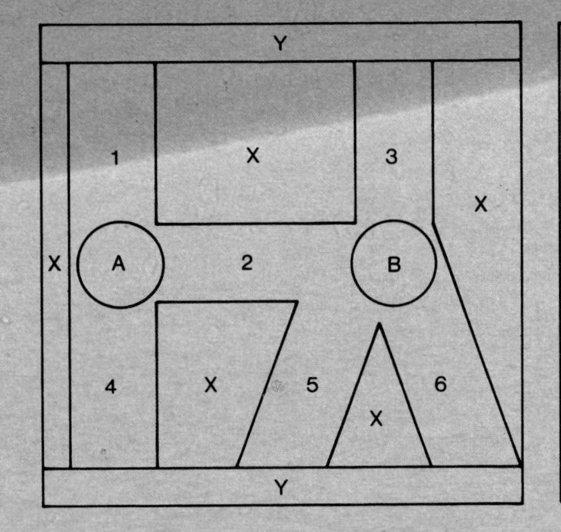

The Six Bridges

A and B are two islands in a river, connected to each other and to the bank by six bridges. Areas marked X are water, areas marked Y are land. Can a pedestrian, beginning at any point and finishing at the same or some other point, cross every bridge without ever retracing his steps? After that, try the following. Can the pedestrian, beginning on one bank, cross each bridge once and finish on either bank without retracing his steps?

The Nine Pipelines

An oil company plans to pump oil from three offshore oil rigs, A, B, and C, to three refineries, 1, 2, and 3, by pipeline. Each rig will supply all three refineries. The pipelines should cross each other in as few places as possible, for it is difficult to make repairs to the pipes near a crossing point. Can the pipelines be laid in such a way that they do not cross at all? If not, what would be the minimum number of crossing points?

The Detachment

A detachment of soldiers reaches a river. The bridge has collapsed, and the river is too fast-flowing to be swum. While the captain is wondering what to do, he sees a small boat that two children are rowing. He commandeers it but immediately realizes that the boat can carry only one soldier or two children. It cannot even hold one soldier and a child. However, the captain finds that he can get his men across the river. How does he succeed in doing it?

Missionaries and Indians

About a hundred years ago a party of three missionaries was hacking its way through the Brazilian jungle in the company of three Indian guides. They came to a river and found a canoe that could hold only two people at a time. Paddling such a canoe was a difficult art. Only one of the Indians and one of the missionaries, who had been diligent in learning the ways of the people, knew how to do it. The missionaries were mistrustful of their Indian companions, who were themselves not enthusiastic about the modern civilization being introduced to them. The missionaries therefore arranged the crossing so that they were never outnumbered by the Indians on either shore. How could they do this in the smallest number of river crossings?

(See solution pages 198-199)

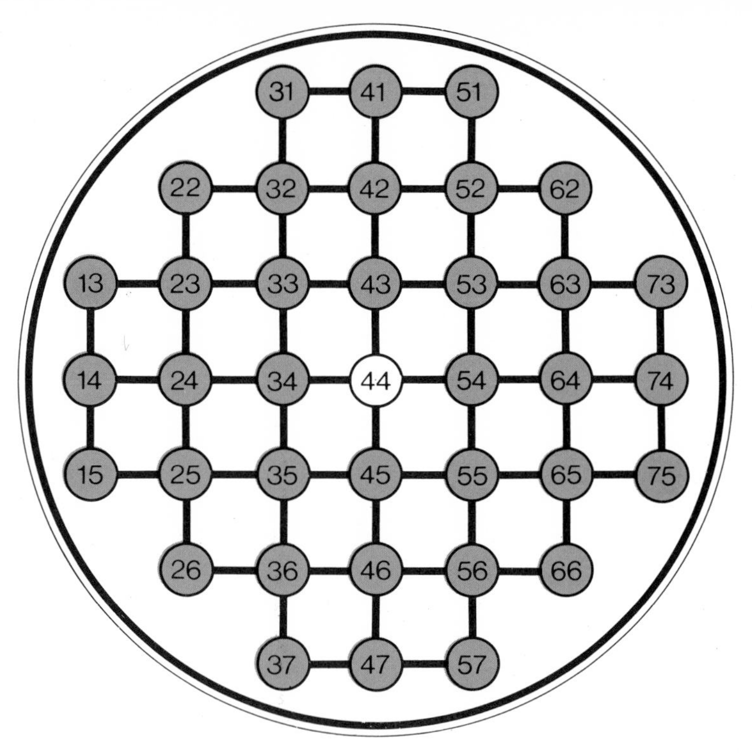

The full solitaire board with 37 cells, which can be occupied by marbles, pegs, or counters. Each cell is numbered according to its row and column.

The Princesse de Soubise is playing solitaire in this French engraving of the 17th century. For most of its history solitaire has had the greatest popularity in France, and French artisans lavished much skill and effort on making beautiful sets from ivory or from the finest and rarest wood.

Peg Solitaire

According to one old story, the game of peg solitaire, often called simply solitaire, was invented in the 18th century by a French nobleman imprisoned in the Bastille, the grim fortress-prison in Paris. He was modifying an already existing game called Fox and Geese. His new invention, like the earlier game, used a board in which an array of holes — called cells — were bored as resting places for pegs or marbles. There are many games and puzzles that can be devised for the solitaire board, but the method of making moves is common to all of them. A peg (assuming that this is the marker used) can be moved only by jumping it over a neighboring peg to a vacant space directly on the other side. Following such a move, the peg over which the jump was made is removed from the board. Jumps can be made only along the lattice lines (as shown in the diagram); a peg cannot jump diagonally.

Two kinds of boards are used for peg solitaire. One, whose plan is shown above, has 37 cells. Another common board lacks the cells numbered 22, 26, 62, and 66 in the diagram; thus it forms a cross-shaped pattern of cells. Any problem devised for a 33-cell board can be attempted on the larger array if the four above mentioned cells are excluded from play. In the problems on the following pages the board pattern to be used is always given.

In the most widely known solitaire puzzle the 33-cell board is used. All cells are filled except the one in the center. The player is required to finish the game with a single peg in the central cell. However, many other puzzles can be devised, and a large selection is given in this chapter.

The number of jumps made in a game of solitaire equals the number of pegs removed. However, a series of consecutive jumps made at one time with a single piece can be regarded as a single move; hence a player can aim not merely at solving a given puzzle but also at finding the solution that requires the smallest number of moves. The basic solitaire puzzle on a 33-cell board — to begin with a single vacancy in the center and to finish with a single peg in the center — requires 32 jumps, which can be grouped into 18 moves.

In the problems that follow, each cell is labeled with a two-digit number. The first digit is the number, from left to right, of the vertical row in which the cell occurs. The second digit is the number of the horizontal row, from top to bottom. In the solutions chapter, a jump is described simply by specifying the cells occupied by a peg before and after it is moved. A chain jump is described by the numbers of the cells successively occupied.

The Latin Cross

A cross whose lower arm is longer than the other three is known as a Latin cross. It is a shape that often occurs in geometric dissection puzzles and is found several times in the section of this book on that subject (page 28). In this puzzle, which is good practice for those beginning to play solitaire, the cross is formed with six pegs placed as shown in the diagram. The object is to remove five pegs in five jumps and leave the remaining peg in the central cell, 44. The puzzle is useful in getting familiar with the difficulties of peg solitaire.

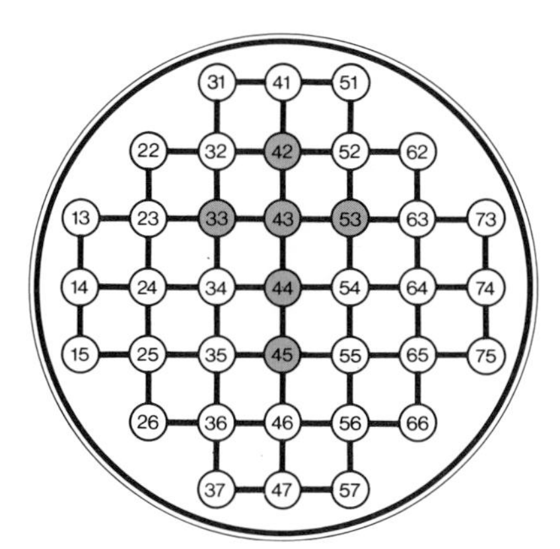

Reduce this pattern to a single peg in cell 44.

The Greek Cross

The diagram below shows the initial pattern of pegs for this problem, which is more challenging than the preceding one. At the outset a Greek cross, having four equal arms, is formed on the board with nine pegs. Eight of these are to be removed in the course of play, and the ninth is to be left in the central cell, 44. Two double jumps occur in the solution provided. This is a six-move solution since chain jumps count as single moves. Knowing how to solve this puzzle is a help in doing the shrine puzzle that is immediately below.

Reduce this pattern to a single peg in cell 44.

The Football Team

The 11 men of a football team are positioned as shown in the diagram, ready for the kickoff. Only one of them will get through to the goal, which once again is the center cell, 44. There are two distinct problems here. In one problem you make use of the full 37-cell board, including cells number 22, 26, 62, and 66. In the other you restrict yourself to the 33-cell array. In both cases the puzzle can be solved in eight moves, of which two are double jumps. Despite the similarity of aim in the problems, the solutions are totally different.

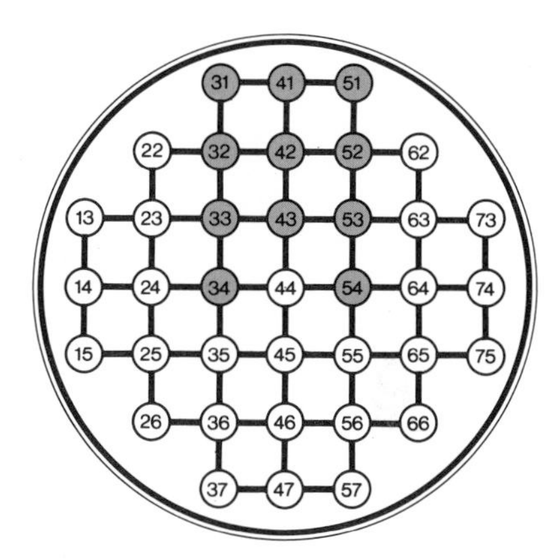

Reduce this pattern to a single peg in cell 44.

The Pyramid of Chefren

Nine pegs are used to construct the pyramid pattern that is laid out on the solitaire board below. It represents one of the lesser Egyptian pyramids, burial place of the pharaoh Chefren. You are challenged to reduce this initial pattern to a single peg positioned in the central cell, 44. Eight jumps are needed to remove eight pegs, but the first two are accomplished with the same peg and thus combine into a single move. Since the cells 22, 26, 62, and 66 are not used, this puzzle can be played on the 33-cell board as well as on the 37-cell board.

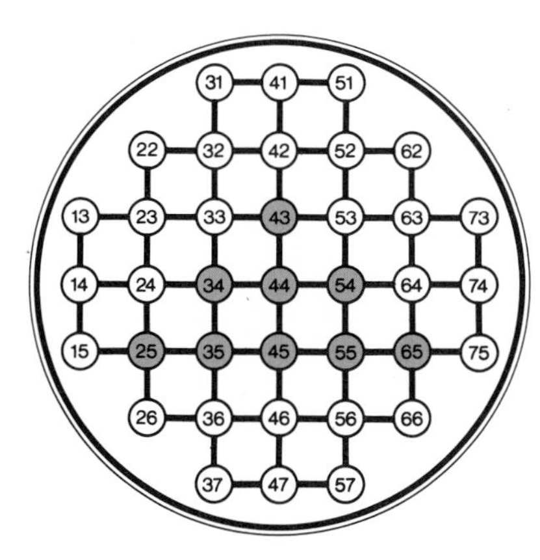

Reduce this pattern to a single peg in cell 44.

The Shrine

Use 15 pegs to make the shape below, which resembles a cross set up on a plinth. The aim of the puzzle is to remove all but one of the pegs in 12 moves, including two double jumps. The final peg is left not in the central cell but in cell 43. If you do not mind a little help in solving the puzzle, you might find it useful to know that after six moves a Greek cross (having four equal arms) is formed. This can be reduced to a single peg in exactly the same way as the initial pattern in the puzzle immediately above.

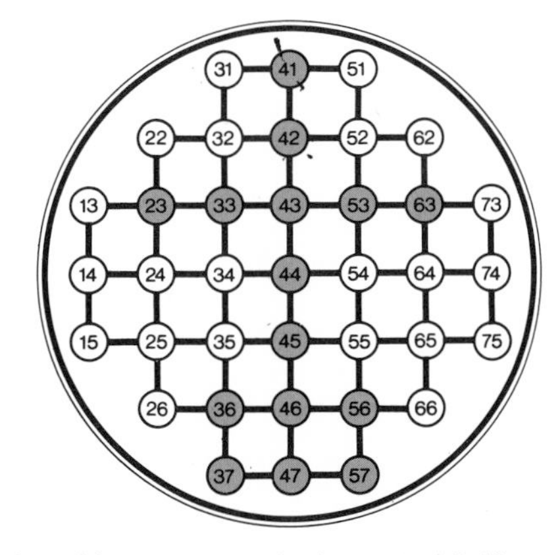

Reduce this pattern to a single peg in cell 43.

The Pyramid of Cheops

The greatest of the Egyptian pyramids was built as a tomb for the pharaoh Cheops. The pattern below is named for it because it is the largest pyramid pattern that can be fitted onto the solitaire board. The aim of the puzzle is to reduce the pattern to a single peg in the central cell, 44. The classic solution required 12 moves. But in 1963 an elegant solution of only eight moves, was discovered by the solitaire expert Harry O. Davis of Portland, Oregon. The early moves place pegs where they can be "swept up" in later chain jumps.

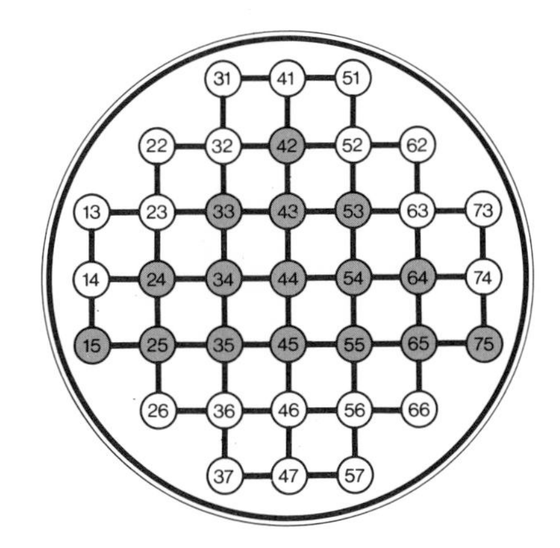

Reduce this pattern to a single peg in cell 44.

(See solution page 199)

The Tiffany Lamp

Only a little imagination is needed for one to see the form of a table lamp with a broad shade in the 16-peg pattern below. You are challenged to remove all of the pegs but one, which must remain in the central cell, 44. Use the 33-cell array only, thus excluding cells 22, 26, 62, and 66. In addition to merely clearing the board, you should search for the most economical solutions by contriving to so place vacated cells that chains of jumps can be made with a single peg. There is a solution of ten moves with two chain jumps.

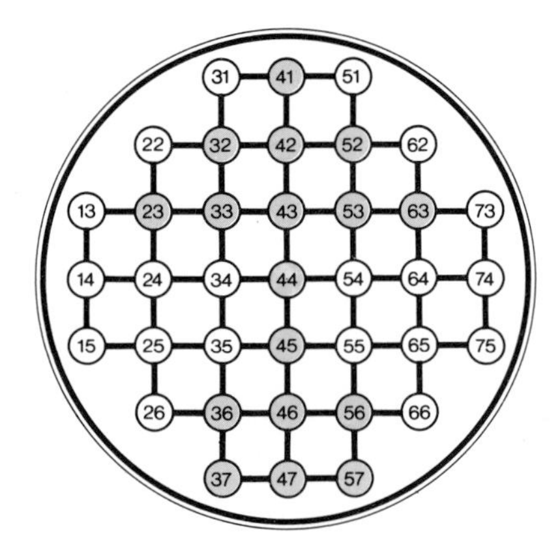

Reduce this pattern to a single peg in cell 44.

Center to Center

This is the classic peg solitaire puzzle. Cells 22, 26, 62, and 66 are vacant at the beginning of the puzzle and are not used during play. All other cells are occupied except the central cell, 44. The pegs are all removed until there is only one remaining in the central cell. This problem has been thoroughly analyzed by solitaire enthusiasts. The puzzle expert Henry Dudeney published a 19-move solution in 1908, but a few years later an 18-move solution was found. It has been proved impossible to solve the puzzle in fewer moves.

Reduce this pattern to a single peg in cell 44.

The Davis Jump

The elegant solution to this puzzle is named in honor of its discoverer, the prolific solitaire puzzler Harry O. Davis. Once again only the 33-cell array of cells is used; avoid cells 22, 26, 62, and 66. Apart from these, the only cell vacant in the initial pattern is 53. Try to remove the pegs until only one remains, in cell 53. For many years the best example known of such a transformation from a single-vacancy position to a single-peg position consisted of 16 moves. However, the Davis jump has only 15, including six chain jumps.

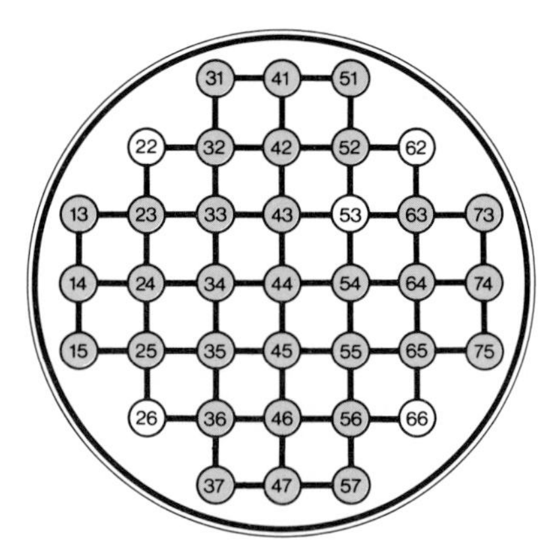

Reduce this pattern to a single peg in cell 53.

Corner to Corner

On the full 37-cell board it is not possible to solve the best-known solitaire puzzle, which begins with a single central vacancy and ends with a single central peg. However, it is possible to solve other puzzles that begin with a single vacancy and end with a single peg. In this puzzle the initial vacancy is in a corner, at cell number 31. The aim is to leave the final peg in cell 57. Two solutions are provided. The first consists of 34 moves, which include a double jump. The second consists of 27 moves, including five chain jumps.

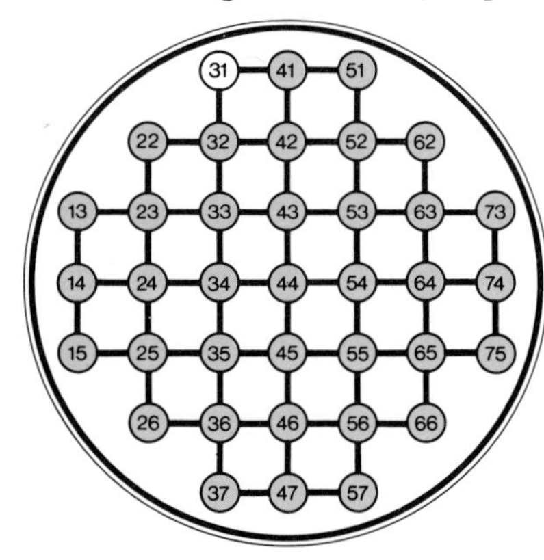

Reduce this pattern to a single peg in cell 57.

The Octagram

The 37 cells of the larger solitaire array form an octagonal, or eight-sided, figure. When eight corner pegs are removed, as in this diagram, the shape formed by the occupied cells is an eight-pointed star, or octagram. The aim of the puzzle that begins with the octagram is to remove all of the pegs except one. The final peg must remain in the central cell, 44. A total of 28 jumps, removing an equal number of pegs, can be used to solve this puzzle, but since they include four double jumps, the solution consists of only 24 moves.

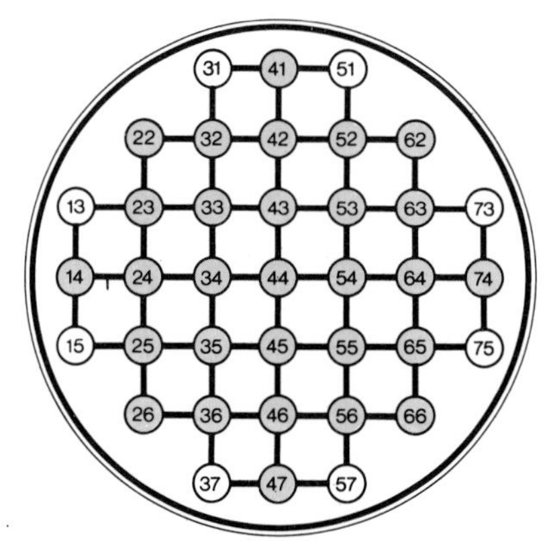

Reduce this pattern to a single peg in cell 44.

The Pentagon

In this puzzle only the 33-cell array is used — cells 22, 26, 62, and 66 are not occupied in the beginning and are not brought into play. In addition to these, the corner cells and cell number 47 are vacated to form the pentagonal, or five-sided, figure below. The aim is to reduce the pegs to a single peg placed in the central cell, 44. There are 15 moves in the solution, and they include only one chain jump. But this is spectacular — nine pegs are removed in a single sweep. This is the kind of coup that the enthusiast tries to achieve.

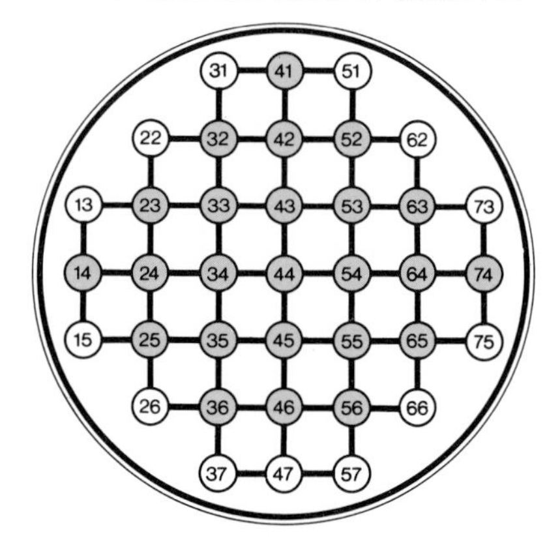

Reduce this pattern to a single peg in cell 44.

(See solution page 199)

The Five Crosses

The pattern shown in the diagram below is composed of five small interconnected crosses. This pattern is made up of 21 pegs. The aim of the puzzle is to reduce the number to one peg positioned in the central cell, 44. A ten-move solution is provided, which includes three chain jumps. In each chain jump four pegs are removed from the board. The full 37-cell array, including cells 22, 26, 62, and 66, is utilized in the solution. In fact it is clear from the diagram that the first move that you make must be a jump into one of these four cells.

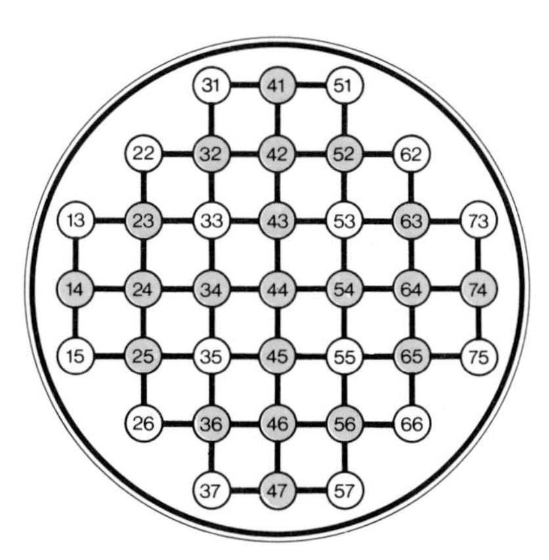

Reduce this pattern to a single peg in cell 44.

The Double Cross

This puzzle requires the full array of 37 cells. Its initial pattern resembles the octagram shown at the bottom center of the page opposite, except that eight pegs have been removed to make an eight-armed cross. The cross consists of 21 pegs, 20 of which must be removed from the board to leave a single final peg in the central cell, 44. There are four double jumps in the solution, which consists of 16 moves.
The first move is a double jump. Since the pattern is symmetrical, you may choose from several such initial moves.

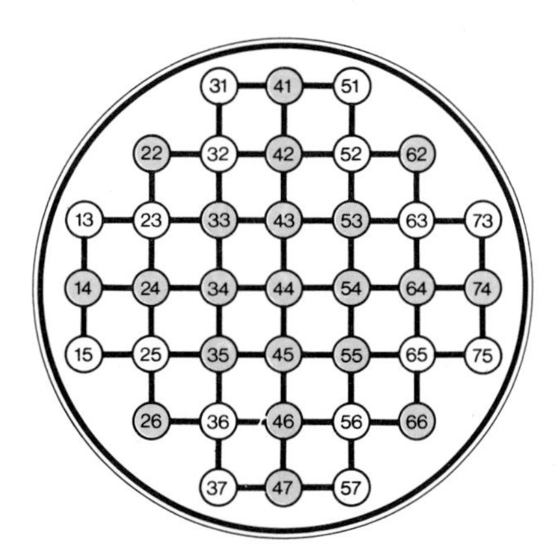

Reduce this pattern to a single peg in cell 44.

The Tilted Square

This inclined-square pattern is formed from 24 pegs, with 13 cells left vacant. The aim is to remove pegs until only one is left in the central cell. If you utilize the full 37-cell array, you can reach the final position in 11 moves, including four chain jumps. One chain consists of five jumps in succession. If you avoid using cells 22, 26, 62, and 66, you can actually find another, more efficient, solution. It utilizes eight moves, one of which is a spectacular series consisting of 11 jumps. Perhaps you can discover an even more economical solution.

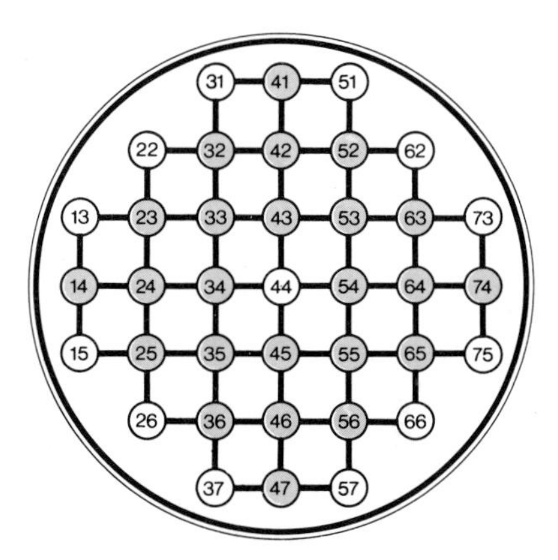

Reduce this pattern to a single peg in cell 44.

The Lonely Cross

This diagram shows not the initial but the final layout of pegs that you are aiming for in this puzzle, which requires the full 37-cell board. First fill the board with pegs; then remove the central peg from cell 44. Now try to form the pattern shown below, in which a cross consisting of five pegs is surrounded by a series of pegs placed in the 16 border cells. Do not assume that the pegs in the border cells can be left untouched in the course of play. It is possible to solve the puzzle in 14 moves, of which only one is a double jump.

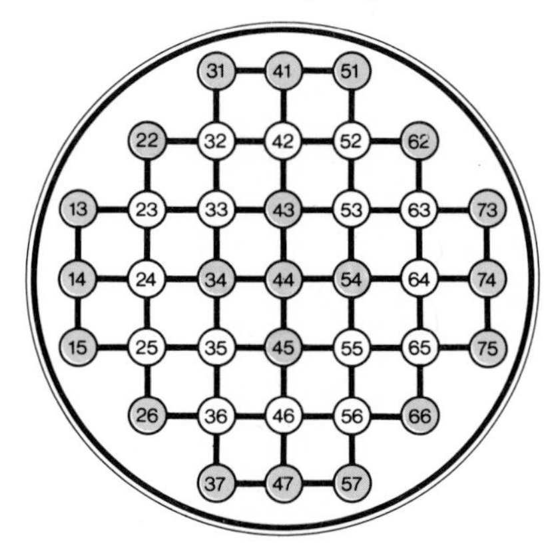

Begin with cell 44 vacant and form this pattern.

The Final Score

When you have successfully completed this puzzle, 20 pegs will remain on the board. Your initial position comprises 36 pegs covering the board, leaving only the central cell, 44, vacant. You are challenged to arrive at the pattern shown in the diagram below. Since 16 pegs are to be removed, 16 jumps are called for. In the solution provided, none of these is part of a chain jump. Since it is rarely certain that the best possible solution to a solitaire puzzle has been discovered, a better solution than this one may yet exist.

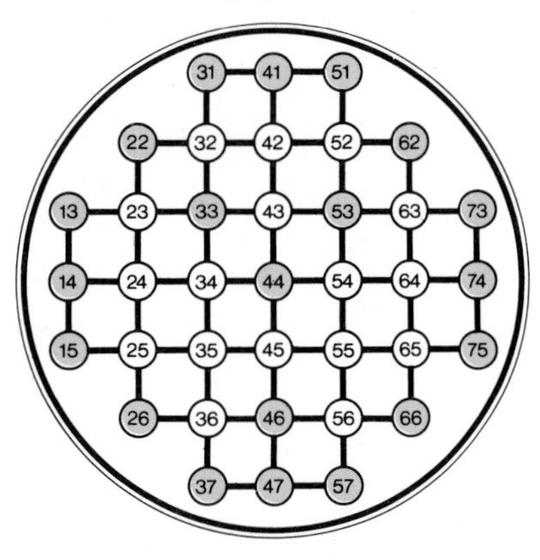

Begin with cell 44 vacant and form this pattern.

The Twelve Guards

Once again the diagram shows the final layout of the pegs for this puzzle. Twelve "guards" are left at the board's four approaches, and all other cells are empty. In the initial arrangement all cells except the central one, 44, are filled. Twenty-four moves are needed to reach the position shown, and all of them are single jumps. The four "gates" — cells number 22, 26, 62, and 66 — are occupied and then vacated. Toward the end of play, a cross with four arms appears. Each arm disappears in turn, and the pattern shown here remains.

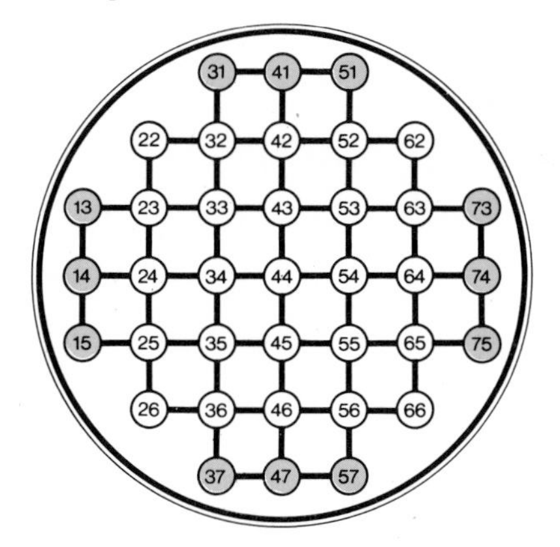

Begin with cell 44 vacant and form this pattern.

(See solution page 199)

Materials
6" × 6" square of larch, mahogany, or other attractive wood, 3/4" to 1" thick
3 feet of wooden dowel, 5/16" thick
Varnish or primer and enamel paint

Tools
Drill with 3/8" bit; fretsaw; pencil; straightedge; compasses.

How to Make the Puzzle
Mark the grid shown in the guide diagram at the right. The grid squares have sides of 3/4". Mark clearly with a well-defined dot the grid line intersections that correspond to the board's cells. (The pattern shown is the full 37-cell array, which is required for many of the puzzles described on the previous pages.) If you wish to make a circular board, draw a circle of 3" radius with the point of a pair of compasses centered on the central dot of the grid.

To make the cells, drill 3/8" holes at the points marking cell positions. Make the holes of equal depth, which should be about half the thickness of the board. (If your drill is not equipped with a depth guide, you can mark the desired depth with chalk on the side of the bit.) If you are making a circular board, cut around the circle you have previously drawn. Sandpaper the edge of the disk. Varnish the wood or apply primer and enamel paint. To make the pegs, cut the dowel into 36 pieces, each 1" long. These, too, may be varnished, or they may be painted in a color contrasting with that of the board. You can paint four pegs of a different color at one end and use them to mark the cells not used (22, 26, 62, and 66) in puzzles that require the 33-cell array.

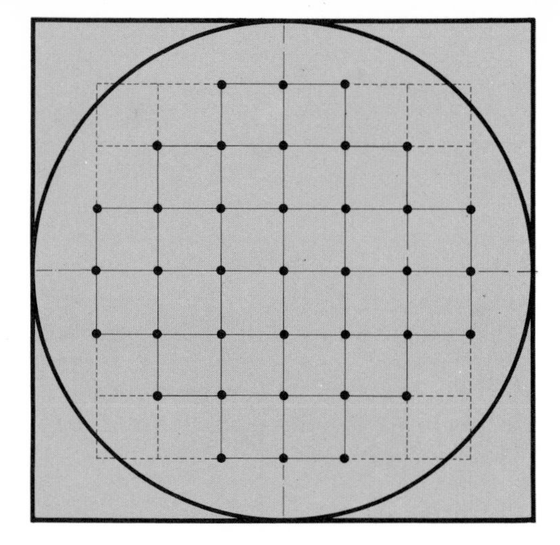

Fix the positions of the cells on your solitaire board by drawing this grid of straight lines separated from each other by 3/4". You can make the board square or trim it to a circular shape of 6" diameter.

An attractively grained solitaire board of larch, made according to the instructions in the text.

The Tower of Brahma

In the great temple of Benares, so the story goes, there is a brass plate on which three vertical diamond shafts are fixed. On the shafts are mounted 64 golden disks, all of different sizes. At the time of Creation, the god Brahma placed all of the disks on one pin, in order of size with the largest at the bottom. The Hindu priests unceasingly transfer the disks from peg to peg, one at a time, never placing a larger disk on a smaller one. When all of the disks have been transferred to a second pin, the universe will end.

This legend is simply the brainchild of Edouard Lucas, who invented the Tower of Brahma puzzle. The model shown below has six disks, which are to be transferred to another peg with the restrictions described above. The number of moves needed to transfer three disks is seven, or $2^3 - 1$ (mathematicians write 2^3 for $2 \times 2 \times 2$). To transfer six disks requires $2^6 - 1$ (or 63) moves (2^6 is $2 \times 2 \times 2 \times 2 \times 2 \times 2$). The priests at Benares would have required $2^{64} - 1$ moves to complete their task. If they made one move every second, it would take nearly six billion centuries.

Materials

Plywood, 14" $\times$ 14" $\times$ $\frac{1}{3}$"
Larch wood, 11" $\times$ 11" $\times$ 1"
Wooden dowel, $19\frac{1}{2}$" long, $\frac{3}{8}$" thick
Wood glue
Paint (optional)

Tools

Drill with $\frac{1}{2}$" and $\frac{3}{8}$" bits; fretsaw; sandpaper; compasses; ruler.

How to Make the Puzzle

Draw a circle of $3\frac{1}{2}$" radius on the plywood, with its center at the center of the square. Keeping the compasses at the same setting, mark six equidistant points on the circle, placing the point of the compasses on each in turn. Draw three circles of $3\frac{1}{2}$" radius, centered on alternate points, as in the diagram, making a trefoil pattern. Cut around the trefoil with the fretsaw and sandpaper its edges. Drill $\frac{3}{8}$" holes at the centers of the three overlapping circles. Cut the dowel into three $6\frac{1}{2}$" lengths, and paint them if you wish. Glue each piece into one of the holes. Draw six circles on the larch wood with radii increasing from $\frac{1}{2}$" to 3" in $\frac{1}{2}$" steps. Cut them out with the fretsaw, sandpaper them, and drill $\frac{1}{2}$" holes through their centers.

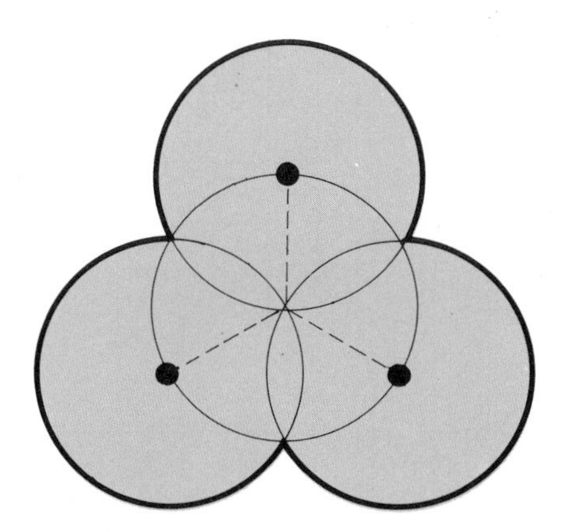

Make six equidistant marks on the central circle. Then center the outer circles on alternate marks. Cut around the trefoil pattern that is formed.

Transfer the disks one by one to other pegs, making sure never to put a disk on top of one that is smaller. You can transfer them all to one peg in 63 steps.

(See solution page 199)

Shunting Problems

Anyone who has lived near a railroad freight yard knows from bitter experience that the business of marshaling cars to assemble a train can be noisy and complex. It always seems to be done in the middle of the night, too. The puzzles on these two pages concern the logistics of moving railroad cars and locomotives. The trains shown date from the age of steam when such problems were commonplace.

Getting the Trains Past

Below are two trains that have come up against a problem that must have been common in the pioneering days of railroading, when there were few double tracks, turntables, or sidings. The two trains, one consisting of an engine and three cars and the other consisting of an engine and two cars, need to pass each other, and they have to make use of the siding to do so. The siding is only long enough to take two cars or one engine and one car. A great deal of coupling, uncoupling, and reversing of engines will be needed. How can the two trains pass each other with the fewest possible engine movements? An engine begins a new move every time it starts from rest or reverses its direction of motion. Each locomotive must continue on its way with the cars that it is now pulling. Cars can be connected to the front or the back of an engine. The letters that label engines and cars give you a clue — the three cars on the left (labeled A) are never uncoupled from each other.

A problem that is amusing on a toy railroad but would be frustrating and expensive on a real one: get the trains past each other, using a siding that has room for only two cars or one engine and one car.

Ordering the Engines

The diagram below shows the layout of a railroad yard. Eight numbered engines are at the positions shown. They are permitted to stop only at these positions and at the vacant position indicated by the arrow. For the following day's work the engines must be placed in numerical order around the circle with the central position vacant. One of the engines cannot move because its fire has been damped down. The other engines can move forward or backward, and the necessary positions can be reached in 17 engine moves. How is it done, and which of the engines is stationary throughout?

The Giant Freight Trains

In the diagram below only the first two cars of each train are visible, but in fact each engine is pulling 80 cars. The trains have to get past each other using only the siding shown. The siding is long enough to accommodate one engine and 40 cars. Find the most efficient way to arrange the shunting. The trains first back up so that ample space for maneuvering is left between them and the switch. Then they accomplish the operation in ten moves. Cars can be coupled to the front or the back of the engines. Each engine is powerful enough to pull all of the cars involved in the problem at the same time.

The Line Gangs' Trains

Two trains carrying track repair teams to their depots found themselves facing each other on a single track. They had to use a siding to get past each other. The situation was similar to that shown in the diagram below, but the left-hand engine was pulling only two cars and the other was pulling only one; however, the siding was only big enough to take one car or one engine. Since the workers were eager to get home, the engineers had to work out the fastest way to get the trains past each other. Each train began the shunting at a sufficient distance from the switch to accommodate the other train.

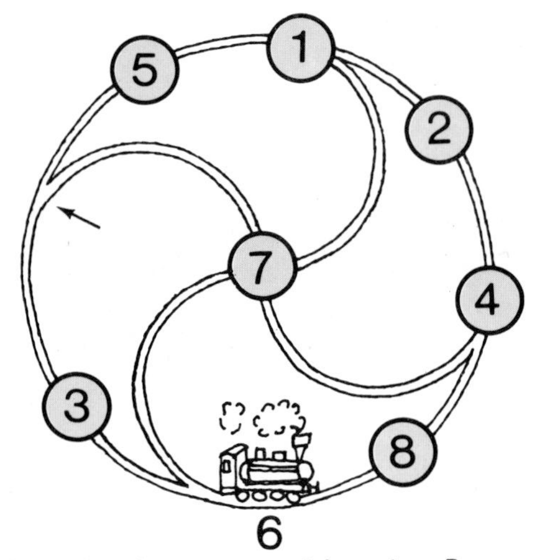

The numbers here represent eight engines. Regroup them in order by moving only seven of them.

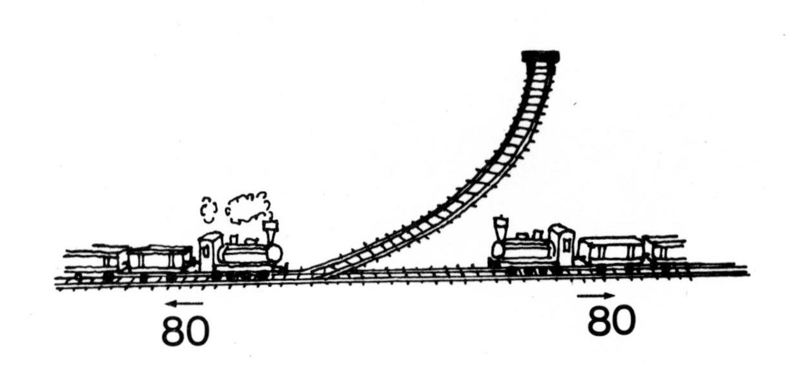

The two engineers will need to cooperate closely to get their 80-car freight trains past each other.

(See solution page 199)

The Double Siding

Two sidings, AC and BC, join the main track in the diagram at the right. They meet at C and lead on to a dead end, D. The stretch of track CD is long enough to hold one freight car or one engine. At present there is a freight car painted with stripes on the left-hand siding and a white-painted car on the right-hand siding. The task of the engineer is to exchange the positions of the freight cars with the smallest number of couplings and uncouplings. He can do it in six operations if he is permitted to finish with his engine facing in the opposite direction. If he must finish with his engine facing to the right, as it is now, he will need ten couplings and uncouplings. How does the engineer accomplish his task in these two cases?

A double problem is posed by this double siding: exchange the freight cars first with and then without a reversal of the direction in which the engine faces.

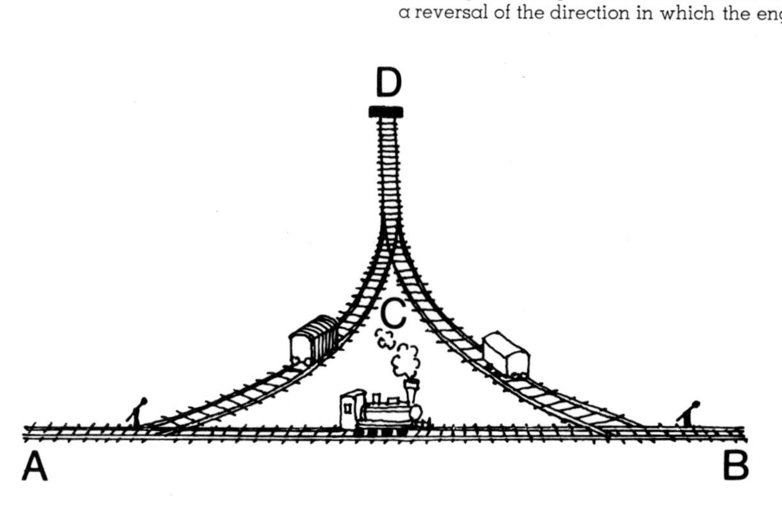

Materials
Plywood, 10" × 6" × 3/8"
Simple wooden picture-frame molding, 16" long
Three wooden balls, each 1" in diameter
Wooden doweling in two diameters, about 1/4" and about 3/8"
Primer and enamel paint

Tools
Fretsaw; drill with 1/4" bit; pencil; straightedge; paintbrush.

How to Make the Puzzle
Copy the outline at bottom right onto graph paper, making the top track the full 10" length of the plywood. Paste the drawing onto the plywood and cut around it. Cut lengths of simple picture-frame molding to the dimensions of the track shown and join the siding to the main track at a 45° angle. Glue the molding to the plywood as shown in the smallest figure. The separation between the parallel tracks should be such that the sliders (described next) can run freely in the grooves thus created. To make the sliders, saw each wooden ball in half, drill a 1/4" hole at the center of each flat face, and glue a piece of the 1/4" dowel in the hole. The length of this dowel will be determined by the thickness of the molding. Drill a 1/4" hole through the axis of a 1" piece of the 3/8" dowel. Cut this piece into six equal thicknesses and glue one to the bottom of the dowel in each slider. Paint the track and sliders. The puzzle of the Line Gangs' Trains is set up below.

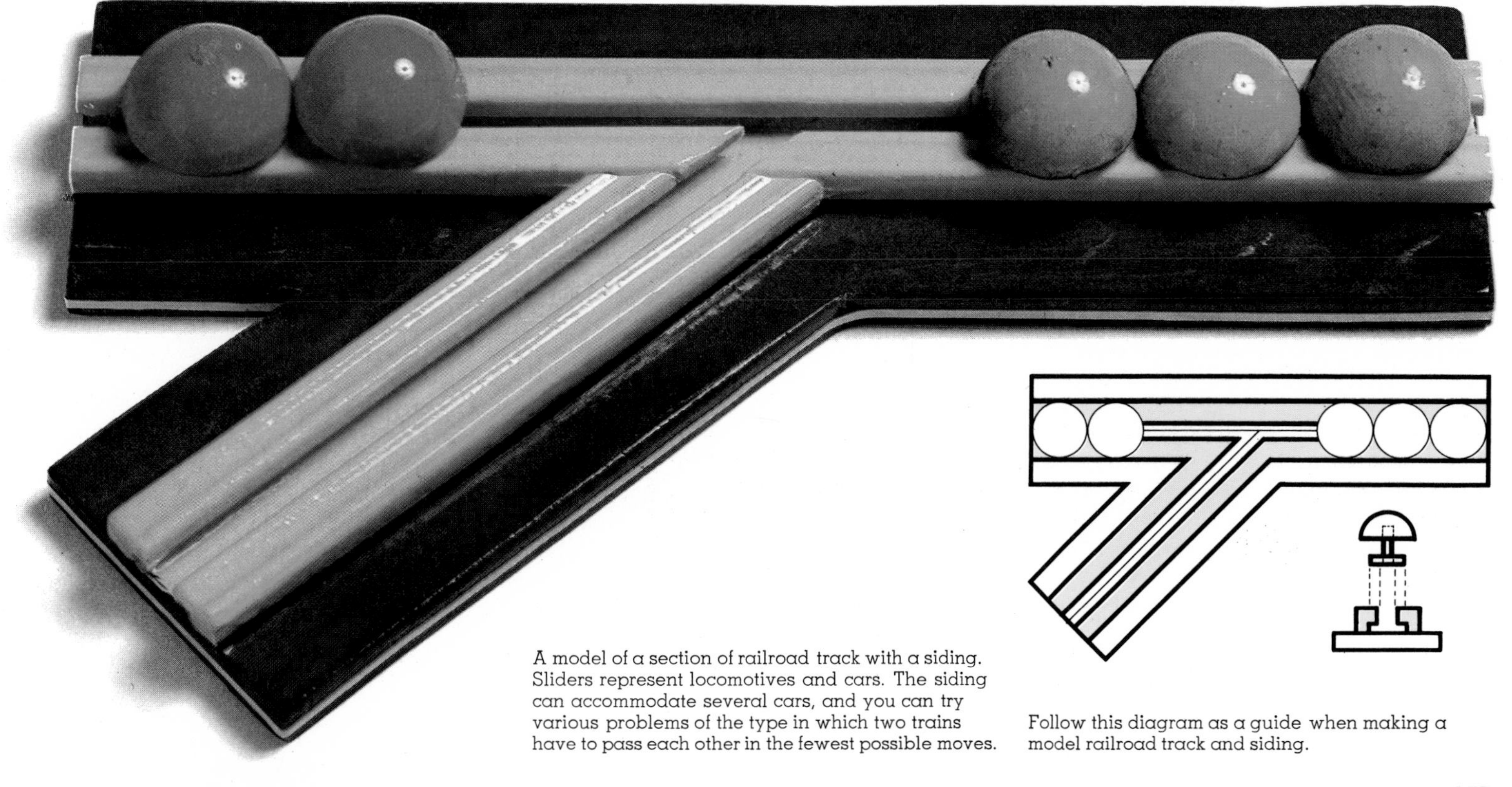

A model of a section of railroad track with a siding. Sliders represent locomotives and cars. The siding can accommodate several cars, and you can try various problems of the type in which two trains have to pass each other in the fewest possible moves.

Follow this diagram as a guide when making a model railroad track and siding.

(See solution page 199)

Puzzles with Checkers

About 2000 B.C. the Egyptians were playing games on checkered boards. There may be an unbroken line of descent from those ancient games to the checkers of today. Certainly a game very much like modern checkers existed in France by the 11th century. The game of checkers played in Britain and America today uses a board of 64 squares, and each player begins with 12 men. In many European countries, however, the so-called Polish game is played, in which the players begin with 20 men each and use a board of 100 squares. Puzzlers have been inspired by the game of checkers. Some of the problems on these two pages use checkers merely as counters.

The Perfect Hexagon

In the lower of the two diagrams below, six checkers are arranged so that their centers form a hexagon, or six-sided figure. Thus there is room for a seventh piece, shown by the shaded circle, to fit precisely among them. If you tried to lay down the six checkers in a six-sided array, you would find it difficult to judge the positions by eye alone; the figure you would make is almost certain to be slightly irregular. However, if you lay the checkers down in the form of an equilateral triangle (as in the upper illustration), you can now form a perfectly regular hexagon by sliding each piece, one at a time, to a new position in which it touches two others. Try to do this in the fewest possible moves. The solution provided has four moves.

Two Transformations

Make the upper of the two patterns shown with eight pieces from a checkers set. Accuracy of positioning is not as important here as it is in the problem on the left; you can judge the right angles and the straightness of the lines by eye. In five moves transform this H pattern into the O pattern shown in the lower diagram. On each move you must slide one piece, without disturbing the others, to a new position where it touches two others. The solution cannot simply be reversed to give a transformation from O to H, for some of the reversed moves would be illegal. In fact seven moves are required to make the H pattern from the O. Furthermore, if the O pattern is made as shown, the H must be formed in a pattern at right angles to it.

A pet monkey tries its hand at checkers in this illustration from a 17th-century book.

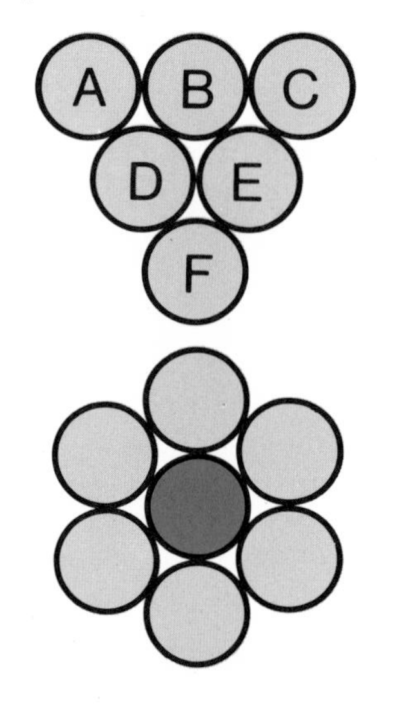

Form the hexagonal ring of checkers by making four moves with some of the pieces in the upper pattern.

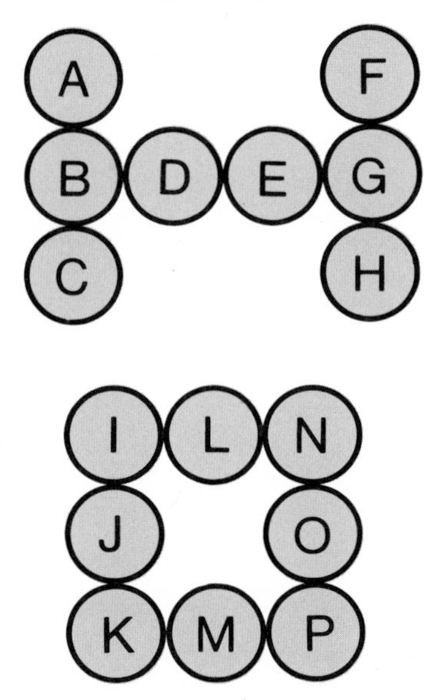

Five moves are needed to change the H into the O, but it takes seven to change the O back into the H.

The Eight Checkers

A very old problem requires the puzzler to place eight checkers on a checkerboard so that no two of them lie in the same row, column, or diagonal. There are fully 4,426,165,368 ways in which you can place eight pieces on the 64-square board, but you do not have to try anything like that number of positions to arrive at a solution. If you place one piece on each row and systematically move them from column to column, a solution will appear in a reasonable time. From this solution you can find others. Slide the pattern successively one row upward (bringing the piece in the top row down to the bottom of its column each time) or successively one column leftward (moving the leftmost piece to the right of its row each time).

You need eight checkers for the problem on the left. One is sufficient for the two puzzles on the right.

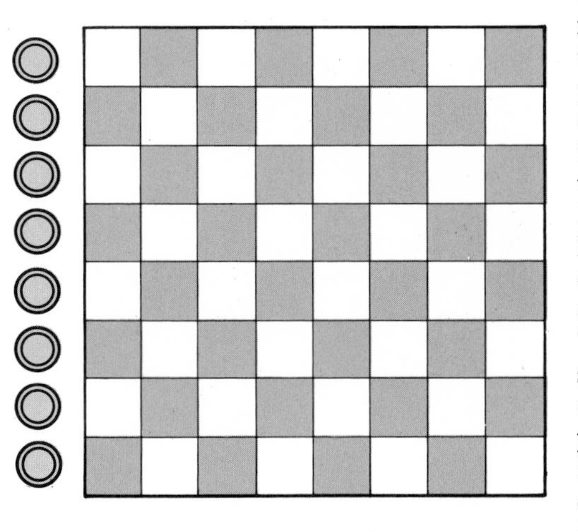

The Queen and Bishop Go Touring

Although these puzzles are based on the moves of two chess pieces, you do not have to know the rules of chess to try them. Use checkers or the appropriate pieces from a chess set or any convenient marker. First the queen's tour problem: move the piece so that it visits all of the squares of the board in 14 queen's moves. A queen's move may be made parallel to a side of the board or diagonally for as many squares as desired, as far as the edge of the board. The queen must finish on the square it started from, and squares may be visited more than once. The bishop's tour problem is to visit all the white squares in only 17 bishop's moves, which are diagonal. The piece may start and finish on different squares.

(See solution pages 199-200)

Switch Sixteen

Copy the diagram below and place eight white and eight black checkers as shown. The aim is to move each checker into the opposite half of the board. A checker can move diagonally into a vacant square or can jump diagonally over a checker into a vacant square. Black checkers move upward only, while white checkers move downward only. There is a 52-move solution.

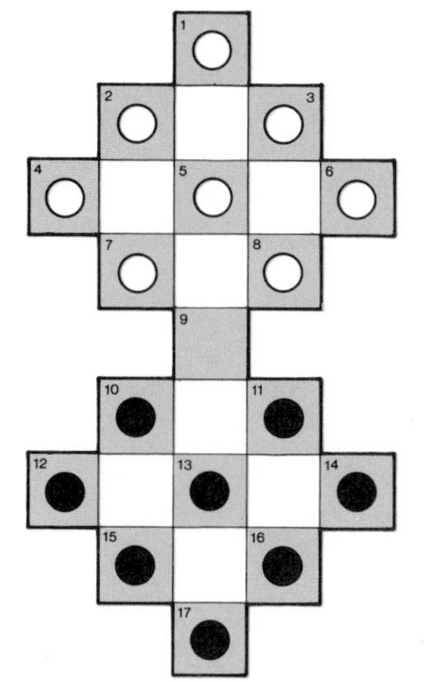

Transpose the pieces in the fewest possible moves.

The Square Dance

Draw a grid of 25 squares like that below, or play on a 25-square region of a checkerboard. Place nine checkers on the central squares. Try to remove eight of them by moving in the following way Jump one checker over another to a vacant square, moving diagonally or parallel to the sides of the board. As each piece is jumped, remove it. The last piece remaining should lie in the center square. If a series of consecutive jumps with one piece counts as a single move, the solution has five moves.

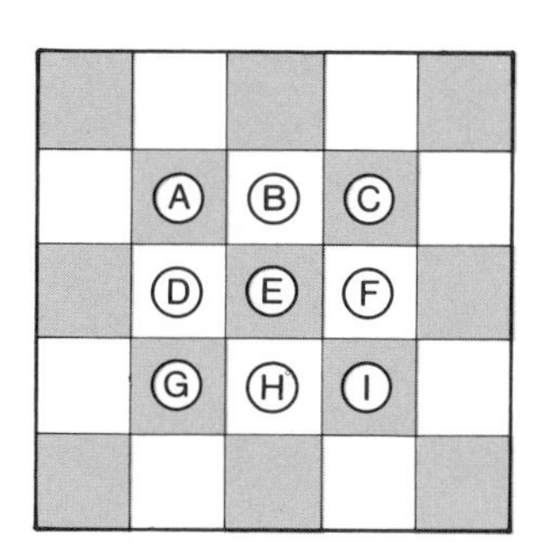

Every move must be a capture in this puzzle. Reduce the checkers to one in the center.

Jumping Checkers

Lay out 17 black and 17 white checkers or counters on a 5 × 7 grid in the way shown here. You can use a checkerboard, but you must keep within the boundaries of the 5 × 7 rectangle. The aim is to transpose the black and white checkers. A checker may move directly into a vacant square or jump into one over a single intervening checker of opposite color. Here is a hint: if you can transpose the checkers in the middle row (15 moves), you can go on to do the same in the other rows.

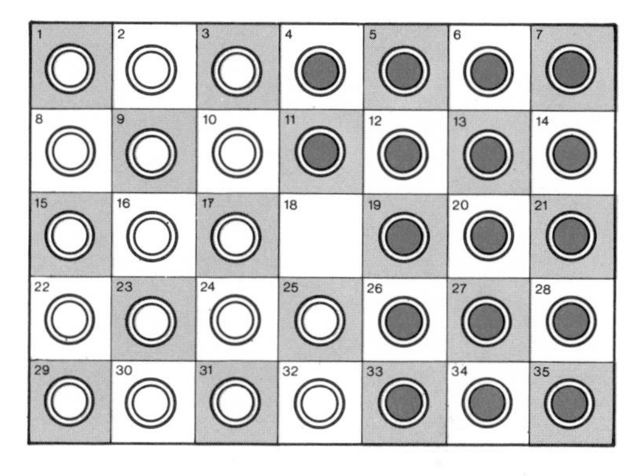

Get the white checkers to the right and the black checkers to the left in the fewest possible moves.

The Juggernaut

Draw a row of ten squares and lay four black and four white checkers in the eight left-hand squares. There should be a white checker at the far left position, and the colors should alternate along the row, as in the picture below. The puzzle is to move pairs of adjacent checkers, without reversing their order, until the white checkers occupy the four right-hand squares and the black checkers occupy the four squares next to those. The puzzle can be solved in as few as four moves of pairs.

It is easy to make a wooden form of this puzzle. Each checker is replaced by a pair of checkers mounted on an "axle" that slides in the slots of a wooden frame — the juggernaut of the title.

Materials

Birch wood, 12" × 2½" × ½"
Eight black and eight white checkers
Wooden dowel, 8" long, ¼" thick
Wood glue
Varnish or enamel paint (optional)

Tools

Fretsaw; drill with ¼" bit; sandpaper.

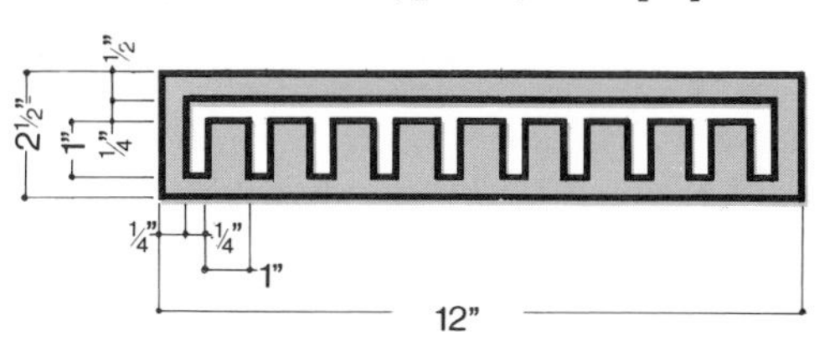

Use the dimensions shown here when you cut out the slot in the frame for your juggernaut puzzle.

The "wheels" of this puzzle are checkers mounted in pairs and free to slide along the slot.

How to Make the Puzzle

Draw the outline of the slot on the wood, following the guide diagram at the left. Drill a small hole through the wood in the area that is going to be removed so that you can pass the fretsaw blade through it. Saw out the slot, and sandpaper its edges. Varnish or paint the frame as well as the checkers if you wish. Cut the dowel into eight 1" sections. Drill a hole ¼" wide and ¼" deep in the center of each of the checkers. Take four of the black checkers and four of the white ones, and glue one end of a piece of dowel into each. When the glue has set firmly, mount each of these checkers with its attached dowel in the frame and glue a like-colored checker to the free end of the dowel. You can now attempt the puzzle as described.

(See solution page 200)

Sliding Block Puzzles

In the 1870s America's greatest puzzle expert, Sam Loyd, "drove the entire world crazy" (as he himself put it) with his newly invented 14-15 Puzzle. It consisted of 15 numbered square blocks that could freely slide in a wooden box that was large enough to accommodate 16 square blocks in a 4 × 4 array. Each block could be slid in turn into the vacancy that would have been occupied by a sixteenth block so that the vacancy would move around the box. A picture of a similar puzzle appears on page 92, where the blocks have been arranged to form a magic square — an array of numbers that add up to the same total in every row, column, and diagonal. Since the invention of the 14-15 Puzzle, countless other sliding block puzzles have appeared on the market. Most of them, like those on these pages, have rectangular rather than square sliding blocks. The aim of all these puzzles is to slide the blocks into a specific arrangement in the smallest number of moves.

It is not surprising that the entire world was "driven crazy" by Loyd's puzzle. The problem that his puzzle posed was impossible to solve. The puzzle was sold with the vacant space at bottom right, and the blocks were numbered in order from left to right beginning at the top, except that blocks 14 and 15 were transposed. The puzzle was to rearrange the blocks into the correct order with the vacancy in the same place. A prize of $1,000 for the feat was offered, but it was never claimed. Success was impossible. It would have been equivalent to a single direct exchange of blocks 14 and 15. But rearrangement of the blocks by sliding them can give rise only to an *even* number of exchanges among the blocks. There are over 600 billion arrangements of the blocks that can be made from the original arrangement. There are an equal number of arrangements that cannot be made — including the one that Loyd asked the puzzler to make. On the other hand, the blocks can be arranged in order if the vacancy ends up in the top left-hand corner. Although it is possible to discover in advance whether or not a particular arrangement can be attained, skill is still needed to solve a puzzle with the 14-15 toy in the smallest number of moves. With the rectangular block puzzles shown here, there is no way of proving that a particular arrangement is possible except by actually playing with the puzzle until it is solved.

The Flying Puzzle

The Flying Puzzle, below left, appeared in 1928 and was inspired by Charles Lindbergh's great transatlantic flight of the previous year. The puzzle player could imagine himself facing the dangers of rain, hail, and darkness without having to leave the comfort of his

The armchair aviator could brave the rigors of transatlantic flight with this puzzle. The plane must be brought to the bottom right-hand corner.

Adversity has crowded around the itinerant son since he left home, and now he longs to return to the embrace of Ma, in the top right-hand corner.

(See solution page 200)

own chair. The block representing the airplane began at the top left-hand corner (New York) and was to be moved to the bottom right-hand corner (Paris). Since the vacant space was half as large as the block representing the plane, the plane could be advanced only by half its own width or height at a time. The puzzle can be solved in 31 moves. (A simultaneous move by two pieces counts as a single move; as do two consecutive moves by one piece.)

Ma's Puzzle

Ma's Puzzle was marketed in 1927. It is noteworthy in having two L-shaped pieces and a vacant space that can be divided into two parts, as it is in the picture. As you might guess, Ma and My Boy have to be brought together despite all the tribulations shown. The two blocks must be united to form a rectangle (either horizontal or vertical) in the top right-hand corner.

The George Washington Puzzle

The last of the sliding block puzzles shown below is an effusive tribute to George Washington. It shows the great man's progress through life amid a host of virtues. The puzzler was required to move the block representing Washington to each corner in the following sequence: top right, bottom right, bottom left, top left. Each corner represented some important period in Washington's life, such as the winter spent at Valley Forge or the presidency. The makers took an optimistic view of the value of the puzzle. The description inside the lid of its box stated: "If you can retrace Washington's career, you may be president." They made it harder to become president by not enclosing a solution.

In giving the solution to a puzzle, it is only necessary to specify the piece or pieces moved at each step. The numbering of the pieces is shown in the construction guide diagrams.

Materials
Any attractive wood, 1/4" thick
Cardboard
Adhesive tape

Tools
Fretsaw; utility knife; sandpaper; pencil; straightedge.

How to Make the Puzzle
Copy one of the plans below onto paper, making each grid square 1" on a side. (If you wish to make the 14-15 Puzzle, shown on page 92, draw a 5 × 5 grid of squares; one square remains vacant.) Paste the plan onto the wood and saw along the heavy lines. Round off the corners and sandpaper the edges. Number each piece and, if you wish, stick on pictures. Cut out a rectangle of thick cardboard with sides 1/2" longer than the sides of the grid. Cut out a 1/4" × 1/4" square at each corner, fold up the sides, and tape the corners to form a tray 1/4" deep.

Follow in the footsteps of the virtuous George Washington by moving his representative block to each corner, in clockwise order from top right.

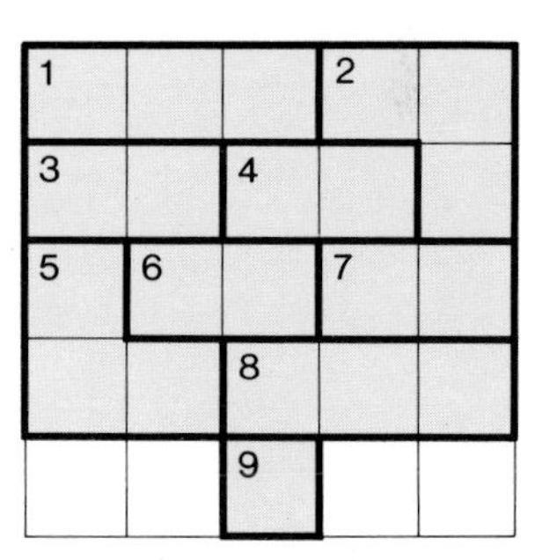

These are the plans of the three sliding block puzzles seen on the left. The rectangular shapes of the blocks complicate the task of moving a particular block to the required part of the puzzle in the fewest moves.

(See solution page 200)

Solutions to the Puzzles

For each of the solutions given on the following pages, the page number where the puzzle can be found is also indicated. Where a puzzle has been named in the previous chapters, the title is also given in the solution; for example, the horse and rider puzzle below. Other solutions have been given numbers that correspond to the puzzle numbers within a particular section, as in the case of matchstick puzzles. If specific figures are shown, the order of the solutions is the same as the order in which the problems appear on the puzzle pages. Only their size is altered.

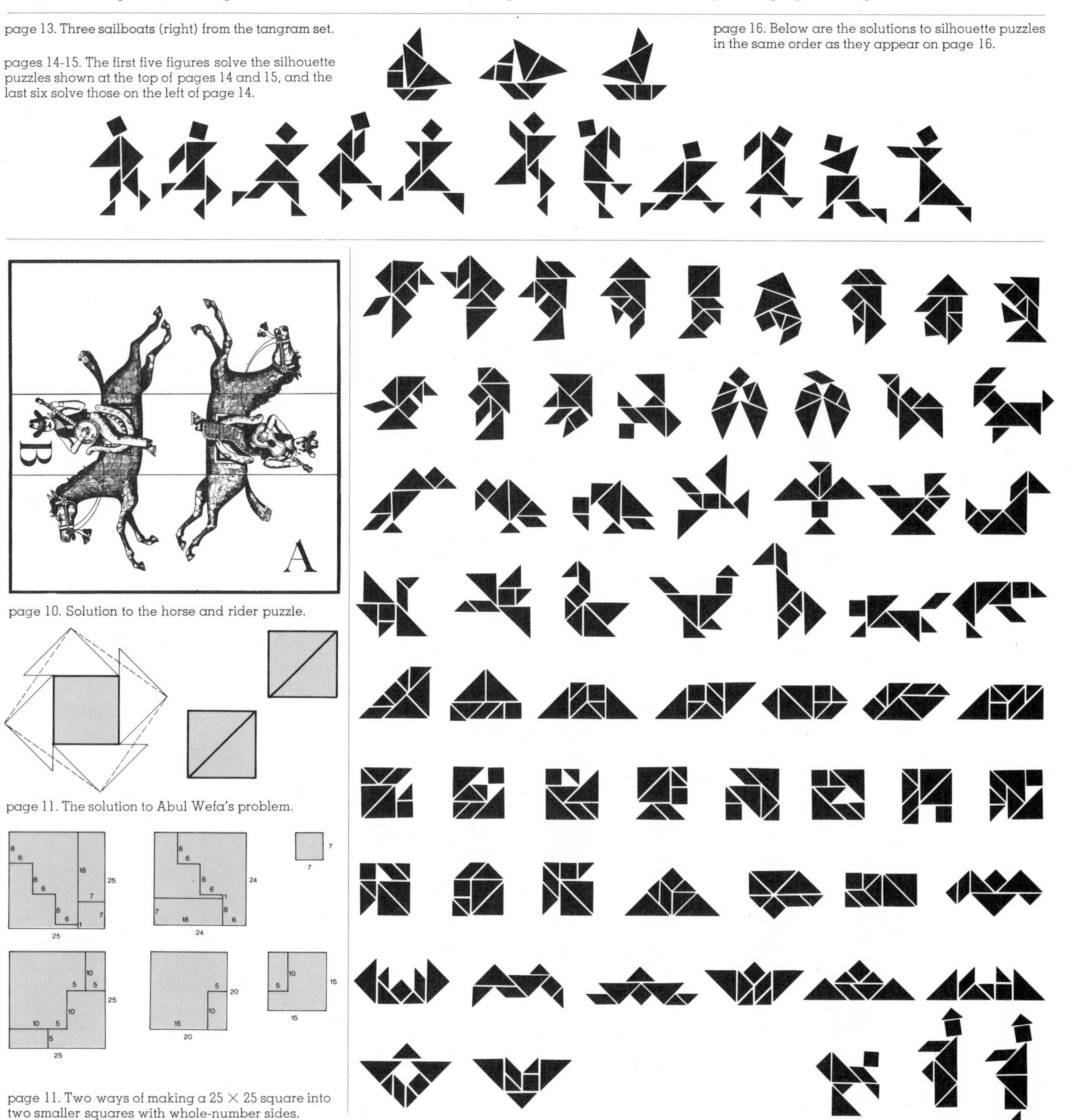

page 13. Three sailboats (right) from the tangram set.

pages 14-15. The first five figures solve the silhouette puzzles shown at the top of pages 14 and 15, and the last six solve those on the left of page 14.

page 16. Below are the solutions to silhouette puzzles in the same order as they appear on page 16.

page 10. Solution to the horse and rider puzzle.

page 11. The solution to Abul Wefa's problem.

page 11. Two ways of making a 25 × 25 square into two smaller squares with whole-number sides.

page 17. Abstract and creeping forms are made with the pieces of the Circular Tangram set above.

pages 18-19. Arrange the pieces of the Pythagoras puzzle as at right, to make the outlined shapes.

pages 21, 22, 23. The solutions given below are, from left to right, for the Circle puzzle, the Broken Heart and the Magic Egg dissection puzzles.

pages 24-26. The cross from page 24 is dissected in the Cross Breaker puzzle. Then the shapes shown on pages 25 and 26 can be made as below. Start by re-forming the original cross.

page 27. The remaining figures, at right, show how silhouettes can be made with the Nine puzzle.

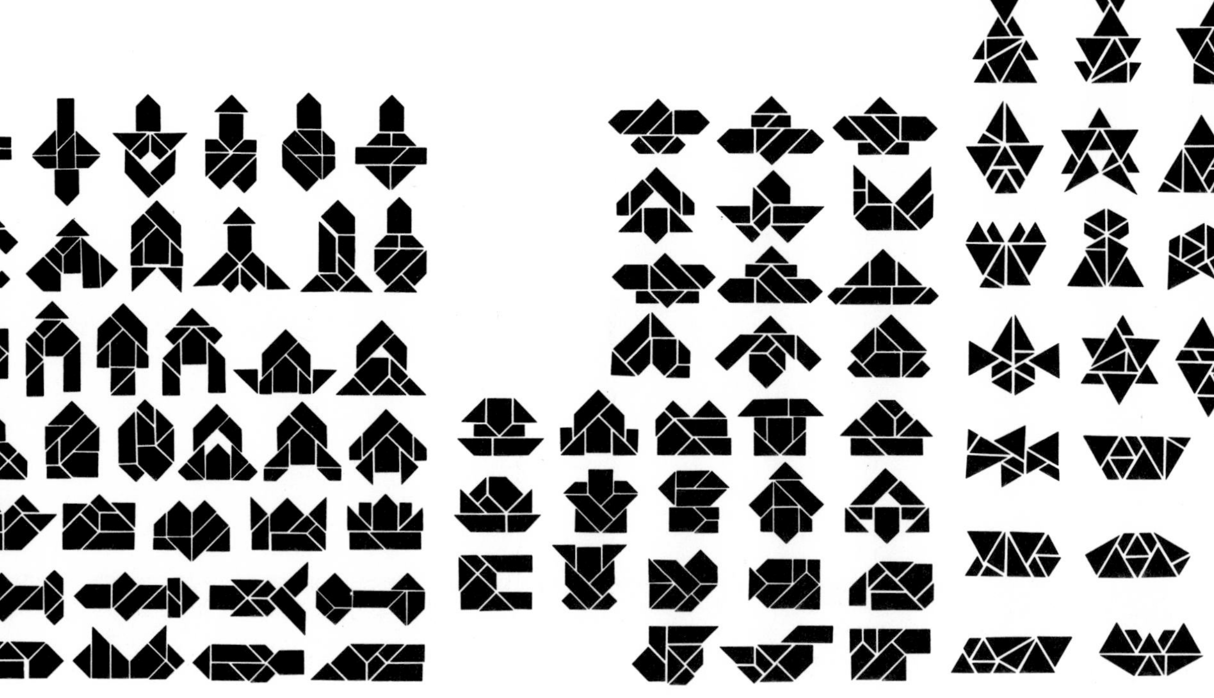

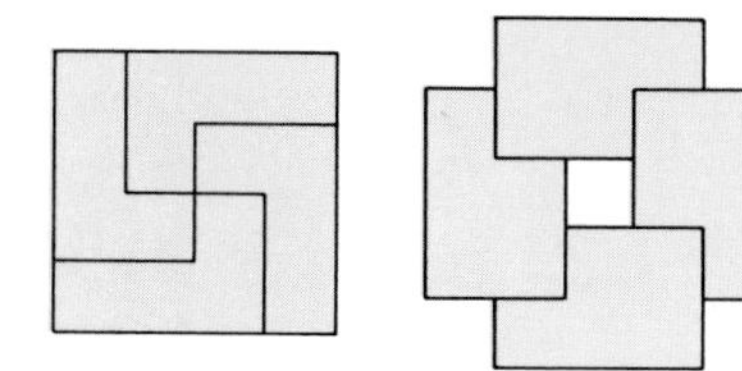

page 28. Two solutions to the Patchwork Quilt puzzle.

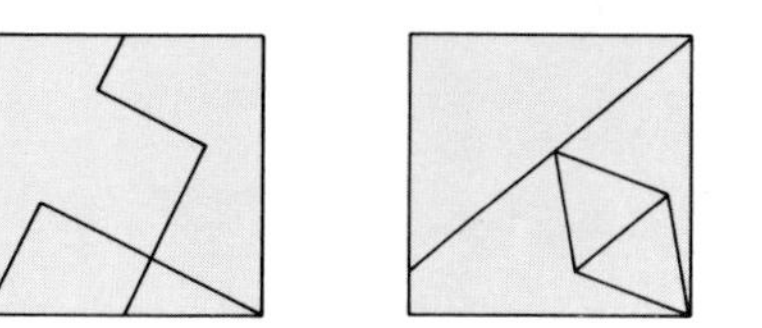

page 29. The pieces of a Greek cross, and a Star of David, can both be arranged to make a square.

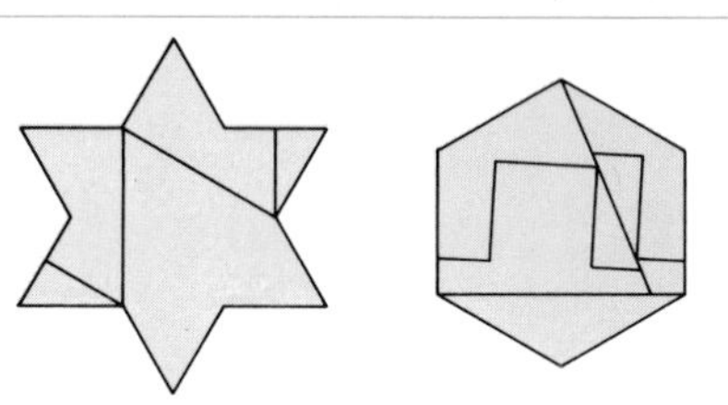

page 30. The left figure was made from parts of a triangle and the hexagon from a Greek cross.

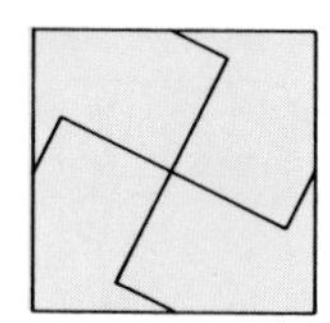

page 29. How to change a Greek cross into a square.

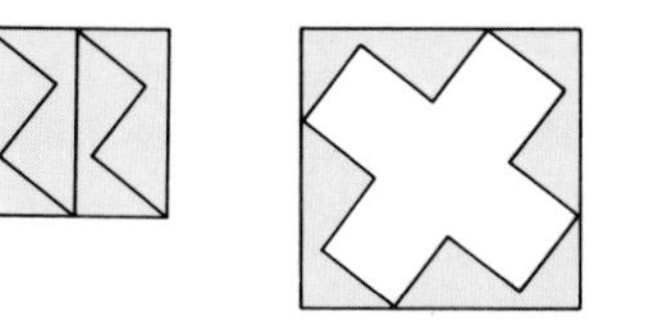

page 29. Two squares from a hollow Greek cross.

page 31. One Latin cross makes a triangle (left), another a hexagon (right), while a square is re-formed to make a Latin cross.

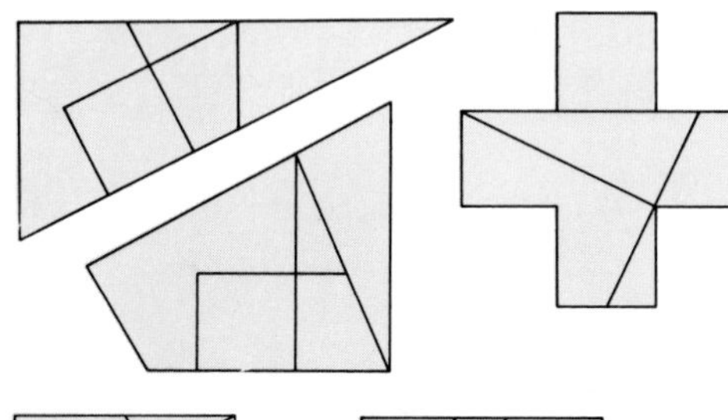

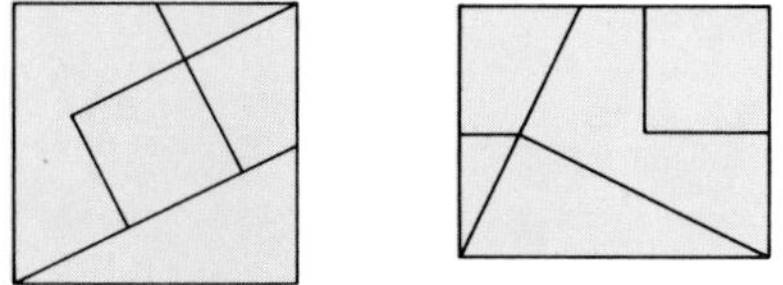

page 29. Five different shapes can be made with the pieces for the five problems, arranged as above.

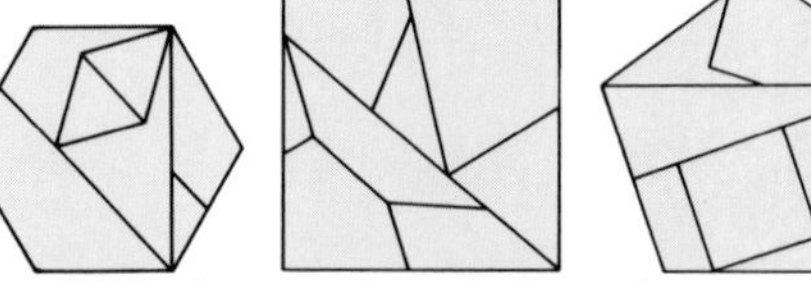

page 29. The hexagon is made from a hexagram.
page 30. The square started as a decagon.
page 30. A Greek cross changes into a pentagon.

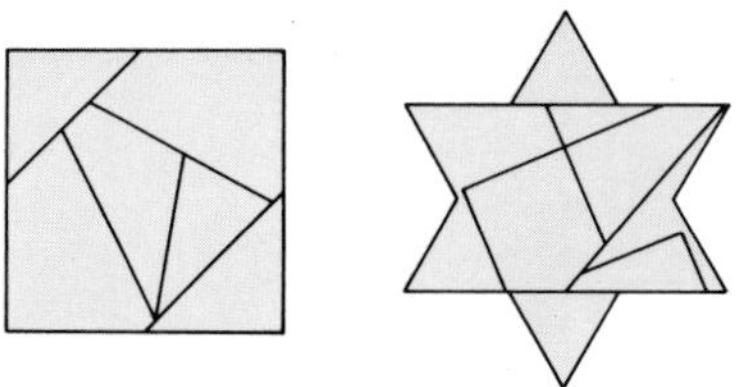

page 30. Left, a pentagon changed into a square; right, a Greek cross into a hexagram.

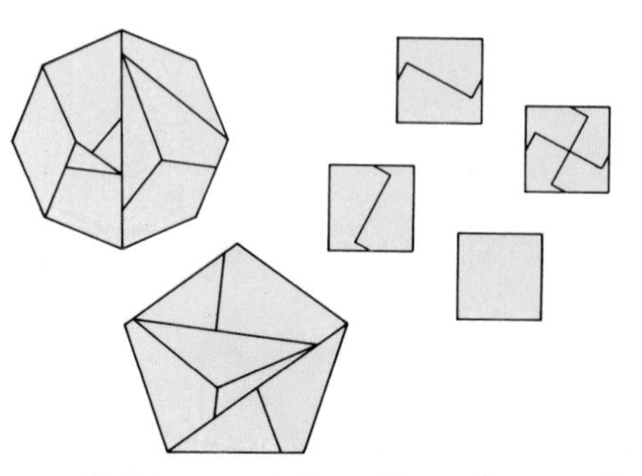

page 31. An octagon is formed from a hexagon, four squares are made from a strange starting shape, and a pentagon is created from a hexagon.

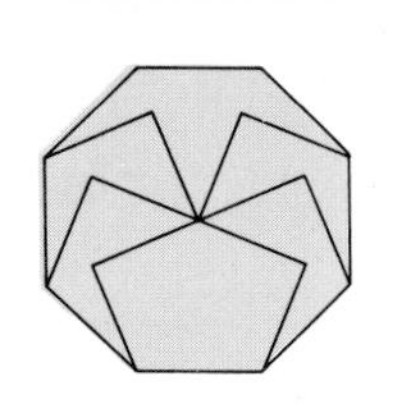

pages 32, 33. One of three stars made from the Supernova, and an octagon made from an octagram.

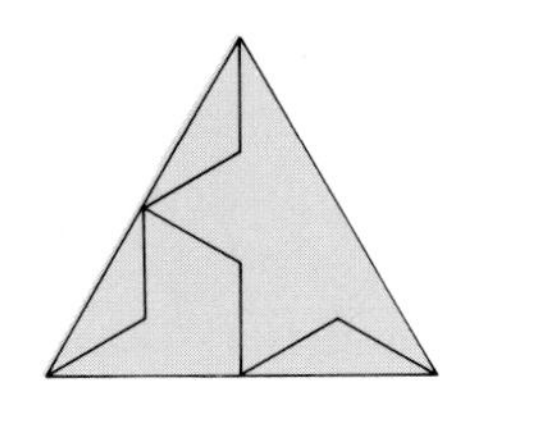

page 33. A hexagram makes a triangle and a dodecagram is re-formed to make a Latin cross.

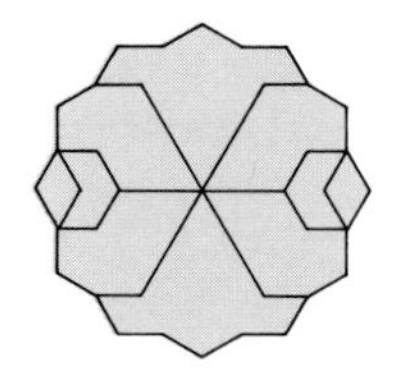

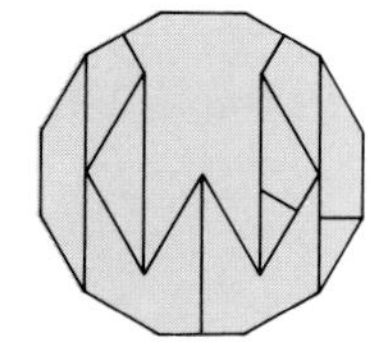

page 33. The left figure is created from a hexagram, and the right one from a dodecagram.

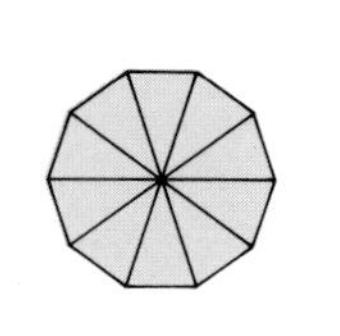

page 33. A decagram and a decagon are made.

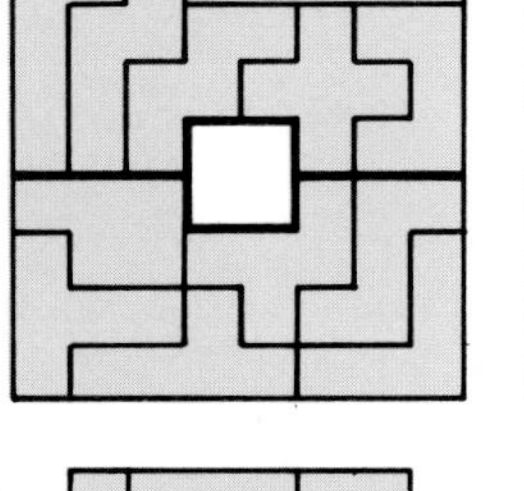

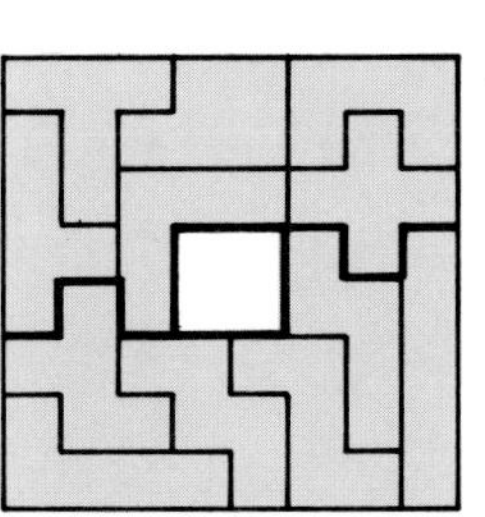

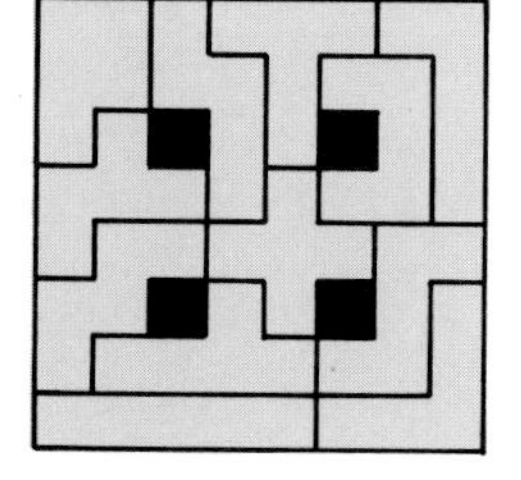

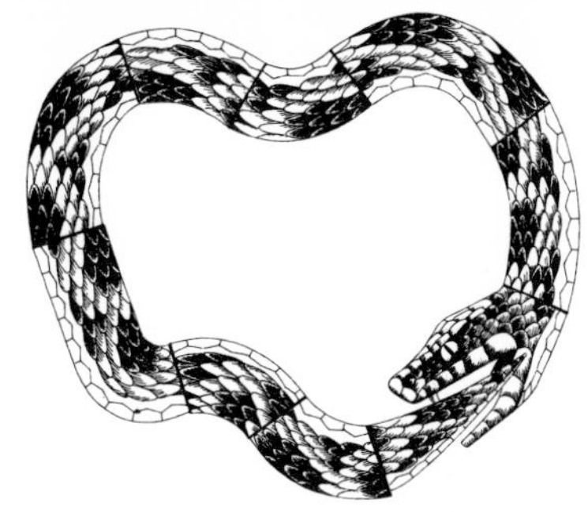

page 34. How the snake can bite its own tail.

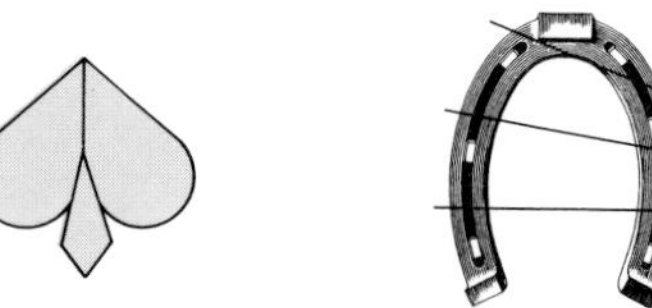

page 34. Cut the heart to make the ace of spades, and cut the horseshoe into seven pieces.

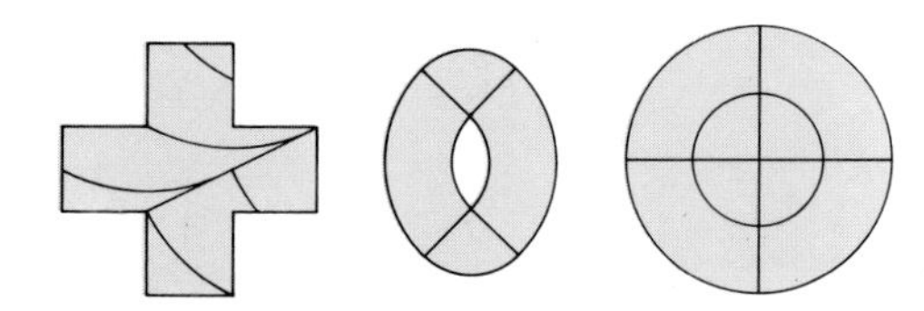

page 34. A cross is made from a crescent (left) and a table (right) from two stools, cut as above center.

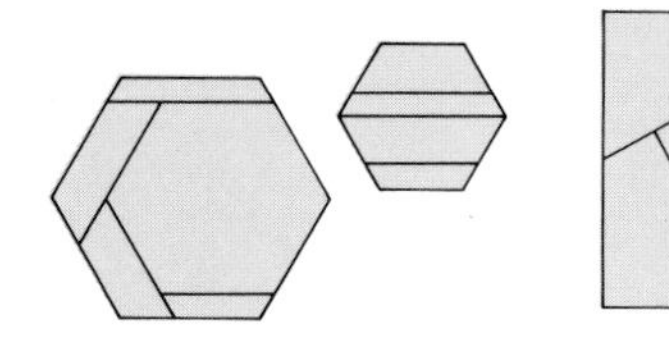

page 34. Hexagons are merged together, and a square piece of wood results from an oddment.

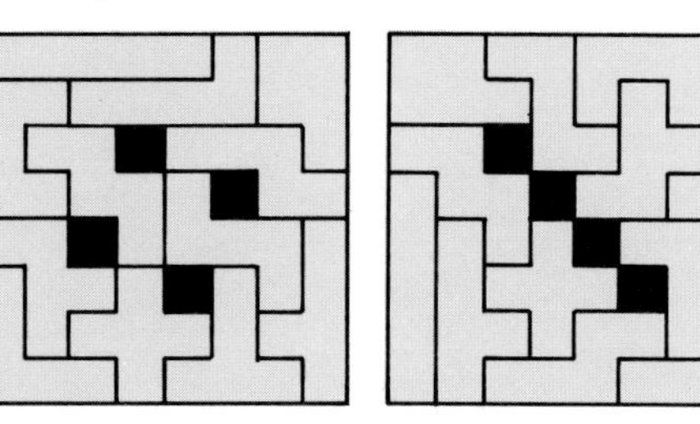

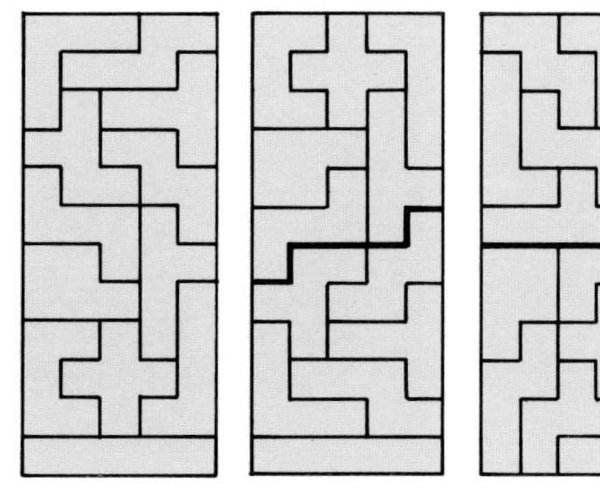

pages 41-42. Some of the possible solutions to the pentomino puzzles. There are 59 ways of making 8×8 squares with central 2×2 holes, 2170 ways of making squares with corners missing, 1010 ways of making 5×12 bars, and so on.

page 35. In the diagrams for the disappearance puzzle at the top of the page, the pieces around the edge of the square are not drawn to be exactly identical before and after reassembly, as they should be. This means that if you made the puzzle, reassembly would not give a perfect square. In the second diagram below this, the diagonal is in reality a long diamond-shaped gap of area one unit. The diagram on its right conceals the fact that the pieces would actually overlap, accounting for the apparently missing area of one unit.

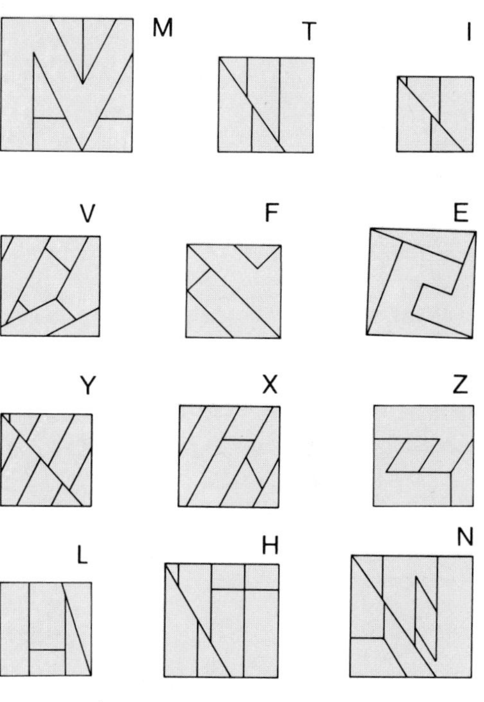

pages 36-37. Letters are dissected and then rearranged to form squares, as above. The letter over each square refers to the original letter that was cut.

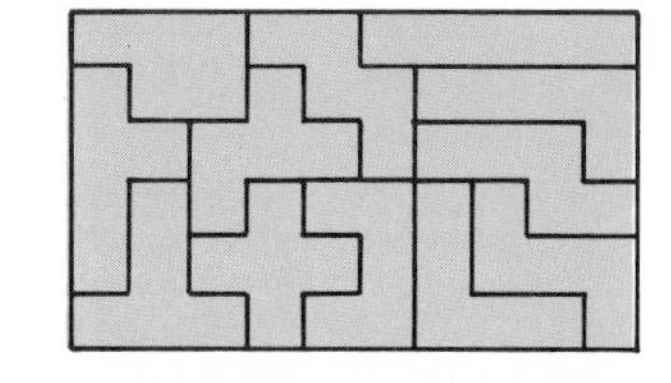

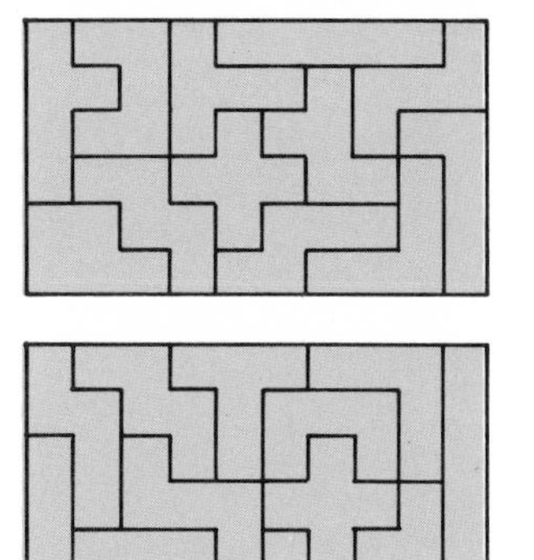

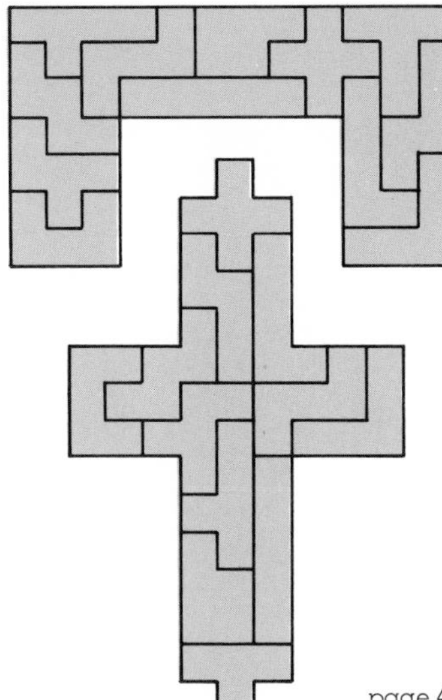

page 42. There are only two possible solutions to the bar (left) but 2339 blocks, 6 × 10 units, can be made. The number of cross and bridge solutions is not known. Heavy lines bisect the last figures.

page 43. Some of the possible arrangements of nine pentominoes to make each of the pentomino letters in turn. In these triplication problems the letter being modeled, and two other pentominoes, are omitted from the final arrangement. Solutions to V and X are given on page 43.

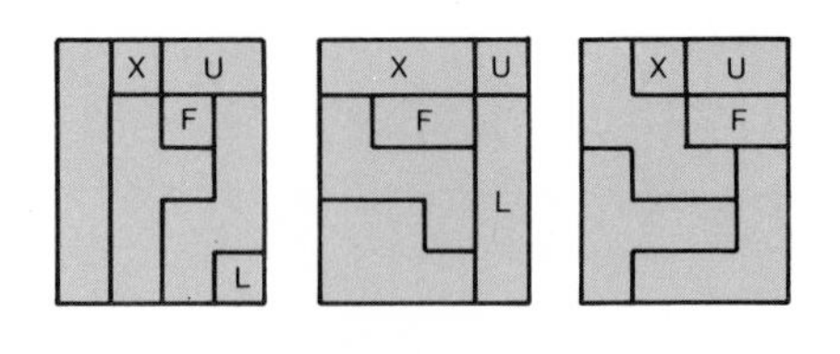

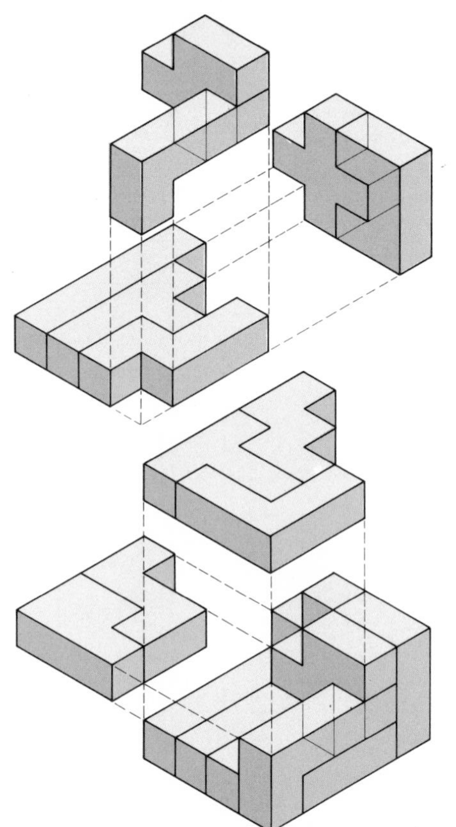

page 44. The top three figures above are, from left to right, the bottom, middle, and top layers of the solid 3 × 4 × 5 block. Where a piece is vertical in this arrangement, and cannot be recognized by its shape alone, the letter it represents is marked on it. The exploded diagram shows how the pieces fit together. This is just one of the 3940 possible ways to make this block (see page 187).

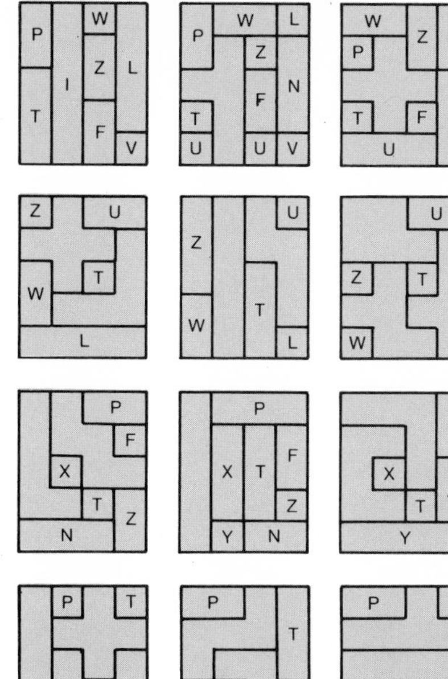

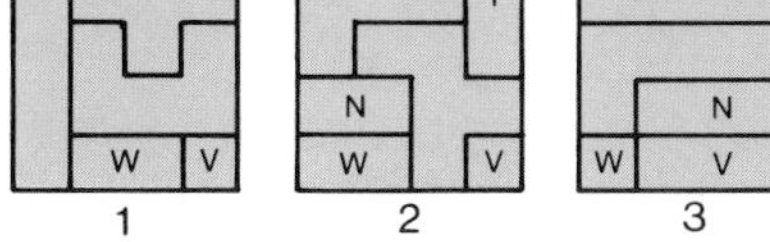

page 45. The layers of solid 3 × 4 × 5 pentomino figures, with letters indicating the pieces that cannot be clearly seen. (See opposite page, bottom right.) Of particular interest is the top group, where the L, N, and V pentominoes combine to make a 1 × 3 × 5 solid that is added to the 3 × 3 × 5 solid formed by the other nine pieces.

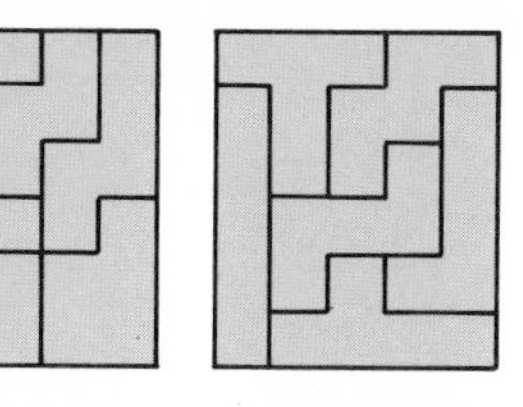

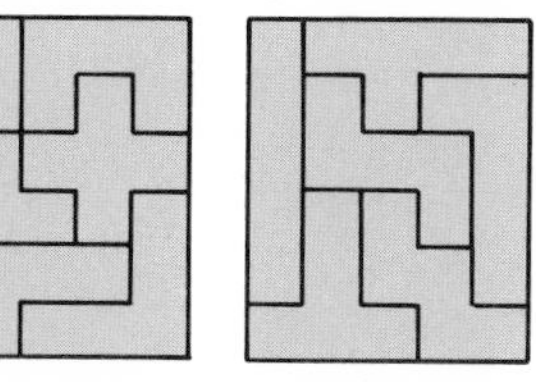

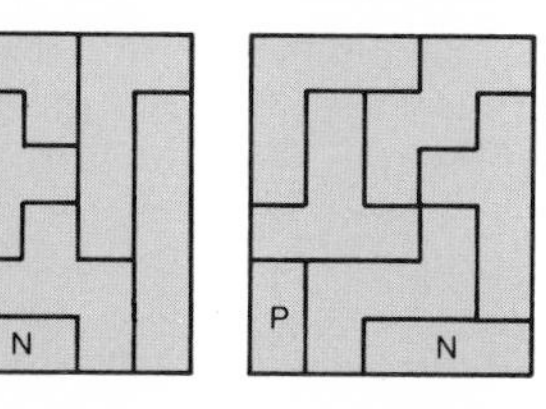

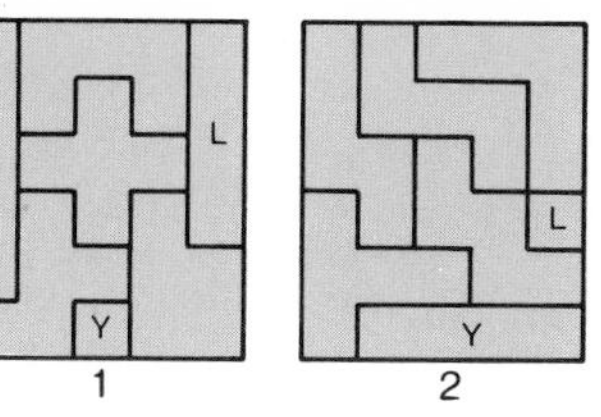

page 45. Four of the 264 ways of building the 2 × 5 × 6 block.

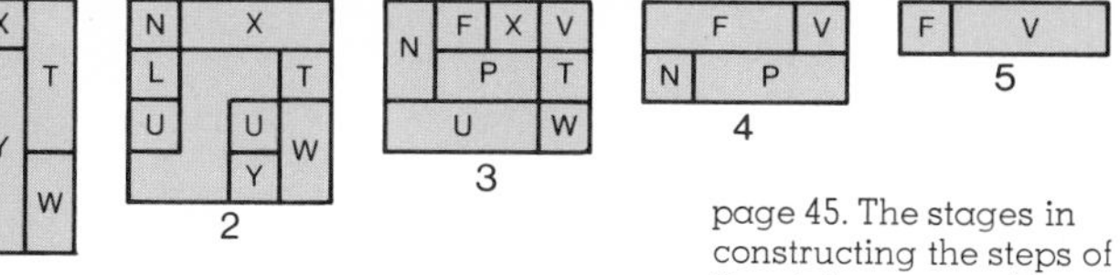

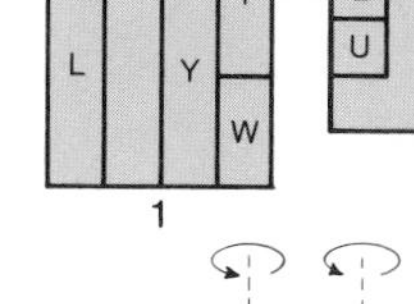

page 45. The stages in constructing the steps of the staircase puzzle.

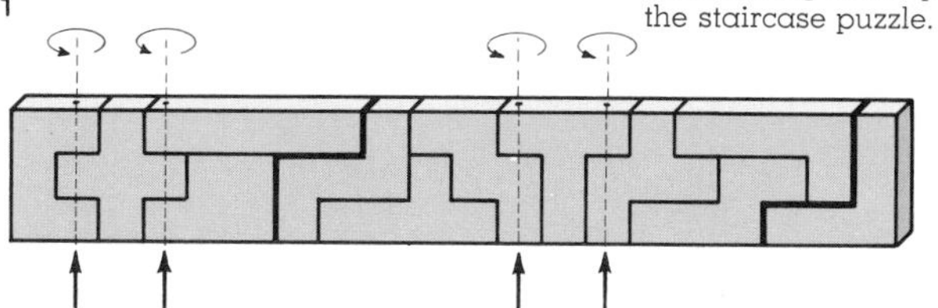

page 45. Build the bar above, stand it on one edge, then fold the puzzle at the heavy arrows, in the directions shown, to make an enclosure.

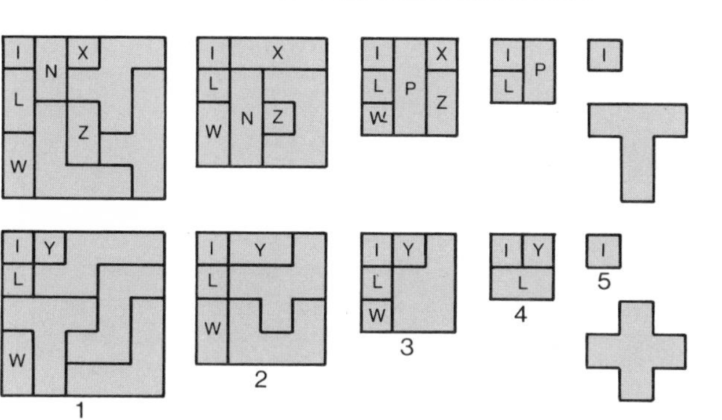

page 45. Two ways to make the pyramid from 11 pentominoes. Pieces on the right are not used.

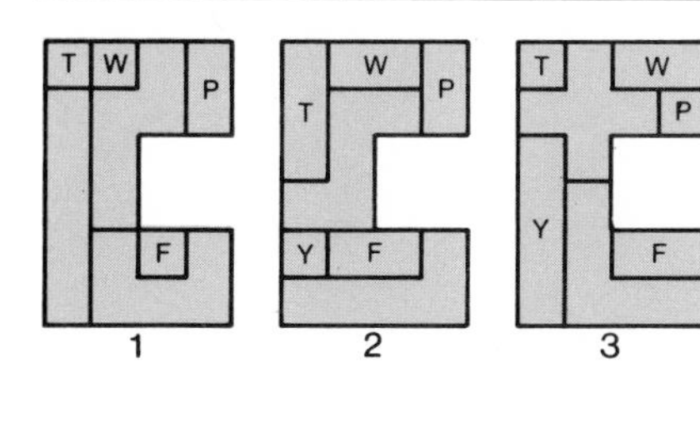

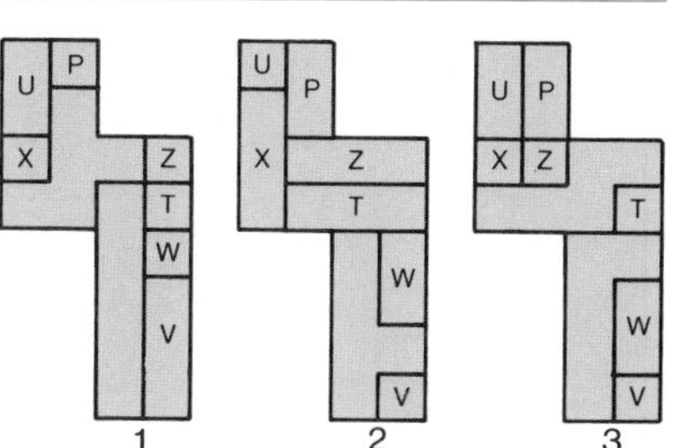

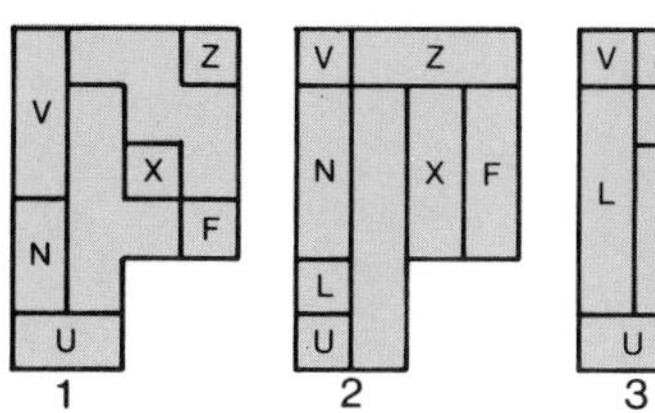

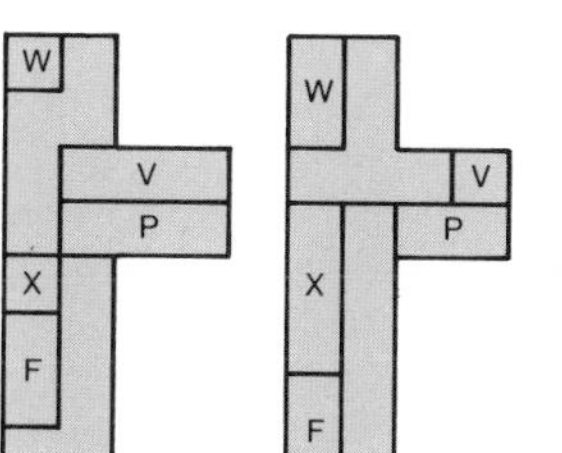

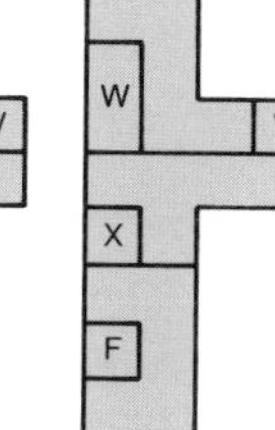

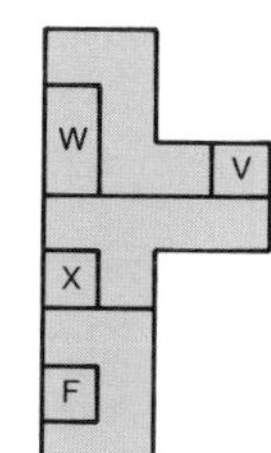

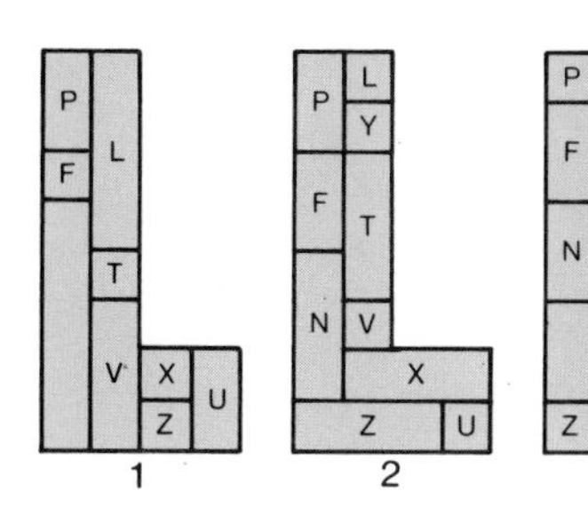

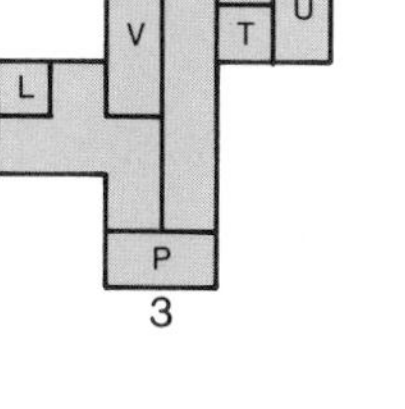

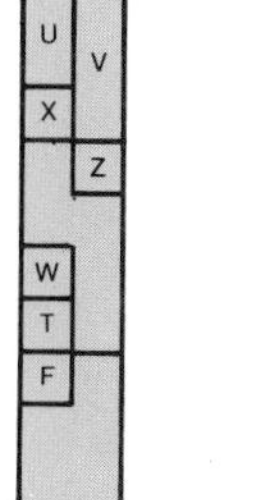

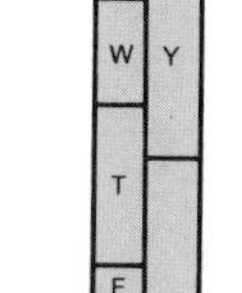

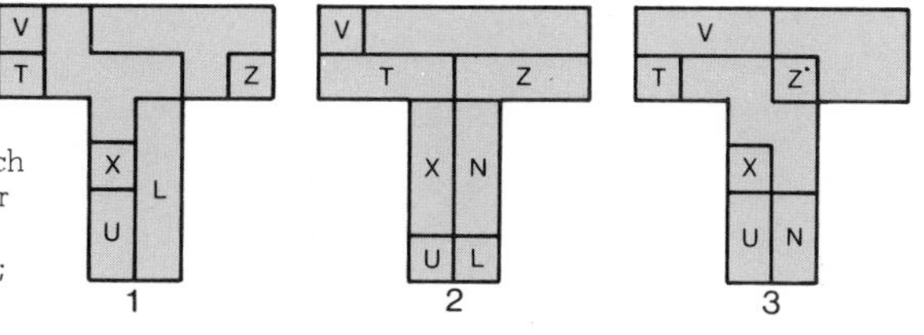

page 45. Three layers make up a solid model of each letter. If the pieces cannot be seen clearly, the letter they represent is marked. The numbers of possible solutions are: F one; I 12; L 99; N 51; P 1082; T three; U ten; V 21; Y seven; Z 24; W and X, none.

pages 47-48. Solutions to the Soma cube figures in the order given on page 47. In each case the exploded diagram shows the shape of each piece and its position in the completed model. Each piece is moved along the dotted lines to make the final figure. The last two figures (bottom right) show two possible ways of making the balancing Soma cube.

pages 50-54. Solutions to matchstick puzzles. Where two stages are necessary, the left diagram shows the position of the matches after the first move, with matches still to be moved indicated in blue. The final arrangement is then given at the right.

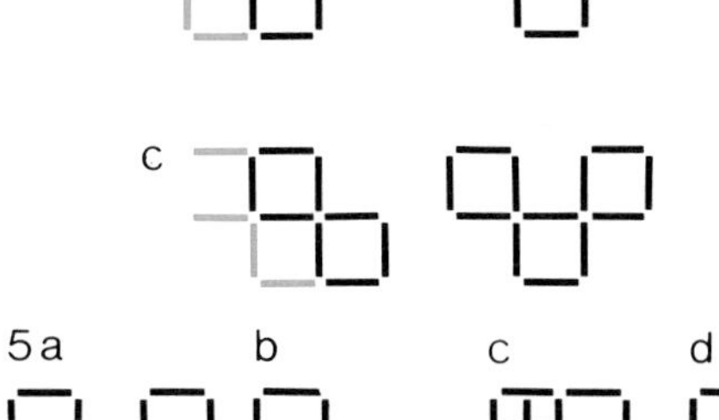

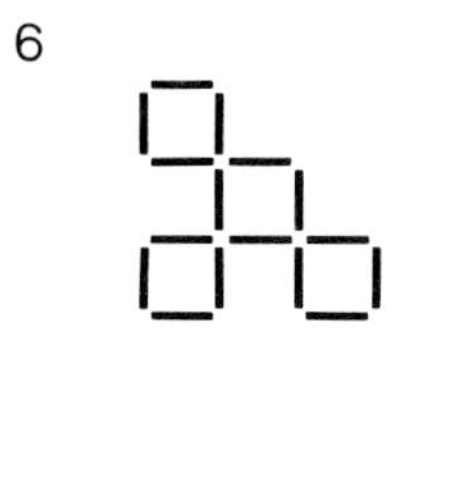

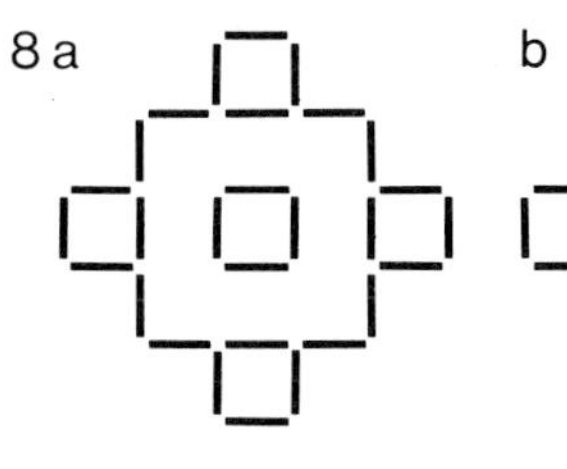

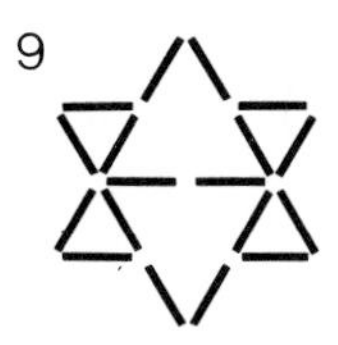

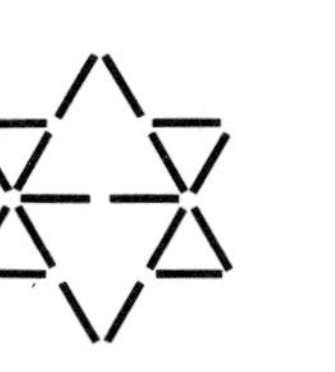

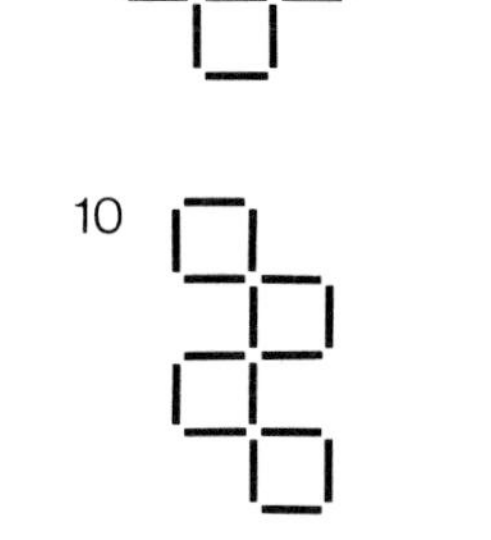

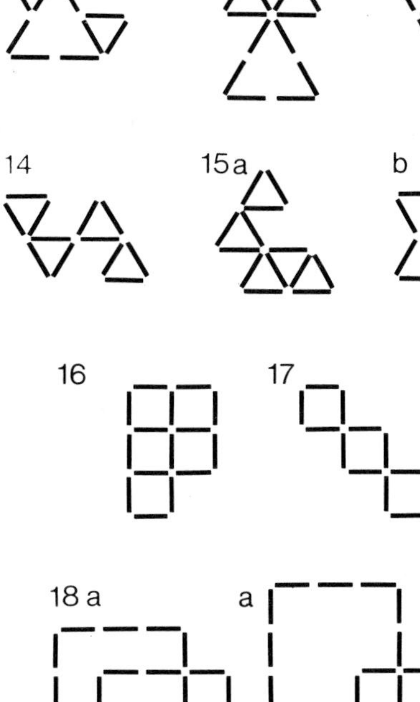

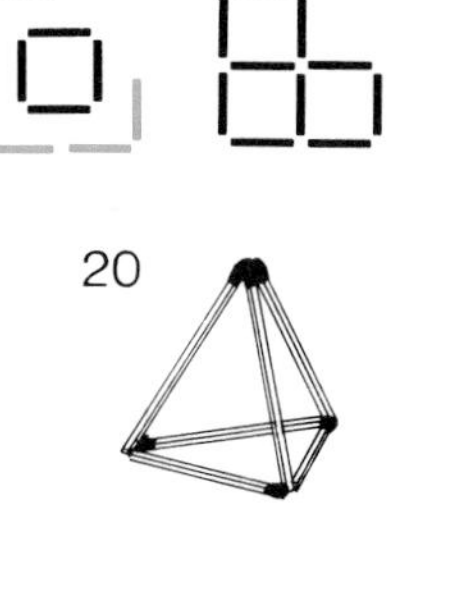

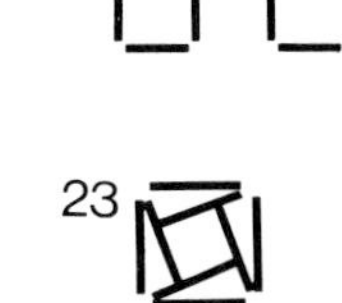

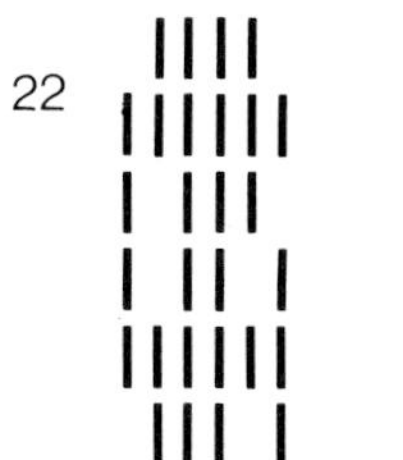

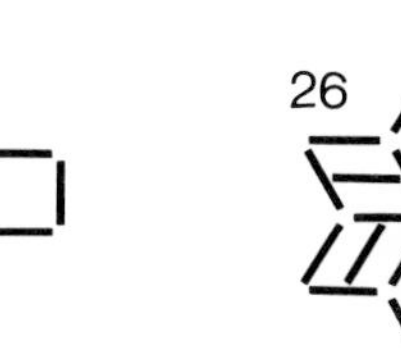

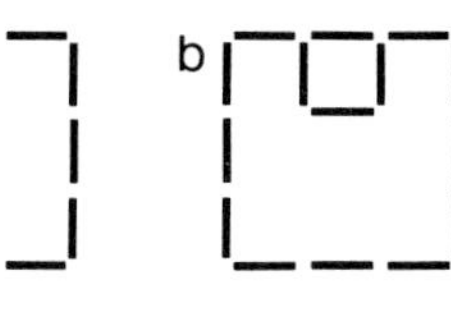

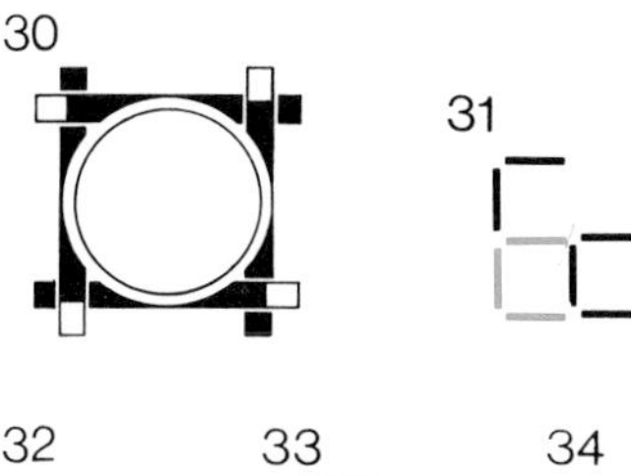

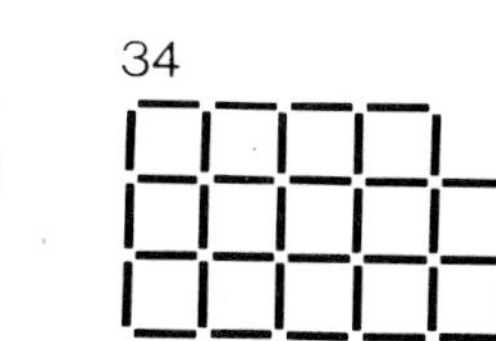

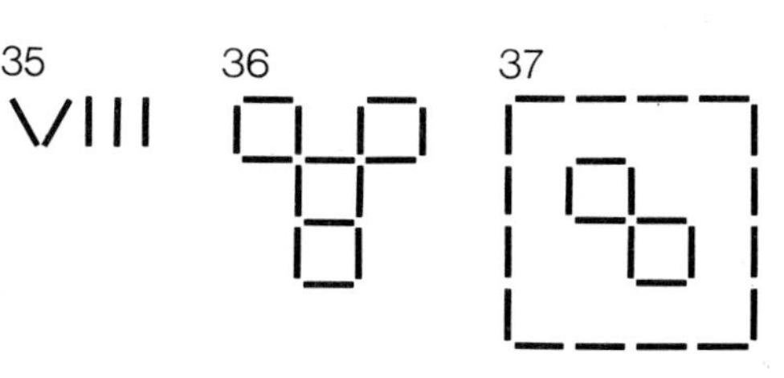

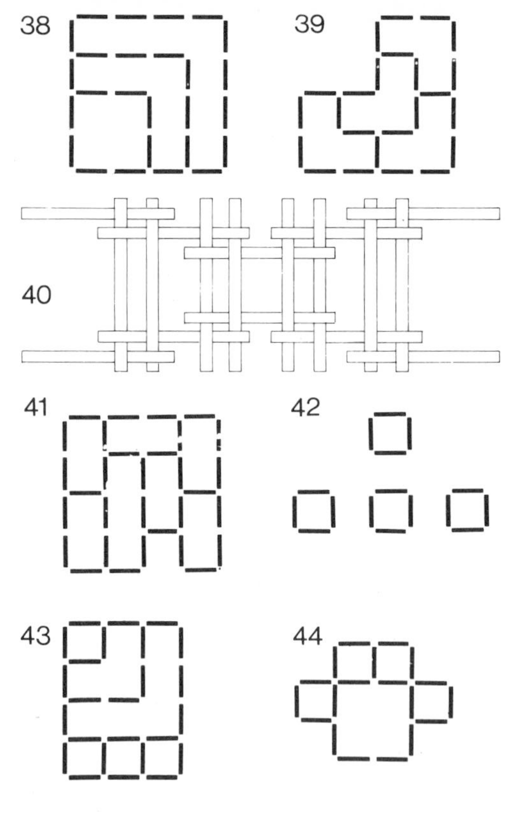

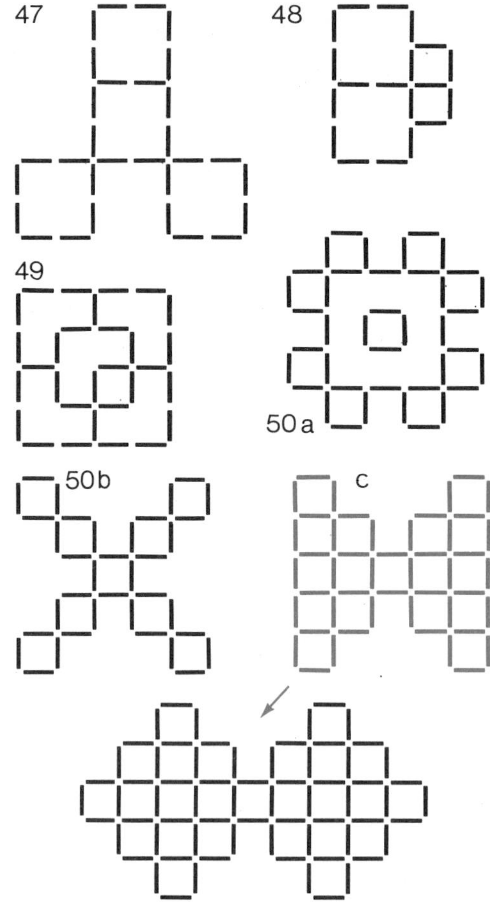

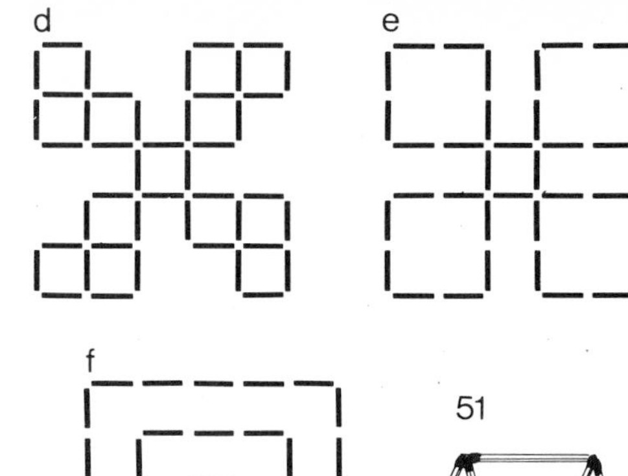

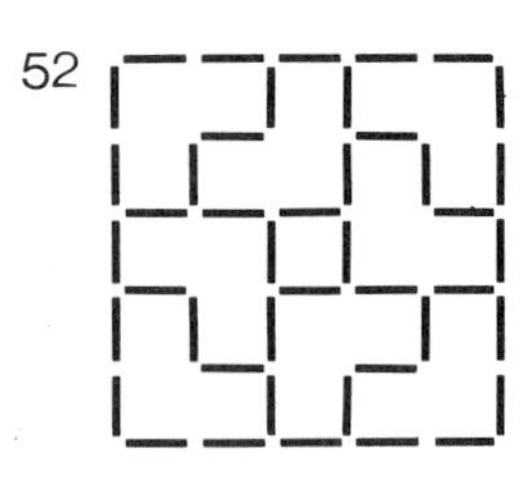

52

pages 54-56. Further solutions to matchstick puzzles. Where two stages are involved to make the final arrangement, matches in position after the first move are colored brown. Diagram 40 shows the position of overlapping matches on viewing the bridge (page 54) from above.

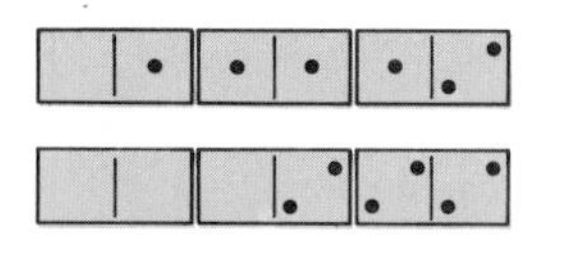

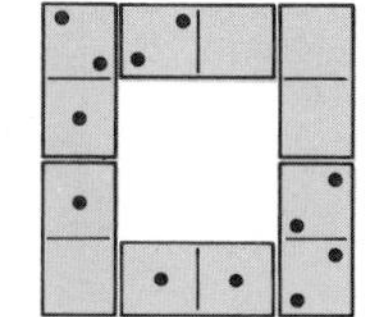

page 58. Double-2 sets of dominoes are arranged as above to make two equal lines and a six-tile square.

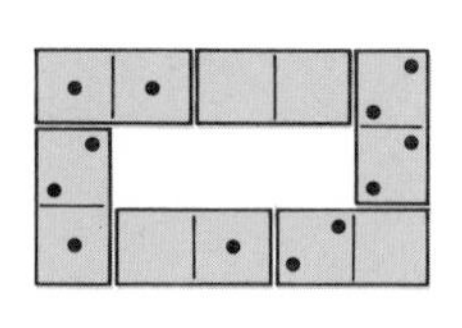

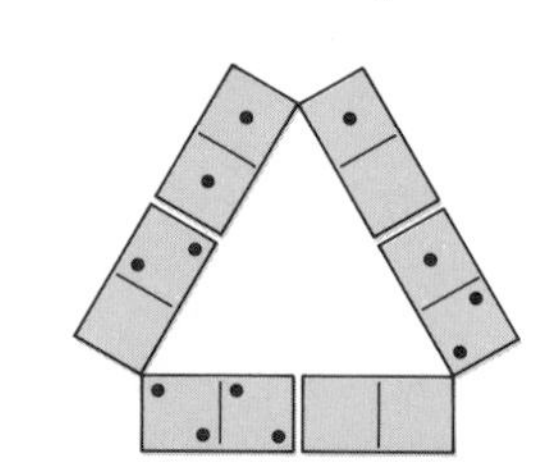

page 58. The same dominoes are used to make a double-2 rectangle and a triangle with equal sides.

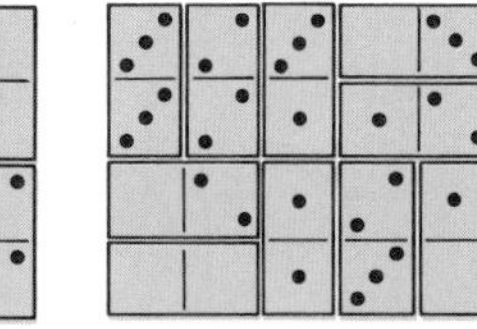

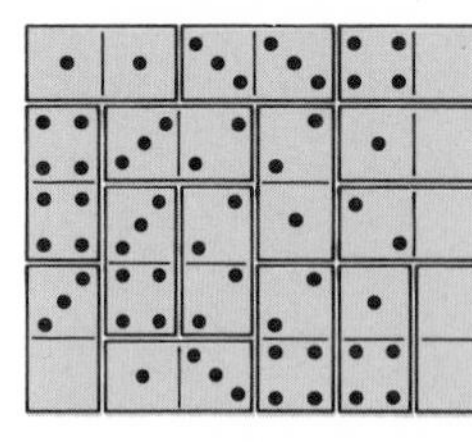

page 58. The magic rectangle (top left) has equal columns while the square in the rectangle (bottom) is wholly magic. Twin rectangles are at the right.

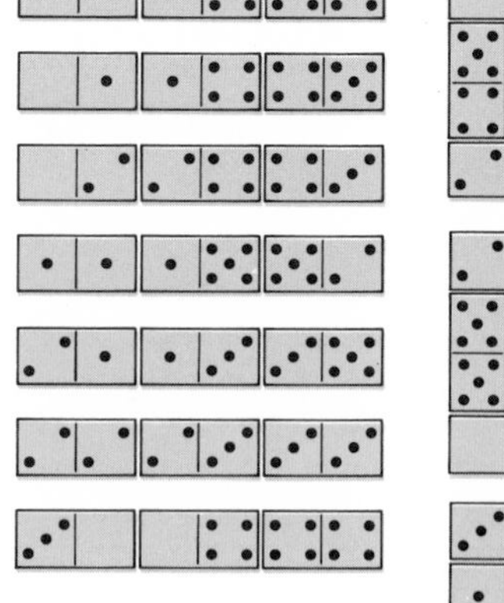

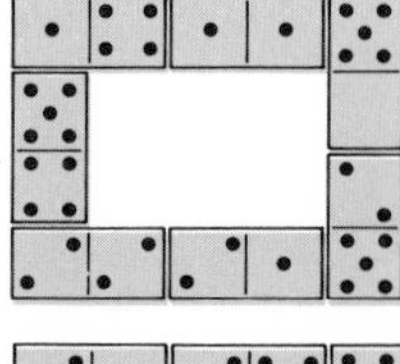

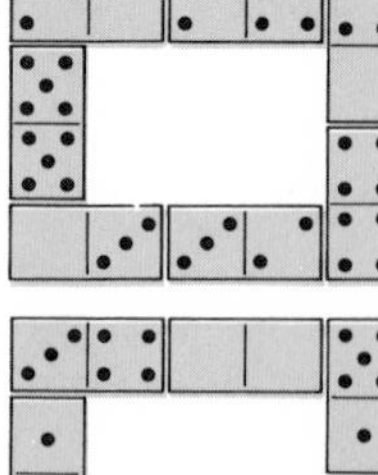

page 59. Three in a row and a trio of rectangles.

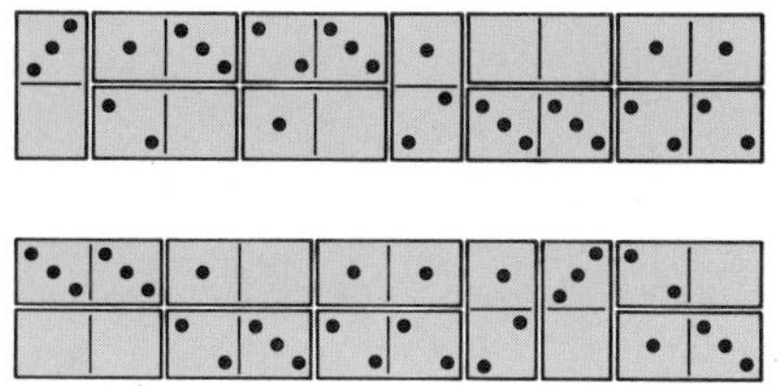

page 58. Two solutions to the magic row puzzle.

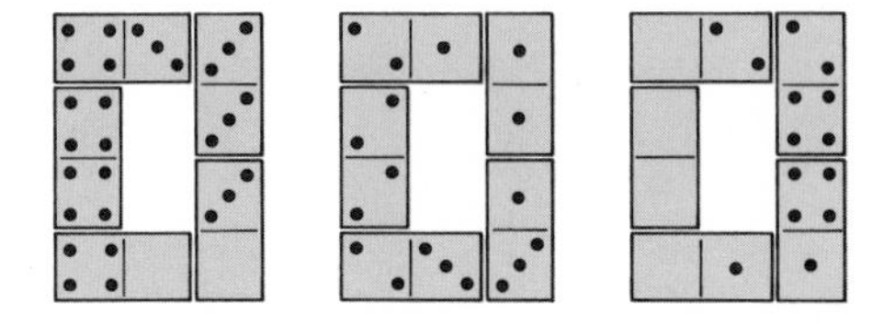

page 58: All the joins match in three of a kind.

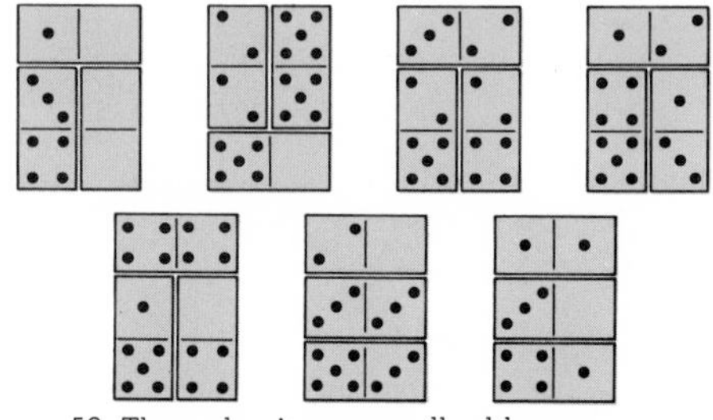

page 59. These domino sums all add up.

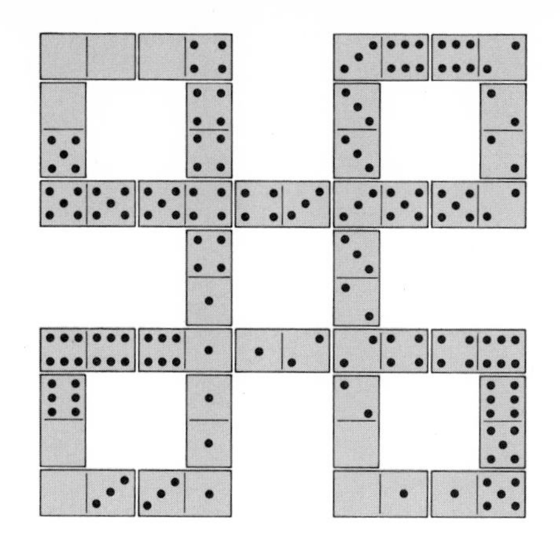

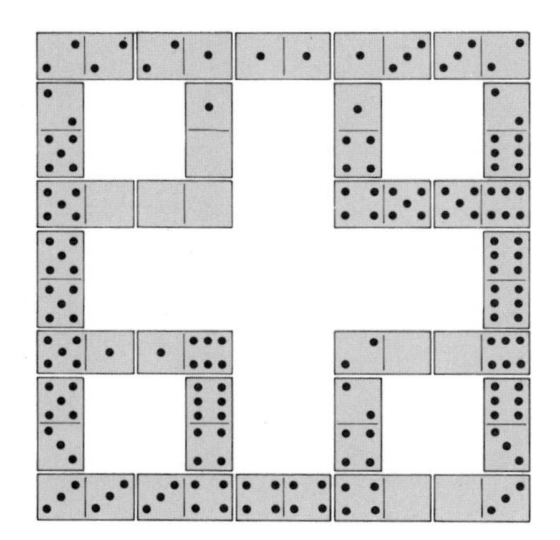

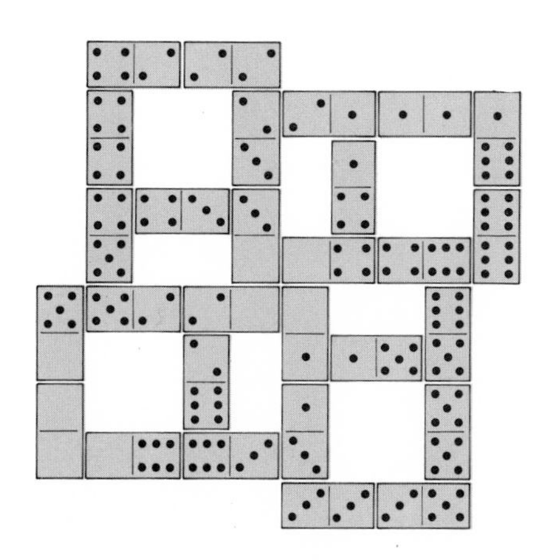

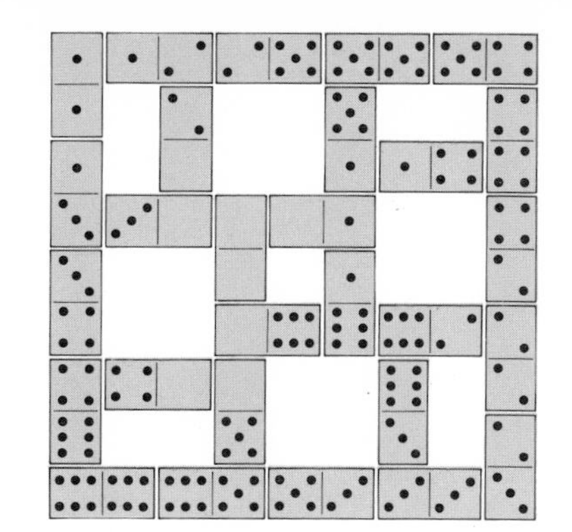

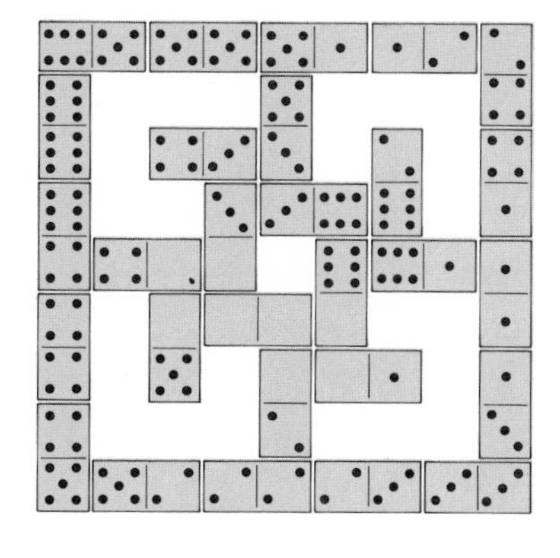

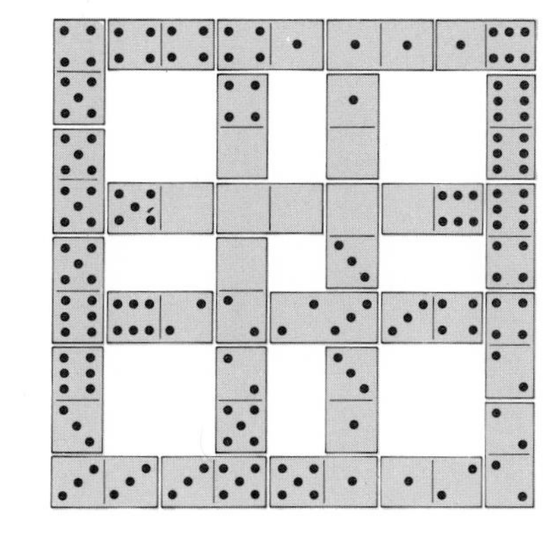

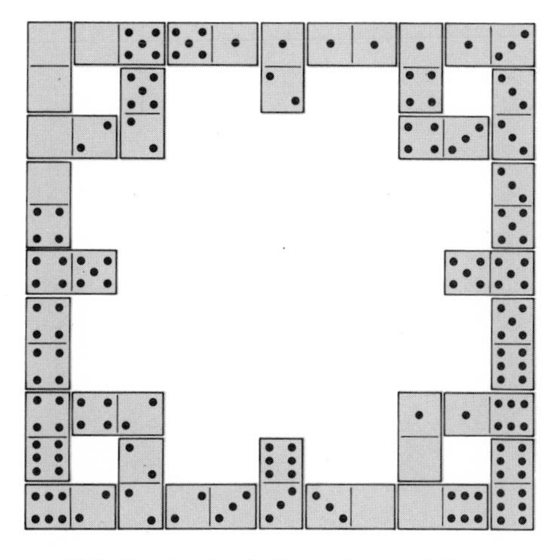

page 59. In the domino lattices above, all the touching half-tiles match — so you can begin to construct them at any point.

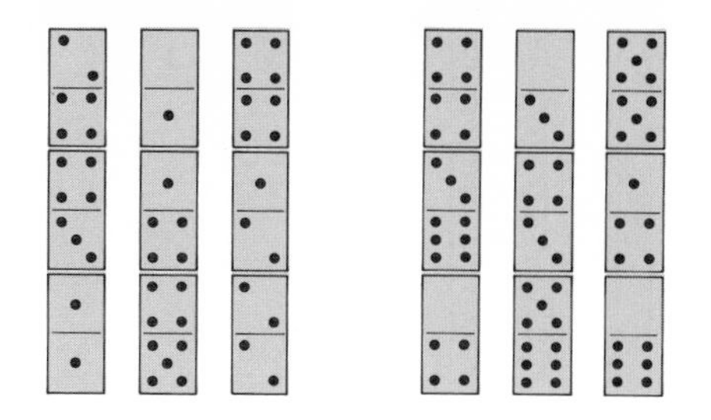

page 60. Two magic squares. The pips on the three tiles in each row, column, and diagonal add up to 15 on the left and 21 on the right.

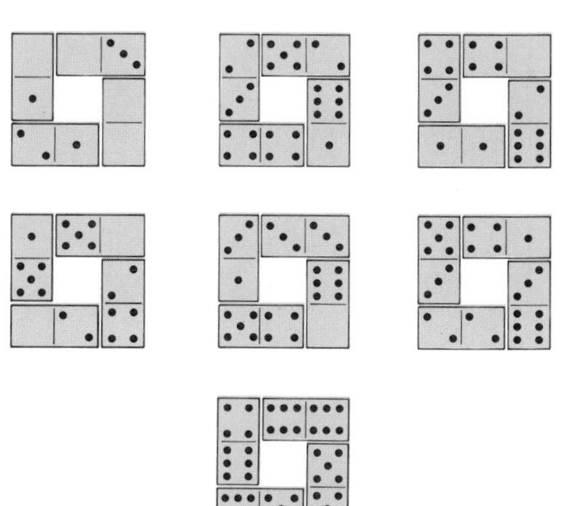

page 60. The sums of the pips on the sides of each window are equal — from 3 (top left) to 16 (bottom).

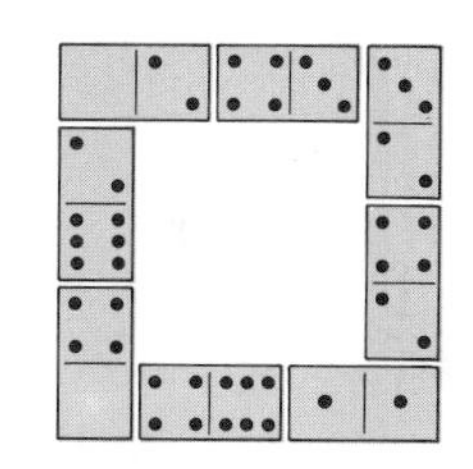

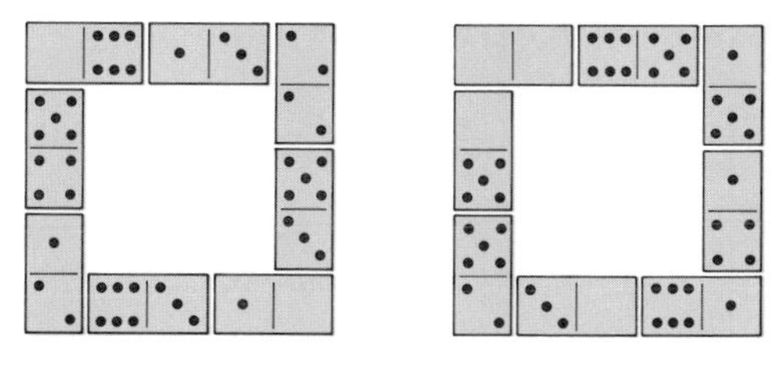

page 60. All 12 sides, each $2\frac{1}{2}$ tiles long, of the three frames above add up to 12.

page 60. A perfect Latin square. No number of pips on a half-tile is repeated in any row or column.

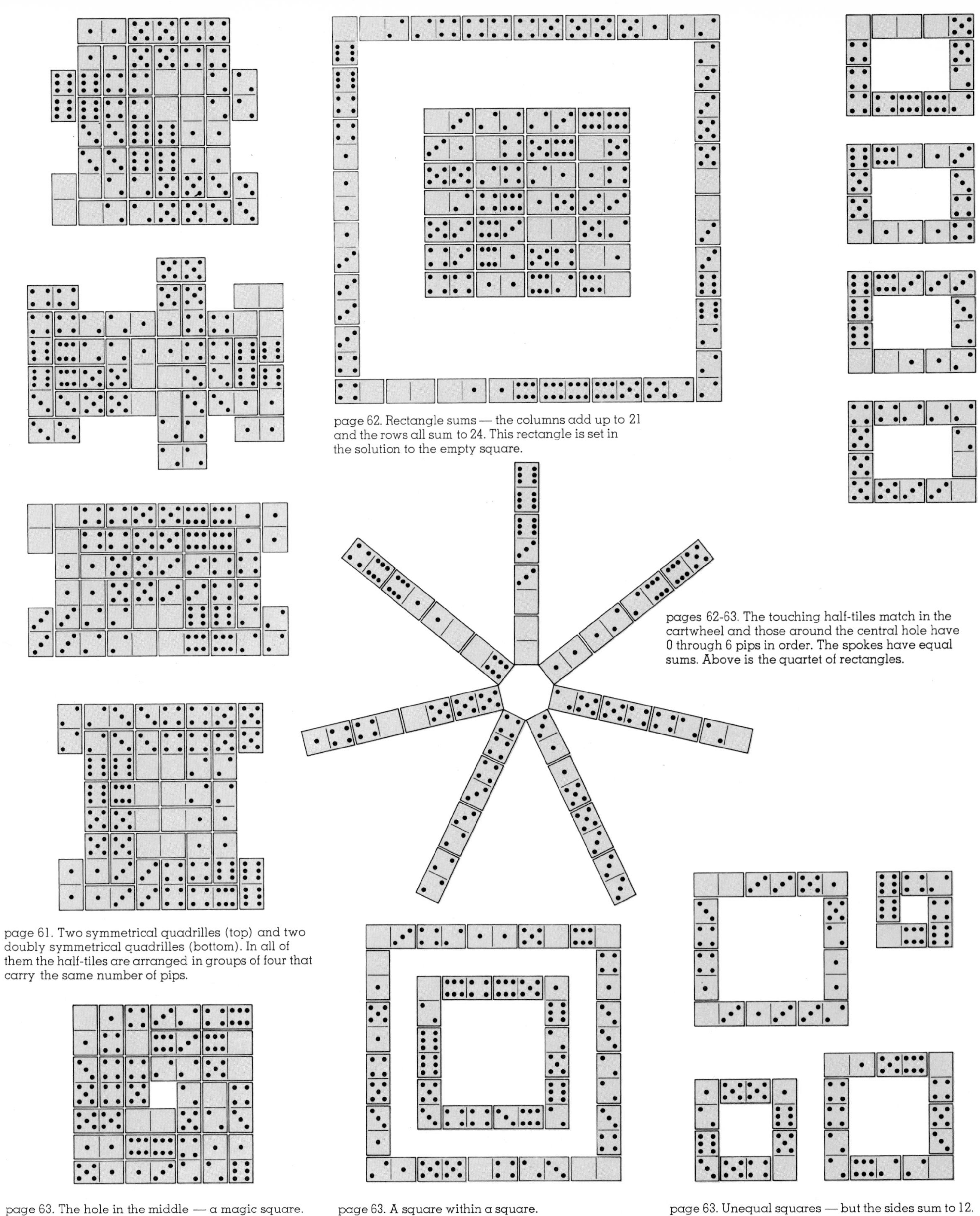

page 62. Rectangle sums — the columns add up to 21 and the rows all sum to 24. This rectangle is set in the solution to the empty square.

pages 62-63. The touching half-tiles match in the cartwheel and those around the central hole have 0 through 6 pips in order. The spokes have equal sums. Above is the quartet of rectangles.

page 61. Two symmetrical quadrilles (top) and two doubly symmetrical quadrilles (bottom). In all of them the half-tiles are arranged in groups of four that carry the same number of pips.

page 63. The hole in the middle — a magic square.

page 63. A square within a square.

page 63. Unequal squares — but the sides sum to 12.

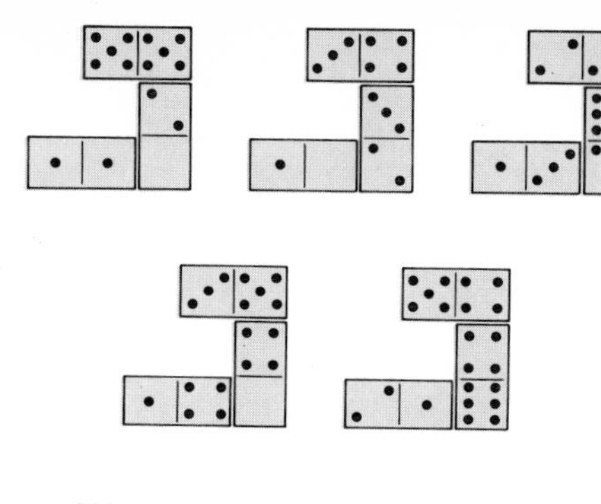
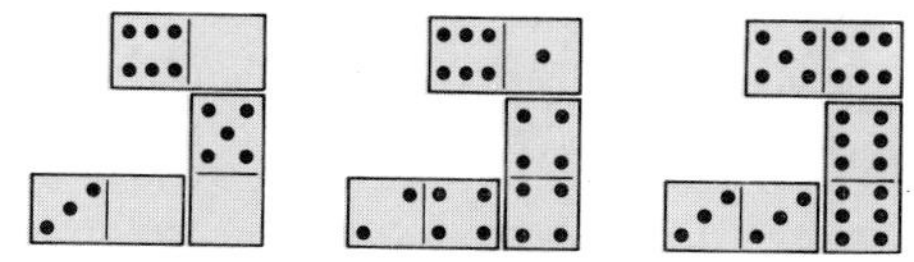

page 63. Eight possible multiplication problems.

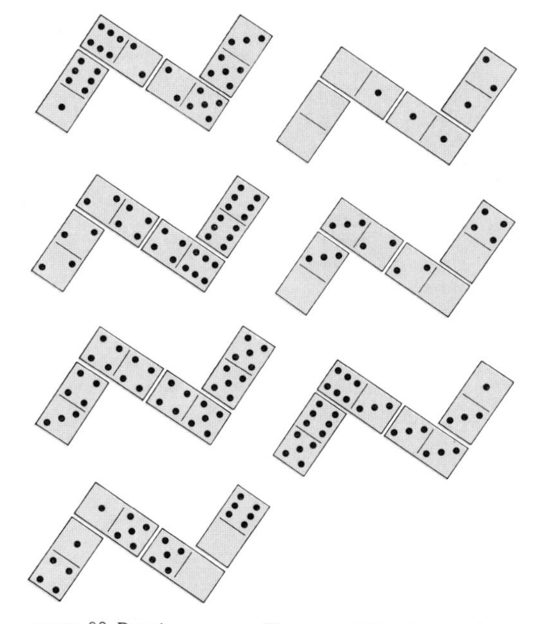

page 63. Domino waves. The sum of the pips on the diagonal bar equals the sum of the other two tiles.

page 63. A pair of double-crossing dominoes.

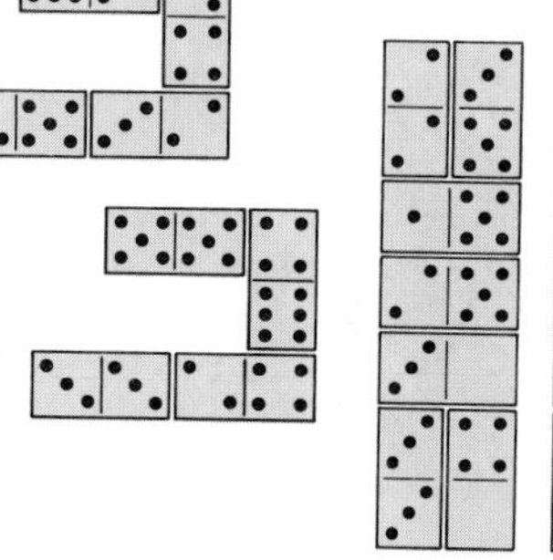

page 64. Three-figure numbers are multiplied by 2 through 6 to give four-figure totals.

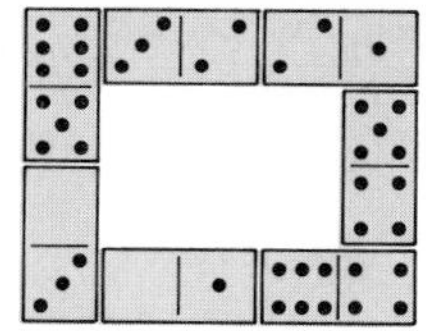
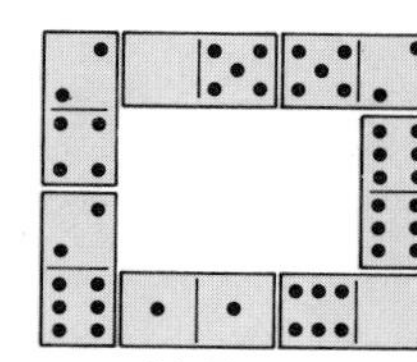
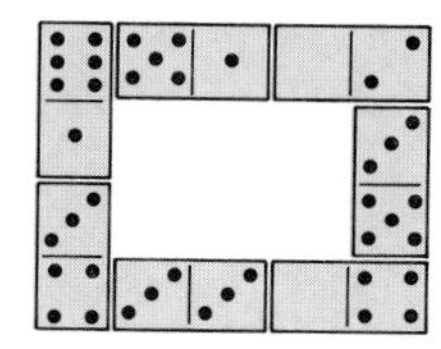

page 64. The rectangular quartet — all sides equal.

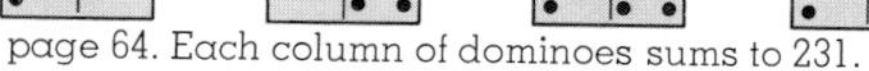

page 64. Each column of dominoes sums to 231.

page 64. Three additions using the double-5 set equal 182. On the right is the largest total that can be made with the double-2 set — 2220.

1	11	6	16
8	14	3	9
15	5	12	2
10	4	13	7

page 92. This reassembly makes the square magic.

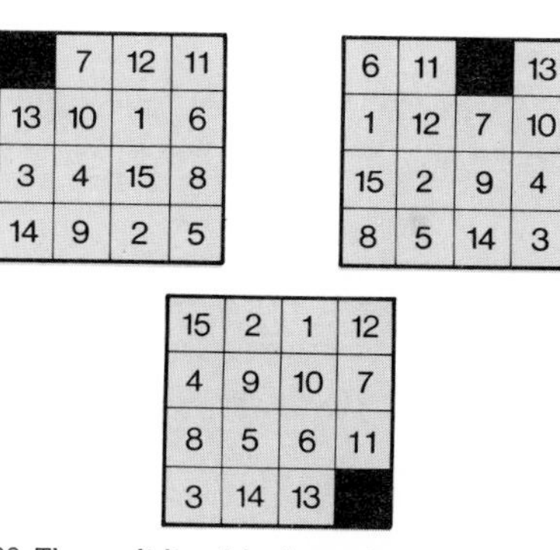

	7	12	11
13	10	1	6
3	4	15	8
14	9	2	5

6	11		13
1	12	7	10
15	2	9	4
8	5	14	3

15	2	1	12
4	9	10	7
8	5	6	11
3	14	13	

page 92. Three sliding block magic squares.

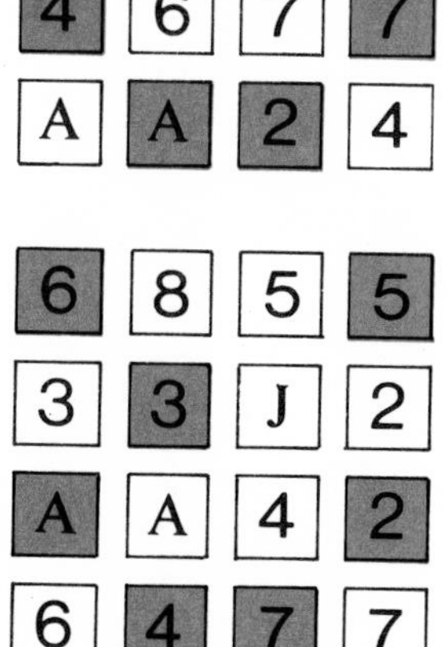

3	3	2	J
8	6	5	5
4	6	7	7
A	A	2	4

6	8	5	5
3	3	J	2
A	A	4	2
6	4	7	7

page 92. Two playing card magic squares of order 4.

5	80	59	73	61	3	63	12	13
1	20	55	30	57	28	71	26	81
4	14	31	50	29	60	35	68	78
76	58	46	38	45	40	36	24	6
7	65	33	43	41	39	49	17	75
74	64	48	42	37	44	34	18	8
67	10	47	32	53	22	51	72	15
66	56	27	52	25	54	11	62	16
69	2	23	9	21	79	19	70	77

page 94. The completed order-9 bordered square.

$5\frac{3}{4}$	4	$5\frac{1}{4}$
$4\frac{1}{2}$	5	$5\frac{1}{2}$
$4\frac{3}{4}$	6	$4\frac{1}{4}$

$4\frac{1}{2}$	4	$6\frac{1}{2}$
7	5	3
$3\frac{1}{2}$	6	$5\frac{1}{2}$

page 94. Two magic squares with fractional values.

18	22	1	10	14
24	3	7	11	20
5	9	13	17	21
6	15	19	23	2
12	16	25	4	8

page 94. There is an odd number cross in the square.

46	55	44	19	58	9	22	7
43	18	47	56	21	6	59	10
54	45	20	41	12	57	8	23
17	42	53	48	5	24	11	60
52	3	32	13	40	61	34	25
31	16	49	4	33	28	37	62
2	51	14	29	64	39	26	35
15	30	1	50	27	36	63	38

page 94. The almost-magic knight's tour square.

1	2	3	4	5	6	7
3	4	5	6	7	1	2
5	6	7	1	2	3	4
7	1	2	3	4	5	6
2	3	4	5	6	7	1
4	5	6	7	1	2	3
6	7	1	2	3	4	5

page 94. Six cuts were made in the magic strips.

52	61	4	13	20	29	36	45
14	3	62	51	46	35	30	19
53	60	5	12	21	28	37	44
11	6	59	54	43	38	27	22
55	58	7	10	23	26	39	42
9	8	57	56	41	40	25	24
50	63	2	15	18	31	34	47
16	1	64	49	48	33	32	17

page 94. *Franklin's 8 × 8 Square*
Benjamin Franklin did not tell us how he constructed his large magic squares, but whatever method he used gave rise to some remarkable regularities in addition to the usual requirements that rows, columns, and diagonals should have the same totals. In the 8 × 8 square designed by him the constant is the usual eighth-order constant of 260. As already mentioned in the text, the half-rows and half-columns are arranged to add up to 130. The "bent" diagonals also total 260. That is to say, if you add the numbers in a half-diagonal to those in one of the half-diagonals at right angles to it, you will get a total of 260. The four central cells total 130; in fact, any square made of four cells in any position adds up to the same total. So do the four corner cells. In the diagram above, some further interesting groupings are picked out with shading. The four-cell clusters in the upper corners, distinguished with the darkest shading, have a combined total of 260. The same is true of the corresponding groups in the lower corners. The lightest shading picks out two cells in each lower corner. The combined sum of the numbers in these four cells is 130. Added to the corresponding numbers in the upper corners of the square, they form a total of 260. The numbers in the eight cells picked out by the intermediate shading, forming two sloping rows in the lower half of the square, make a total of 260. In addition, every V-shaped pattern parallel to these has the same total. And the same is true of the corresponding V-shaped patterns pointing in from the other three sides of the square and all the patterns parallel to them. Franklin made a tantalizing reference to "five other curious properties" that he claimed the square to have, but he did no say what they were. The magic square enthusiast can enjoy continuing his search for them.

page 95. *Franklin's 16 × 16 Square*
The 16th-order magic square devised by Benjamin Franklin (below) is rich in groupings related to the square's constant of 2056. If the sum of the numbers in any half-diagonal is added to the sum of those in either of the half-diagonals at right angles, the sum is 2056. (The diagonals themselves, however, do not have the correct sums. The diagonal from top left to bottom right falls short by 128, that from top right to bottom left exceeds it by the same amount.)
The darkest shading here picks out a V-shaped pattern of 16 cells in the top half of the square. The sum of the numbers in these cells is 2056. The corresponding patterns on the other sides of the square have the same sums. The dark shading also picks out a square of 16 cells. Not only this square, but any 16-cell square, wherever it is positioned, has a sum of 2056. Yet again, any half-row or half-column, like the one picked out in the darkest shading, has a sum of 1028. The second darkest tone picks out a set of 32 cells around the square. The 16 on the left total 2064, which exceeds the constant by 8. The 16 on the right total 2048, which falls short of the constant by the same amount. All 32 cells therefore add up to twice the square's constant. Four cells in each corner are distinguished by the lightest shading. Together these total 2056. While it is easy to think of desirable improvements in the square — making the diagonals equal, for example — it would be extremely difficult to make changes in the arrangement of any of the numbers without disturbing some of the delicate arithmetical balances that already exist.

200	217	232	249	8	25	40	57	72	89	104	121	136	153	168	185
58	39	26	7	250	231	218	199	186	167	154	135	122	103	90	71
198	219	230	251	6	27	38	59	70	91	102	123	134	155	166	187
60	37	28	5	252	229	220	197	188	165	156	133	124	101	92	69
201	216	233	248	9	24	41	56	73	88	105	120	137	152	169	184
55	42	23	10	247	234	215	202	183	170	151	138	119	106	87	74
203	214	235	246	11	22	43	54	75	86	107	118	139	150	171	182
53	44	21	12	245	236	213	204	181	172	149	140	117	108	85	76
205	212	237	244	13	20	45	52	77	84	109	116	141	148	173	180
51	46	19	14	243	238	211	206	179	174	147	142	115	110	83	78
207	210	239	242	15	18	47	50	79	82	111	114	143	146	175	178
49	48	17	16	241	240	209	208	177	176	145	144	113	112	81	80
196	221	228	253	4	29	36	61	68	93	100	125	132	157	164	189
62	35	30	3	254	227	222	195	190	163	158	131	126	99	94	67
194	223	226	255	2	31	34	63	66	95	98	127	130	159	162	191
64	33	32	1	256	225	224	193	192	161	160	129	128	97	96	65

Mazes and Labyrinths
Many of the labyrinths traditionally made in past centuries are not puzzle mazes, for they do not have branching paths, but consist simply of a single winding path that was to be walked or run. Mazes shown in this chapter that have branching paths are here reproduced with their solutions.

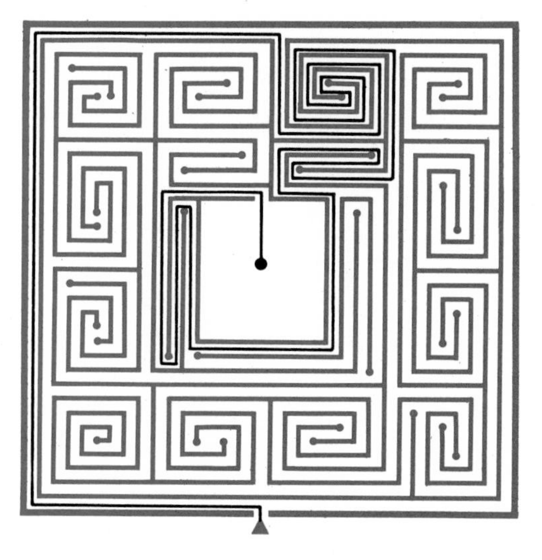

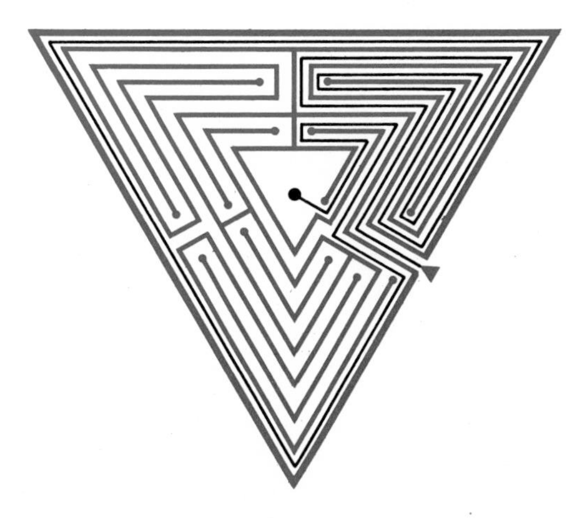

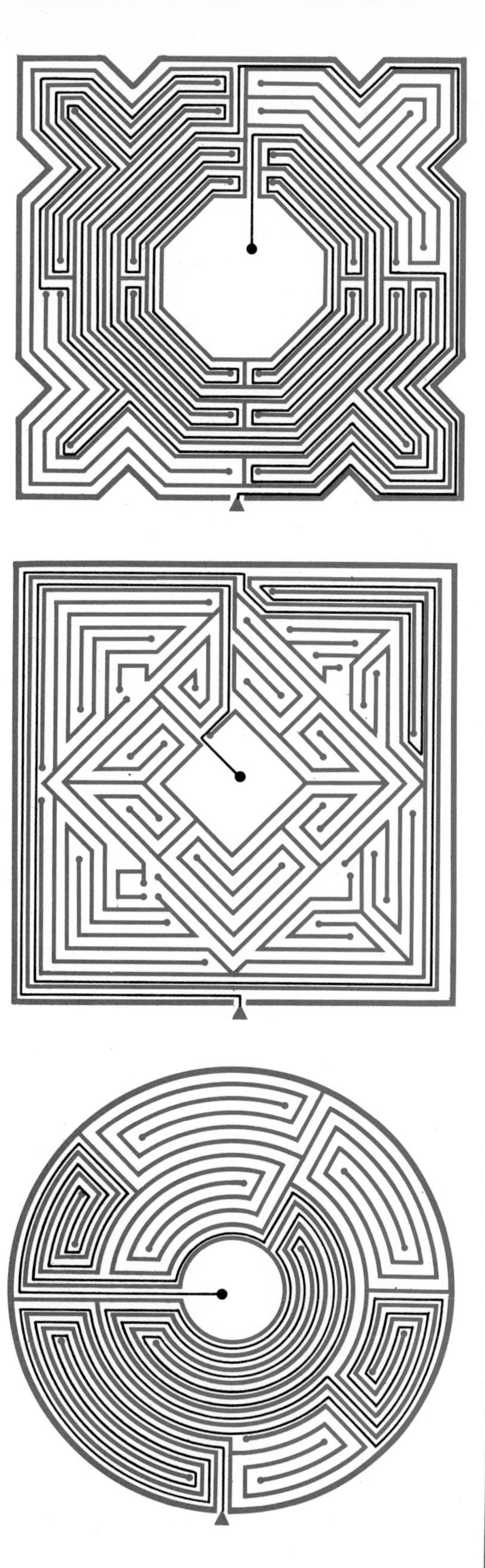

page 135. Six of the designs for garden mazes made by G. A. Boeckler in the 17th century. Boeckler liked to design all of his mazes — few of which were actuallly planted — in highly symmetrical patterns, but it is doubtful whether this fact would help the wanderer find his way through them.

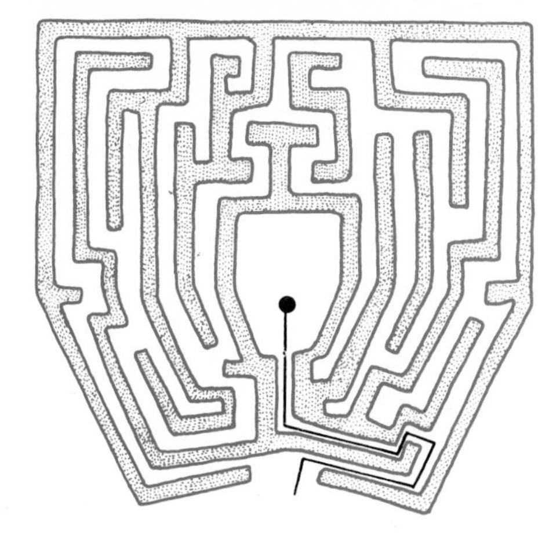

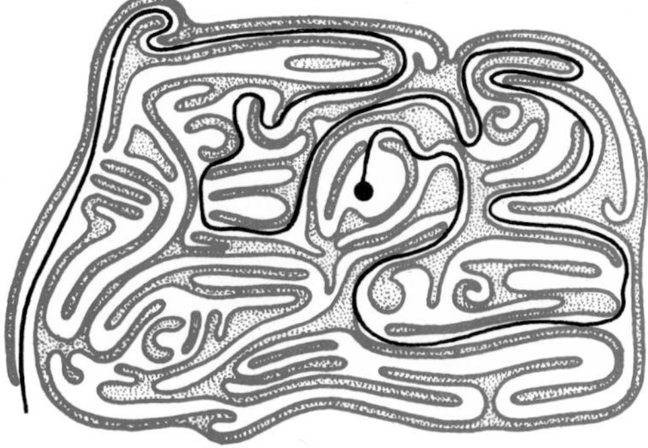

page 136. If you miss your way in the hedge maze at Williamsburg, Virginia (top), you will have a long walk. But the correct route to the center is very short. In the maze at Glendurgan, Cornwall (above), on the other hand, there is no avoiding a long and winding journey to the goal.

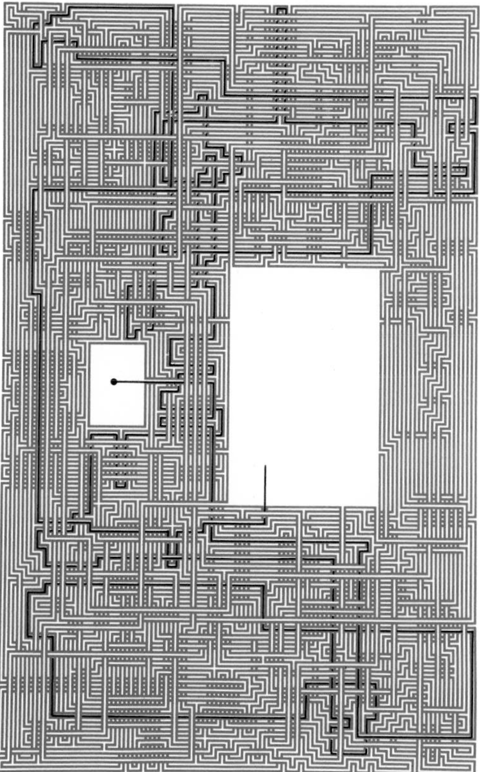

page 139. A route that connects the large and small empty areas in the complex maze of Greg Bright.

page 140. One of the many ways in which you can travel from the outside to the center of this maze.

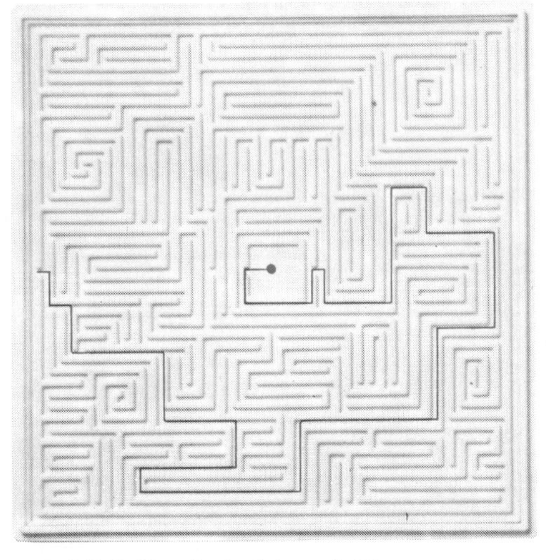

page 141. Rolling the ball through this maze, you would have the double problem of making it take the correct turn each time while keeping in mind the route shown here.

Solutions to Number and Logic Puzzles

page 159. *The Number Disks.* Arrange the disks into the groups 715, 46, and 32890; the first two numbers, when multiplied, yield the third as product.

page 159. *Finding the Ages.* Suppose that Tommy will be half as old as his father in x years. The combined ages of Tommy and his parents will have increased by $3x$ years. But in this time, the combined ages will have doubled — that is, increased by 70 years. So $x = 23^1/_3$ years. Now suppose that Tommy's present age is T years. His father is 6T years old. When his father is 6T + $23^1/_3$ years old, he will be twice as old as Tommy, who will be T + $23^1/_3$ years old. So we can write: $6T + 23^1/_3 = 2 \times (T + 23^1/_3)$. It quickly follows that $T = 5^5/_6$. So Tommy is 5 years and 10 months old. His father's age is six times this, or 35 years. And his mother's age is $29^1/_6$ years, or 29 years, 2 months.

page 160. *The Number Frame.* Circles C and F are each connected to six other circles. They must therefore contain 1 and 8, for only these differ by more than six from other numbers in the sequence. Place 1 in C and 8 in F. Then 2 can go only in H, and 7 in A. It is then not difficult to place the other four numbers. This arrangement can be flipped from left to right or from top to bottom to give solutions that are equally good.

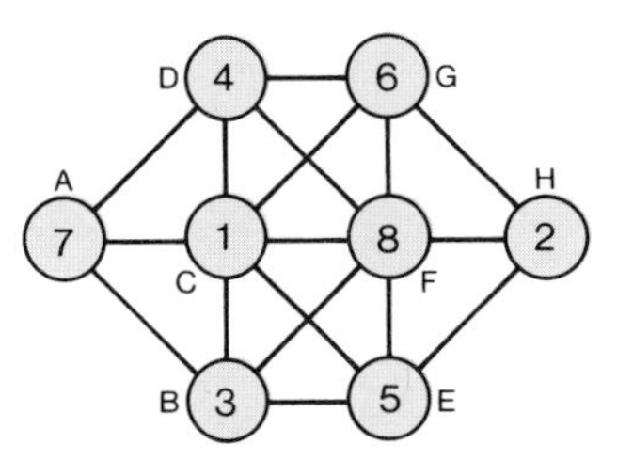

page 160. *Salvation by Numbers.* The dark disks indicate how the mathematicians positioned themselves in the circle: counting begins at the top of the circle.

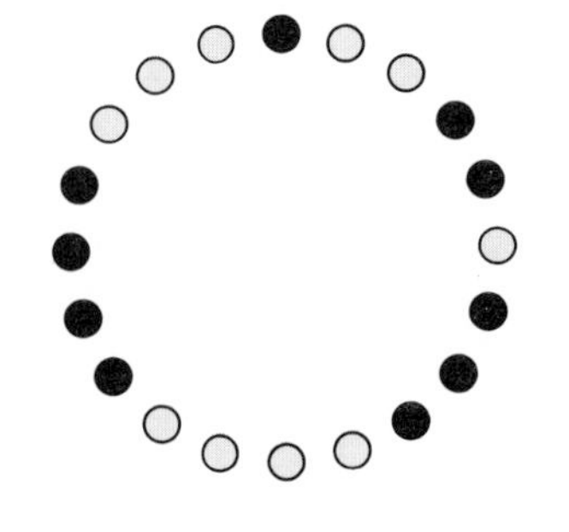

page 160. *Balancing the Scales.* Throughout these operations, the scales balance. They finish with a circle on one side and triangles on the other.

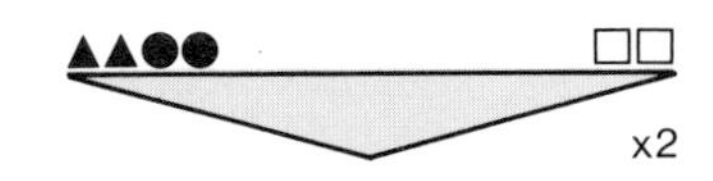

Double the loads on the first scales.

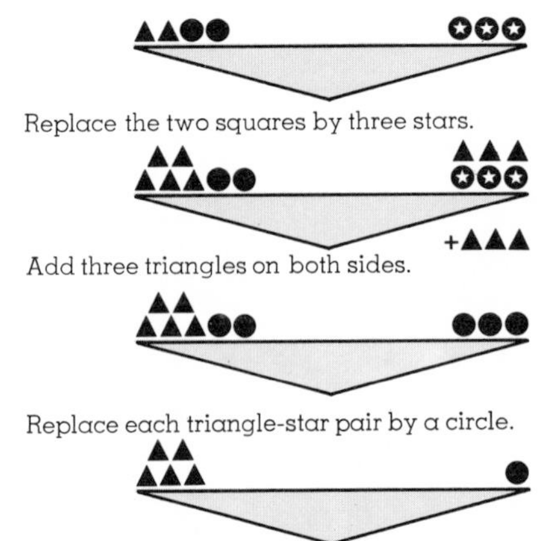

Replace the two squares by three stars.

Add three triangles on both sides.

Replace each triangle-star pair by a circle.

Take two circles from each side.

page 160. *The Stopped Clock.* Before he went out, Mr. Smith started the clock (though, of course, it was showing the wrong time). So when he came back he could see how long he had been away. He had noted the correct time when reaching and leaving Mr. Jones' house, so he knew how long he had spent there. It was then an easy matter to calculate how long he had spent walking. Half of this was the time he had spent walking back, and added to the time of departure from Mr. Jones' house told him the time at which he arrived back home.

page 160. *The Magic Chain.* The result of your friend's calculation will always be 9. So, if you begin at the square, you are certain to finish on the star. You can choose any starting point, together with its corresponding finishing point.

page 160. *A Mystic Number.* Whatever number your friend originally chooses, he will end up with 1089 — so you can demonstrate the trick only once.

page 160. *Sharing the Apples.* Mary began with 15 apples. Brother-sister pairs are: Ann and George; Betty and Harry; Cathy and Ed; Dee and Frank.

page 160. *The Bookworm's Puzzle.* Some arrangements of books that give the required fractions are as follows (it is sometimes possible to find alternative arrangements of numbers giving the same fractions).

$$\frac{5832}{17496}=\frac{1}{3} \quad \frac{4392}{17568}=\frac{1}{4} \quad \frac{2769}{13845}=\frac{1}{5} \quad \frac{2943}{17658}=\frac{1}{6}$$

$$\frac{2394}{16758}=\frac{1}{7} \quad \frac{3187}{25496}=\frac{1}{8} \quad \frac{6381}{57429}=\frac{1}{9}$$

Page 160. *Feeding the Cattle.* Imagine that the cattle supported by the field are divided into two groups — one that eats the original grass and one that eats the new grass as fast as it grows. Let the number of cattle that would eat the original grass on ten acres in 16 weeks be x. Then the remaining $12 - x$ cows eat the new grass as fast as it grows. The same number, $(12 - x)$, can eat the new growth when there are 18 cows in the field, leaving $x + 6$ cows to eat the grass initially present. But to do this in eight weeks, they must be twice as numerous as the corresponding cattle (of which there were x) in the 16-week period first considered (that is, $2x$). So we can say: $x + 6 = 2x$, and thus $x = 6$. In the 40-acre field, four times as many cattle can live off the new growth — 24. As we have just seen, six cows can live on the initial grass on ten acres for 16 weeks. The same amount of grass could feed 16 cows for six weeks. And so four times as many, or 64, cows could be supported for six weeks by the grass initially present on 40 acres. So altogether $64 + 24 = 88$ cows can be supported on the 40-acre field for six weeks.

page 161. *The Archeologist.* Multiplying the final 9 of the divisor by 3 (step 5) shows that c is 7. Then multiplying the 9 by 5 (step 3) shows that f is 5. And d must be 8 to give a final 2 at step 1. The figures 47 can result at step 4 only if b is 4. It follows that e is 9. And a can only be 7 or 8, since when the divisor is multiplied by the 8 of the quotient and the result is subtracted from the first four figures of the dividend, the remainder has only three figures. Trial quickly shows that a cannot be 8. Hence the whole calculation is as shown.

```
      853                d53
749/638897          ab9/6.8..c
    5992                ..e2     1
     3969                .9..    2
     3745               ..4f     3
      2247               ..4c    4
      2247               ..4c    5
```

page 161. *A Blot on the Copybook.* Since a two-digit number results when a is added to 2, a must be 7 or 9 (remember that 1 may be carried over from the next column). But if a were 9, then c would be 1 or 2—and both of these are impossible. Hence a is 7, b is 1, c is 0, and 1 is indeed carried over from the right. Trial and error establish the right positions for other digits.

```
 28.     289
+a.4    +764
bc..    1053
```

page 161. *Don't Repeat Yourself.* Figure c cannot be 1, for then d and e would be the same as a and b respectively. Nor can c be 5, for then e would have to be either 0 (ruled out in the statement of the problem) or another 5. And c cannot be 9, for that would result in a three-digit number when it multiplied ab. Also, a cannot be greater than 4—otherwise there would be a three-digit answer to the multiplication. Try setting a equal to 4: then c can only be 2. Trial and error quickly show that there are then no possible values for b. If a is taken to be 3, then c can again only be 2; but the rest of the calculation cannot be filled in. Continuing in this way, you can progressively eliminate possibilities until you try $a = 1$, $c = 4$, $b = 7$, when everything clicks satisfyingly into place.

```
 ab     17
x c    x 4
 de     68
+..    +25
 ..     93
```

page 161. *A Blank Division.* Some of the figures can be seen to be zeros immediately, and have been written in here. Thus, from line 6 onward, all the figures brought down must be zeros. And in lines 2 and 8, two or more figures are brought down in the working out, and corresponding zeros occur in the quotient. In line 9 a whole number of thousands occurs on multiplying by b. So the final figure of the divisor, a, must be 0 or 5. But a cannot be 0, since c, and hence d, would then be 0. So a is 5, and so are c and d. The only number ending in 5 that will yield 5000 when multiplied by a single figure is 625. Hence b is 8, and none of the other figures in the quotient is greater than 1, since only three-figure numbers occur at lines 1, 3, 5, and 7. The whole of the long division quickly follows.

```
      .0...00b
..a/......
    ...          1
     ...         2
     ...         3
      ...        4
      ...        5
       ..0       6
       ..c       7
        d000     8
        d000     9
```

```
      1011.1008
625/631938
    625
     693
     625
      688
      625
       630
       625
        5000
        5000
```

page 161. *The Clerk's Problem.* Adding 1 to jk turns it from a two-figure to a three-figure number; therefore j must be 9 and k must be 8 or 9. Hence g is either 8 or 9. But this means that c must be 9, while either ab is 89 or a is 9. But ab cannot be 89, for then g would be 8 and h would be 0, so that j could not be 9. Hence a is 9 and g is 8.

Since k must be 8 or 9, e and h must add up to 17 or 18 (since 1 may be "carried" from the addition of f and i). Either e or h must be 9, and the only possibility is that b and d are each 9. It follows that the result of the multiplication is 9801. Therefore neither l nor m can be less than 9. The whole calculation is shown.

```
    ab       99
   xcd      x 99
   ef.      891
  ghi      891
 jk..      9801
+ 1im     + 199
.....     10000
```

page 161. *Deciphering the Division.* Two digits are brought down at steps 2 and 4. Hence digits e and f are 0. When the divisor is multiplied by 8 (step 3), a three-figure number results; so the divisor is less than 125. But a four-figure number results when the divisor is multiplied by g (step 5). So g is 9.

When the divisor is multiplied by d and the result is subtracted from the first four digits of the dividend, a two-digit number results (step 2). This is possible only if d is greater than 7. But d must be less than 9 (otherwise it would give a four-figure result at step 1), and so it is 8. The quotient is therefore 80,809. To yield a number of eight digits, this must be multiplied by a number greater than 123. Since the divisor is also less than 125, it can only be 124.

```
      de8fg
abc/........
    ...          1
     ....        2
      ...        3
      ....       4
      ....       5
```

```
      80809
124/10020316
    992
     1003
      992
      1116
      1116
```

page 161. *The Storekeeper's Accounts.* Figure e must be 1—otherwise there would be a four-figure number in line 1. The last figure in line 3 is 5; therefore either b or c is 5. But if c were 5, there could not be a 5 in second place in line 3. Hence b is 5. Then h is either 0 or 5, and f (which equals a) is either 4 or 9 correspondingly. Trying $a = 9$, it turns out that there is no value of c that will give 5 in the second and fourth places in line 3. Hence a is 4, and c is 7, giving the result 4515 in line 3. Then h is 0. It only remains to find an even value for d that will satisfy the rest of the calculation. Trial and error show it to be 2.

```
   6ab            645
  x cde          x721
    .fg    1      645
  ...h     2     1290
 .5.5      3    4515
....4.          465045
```

page 161. *A Coded Calculation.* Neither A, B, nor J can be 1, since the divisor does not reappear in lines 1, 3, or 5. In line 5, H must be 0. Since H results from multiplying A by J, either J is 5 and A is some even number, or vice versa. But A cannot be 5, for then the final digit in line 1 would also be A. Hence J is 5 and A is even. Line 3 shows that when A is multiplied by B, a number results whose final digit is A. This can happen only if B is 6 and A is 2, 4, or 8. Lines 4, 5, and 6 show that A must be less than 3 and so must be 2. When these results are filled in, other values follow.

```
      ABJ                 265
ECA/ FDBHJ          372/ 98605
     CGG      1          744
     AGAH     2          2420
     AAEA     3          2232
      KDDJ    4           1885
      KDBH    5           1860
        AJ    6             25
```

page 164. *The Battle of Baffleburg.* Let A stand for "Albright will win a prize," B for "Branebender will win a prize," and so on. Then the possibilities excluded are, in turn: ab; BC and bc; de; dE; Cd and cD; AE. The only possibility remaining is AbCDe. Only Branebender and Egghead will fail to win prizes.

page 164. *Murder at the Manor.* Let A, B, C, and D represent respectively the statements that the admiral, the butler, the count, or the deacon is telling the truth. Sir Harold excludes these possibilities in turn: Ab; BC; cd; BD. Remove the corresponding cards from the pack (ignore the E position as you work with the cards). You will be left with six cards, corresponding to the possibilities: abcD; abCd; abCD (each possibility is represented by two cards). So the admiral and the butler are certainly lying; it is not possible to tell, from this evidence, whether or not the other people mentioned are telling the truth.

page 164. *The Bad, the Sad, and the Mad.* Let A stand for "Annie gets mad," B for "Benny is bad, and C for "Connie is sad." When sorting the cards, work only with the A, B, and C positions. According to Benny's Ma, A and C follow when B is true, and B follows when A is false. So she rules out the possibilities aB, Bc, and ab. Annie's Pa rules out Ac. When the corresponding cards have been removed from the pack, 16 cards remain. Considering only the A, B, and C positions, you will find that they represent the possibilities ABC and AbC. So Benny may or may not be bad, but unfortunately Annie is bound to get mad and Connie to be sad.

page 164. *Directions and Misdirections.* Represent the instruction "go through Ashville" by A, and so on. Then the directions that the motorist received were: AB; bC; cd; bD. None of these *combined* instructions was correct, though either of its two parts might have been. Remove the cards representing each of the combinations. All the remaining cards have a hole at the A position and a notch at the B position, so all of them represent aB. The driver's shortest route took him through Beefburg but not Ashville.

page 164. *The Children's Ages.* Let A, B, and C represent the statements that Alice, Bill, or Charles is the youngest, respectively; and let D label the statement that Alice is the oldest. You can immediately remove the cards that represent AB, AC, AD, and BC. The facts remembered by Mrs. Rackbrain further rule out the possibilities ab and cd. The only cards left when these have been removed correspond to aBcD; Alice is the oldest, Charles is the next in age, and Bill is the youngest.

page 164. *Keeping the Peace.* Let A stand for "Abria will send a contingent," and so on. The possibilities excluded are, in turn: AB; de; Bc and bC; cD and cD; aE and dE. When the cards corresponding to these are removed from the pack, the only card remaining is that representing aBCDe. Only Bemblia, Costlia and Detria send contingents.

page 165. *The Colormatch Square*
In each solution the tiles are listed from left to right and top to bottom.

1	0	1	7	10	3	6	12	9	15	11	2	5	13	14	8	4
2	0	1	7	10	3	6	13	11	14	8	5	15	9	2	4	12
3	0	4	8	5	3	2	1	6	15	11	7	10	12	13	14	9
4	0	4	8	5	3	2	1	6	15	11	7	10	13	14	12	9
5	0	4	9	7	3	2	5	14	15	11	6	8	12	13	10	1
6	0	4	12	9	3	2	1	7	15	10	5	14	13	11	6	8
7	0	5	11	2	3	6	12	9	15	10	1	7	14	8	4	13
8	0	5	11	3	2	4	13	15	10	1	7	14	9	6	12	8
9	0	5	11	7	3	6	13	14	15	10	4	8	12	9	2	1
10	0	5	14	8	2	4	9	3	10	1	7	15	11	6	12	13
11	0	5	15	10	3	6	12	9	14	8	1	7	11	2	4	13
12	2	4	9	7	10	0	5	15	11	3	6	12	13	14	8	1
13	2	4	12	9	10	0	1	7	11	3	6	13	15	14	8	5
14	2	4	13	11	10	0	5	15	8	1	7	14	3	6	12	9
15	2	4	13	11	10	0	5	15	9	3	6	12	7	14	8	1
16	6	8	1	2	10	0	5	11	9	3	7	15	4	12	13	14
17	6	8	1	2	10	0	5	11	9	3	7	15	4	13	14	12
18	6	8	4	12	10	0	1	2	9	3	7	11	5	14	13	15
19	6	8	4	12	10	0	1	2	9	3	7	11	5	15	14	13
20	6	8	5	15	10	0	4	12	11	3	2	1	13	14	9	7
21	6	12	9	3	10	0	4	13	11	2	1	7	14	8	5	15
22	6	12	9	3	10	0	5	14	8	1	7	11	2	4	13	15
23	6	12	9	3	10	0	5	15	8	1	7	14	2	4	13	11
24	6	12	9	3	10	0	5	15	11	2	4	13	14	8	1	7
25	8	0	1	6	3	2	5	11	14	9	7	15	10	4	12	13
26	8	0	1	7	3	2	5	14	15	11	6	9	12	13	10	4
27	8	0	4	13	3	2	1	6	15	10	5	11	12	9	7	14
28	8	0	5	11	3	2	4	13	15	10	1	7	14	9	6	12
29	8	0	5	14	3	2	4	9	15	10	1	7	13	11	6	12
30	8	1	7	10	0	4	13	11	3	2	5	15	14	9	6	12
31	8	4	9	7	2	0	5	15	11	3	6	12	14	13	10	1
32	10	0	1	3	9	2	5	15	7	11	6	13	14	12	8	4
33	10	0	4	8	9	2	1	3	5	11	7	15	6	12	13	14
34	10	0	4	8	9	2	1	3	5	11	7	15	6	13	14	12
35	10	0	4	12	9	2	1	3	7	11	6	13	15	14	8	5
36	10	0	4	13	11	2	1	7	14	8	5	15	9	3	6	12
37	10	0	5	15	11	2	4	13	12	9	3	6	1	7	14	8
38	10	0	5	15	11	2	4	13	14	8	1	7	9	3	6	12
39	10	4	9	2	8	0	5	11	1	3	7	15	6	12	13	14
40	10	4	9	2	8	0	5	11	1	3	7	15	6	13	14	12
41	10	4	12	13	8	0	1	6	3	2	5	11	14	9	7	15
42	10	4	12	13	8	0	1	7	3	2	5	14	15	11	6	9
43	10	4	13	11	8	0	5	15	1	3	6	12	7	14	9	2
44	14	8	1	7	10	0	5	15	9	3	6	12	4	13	11	2
45	14	8	1	7	10	0	5	15	11	2	4	13	12	9	3	6
46	14	8	4	12	10	0	1	3	9	2	5	15	7	11	6	13
47	14	8	4	13	10	0	1	7	9	3	6	12	5	15	11	2
48	14	8	5	15	10	0	4	12	9	2	1	3	7	11	6	13
49	14	8	5	15	10	0	4	12	9	3	2	1	6	13	11	7
50	14	12	8	4	10	0	1	3	9	2	5	15	7	11	6	13

Solutions to Positioning Puzzles

page 166. *The Moving Peg Puzzle.* Move the pegs as follows: 6-9, 12-6, 15-12, 9-15, 10-9, 8-10, 7-8, 9-7, 3-9, 6-3, 12-6, 13-12, 10-13, 16-10, 15-16, 9-15, 10-9, 8-10, 5-8, 6-5, 4-6, 7-4, 9-7, 11-9, 10-11, 8-10, 2-8, 3-2, 1-3, 7-1, 9-7, 6-9, 12-6, 14-12, 11-14, 17-11, 15-17, 9-15, 3-9, 6-3, 12-6, 9-12, 11-9, 10-11, 8-10, 9-8.

page 166. *The Donald Duck Puzzle.* The following abbreviations are used: d = down, u = up, l = left, r = right.

6 (d+r), 4, 8, 10+9, 5, 7, 6+9, 10, 8, 4, 6+7, 5, 10+8, 8 (u), 10, 7+9, 9, 7, 7 (d), 6+8, 4, 2, 1, 6+8+7, 9 (1+u), 10, 2+4, 1, 6, 8 (u+1), 7, 1, 2, 4, 10, 3+5, 6+8+7, 2+4, 10, 9 (d), 1, 6 (d+r), 2, 4, 1, 6, 8, 7 (1), 3+5, 9, 6, 8 (u), 1, 4, 2+7+8+3, 5, 1, 7+8, 2, 4, 8 (1+u), 10, 6+9, 1, 8+7, 10, 9 (u+1), 1.

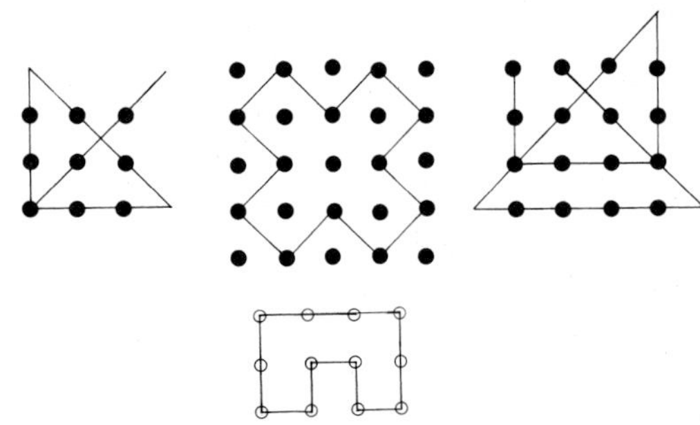

pages 166, 167. Join the points of the nine-dot problem, and the *Cross and the Dots*, the *Sixteen Dots*, and the *Shortest Route* puzzles.

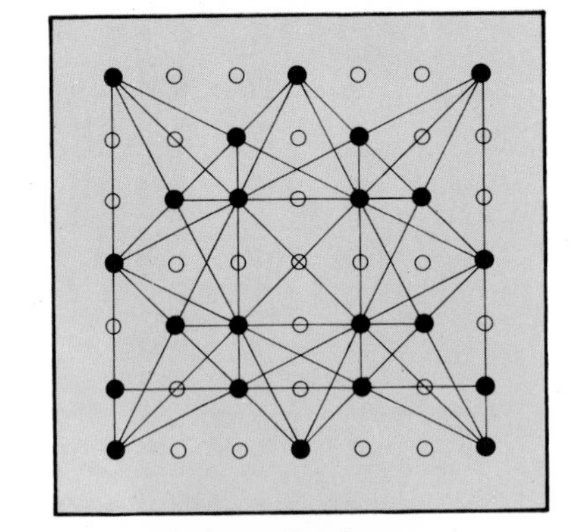

page 167. *The Plantation Puzzle.*

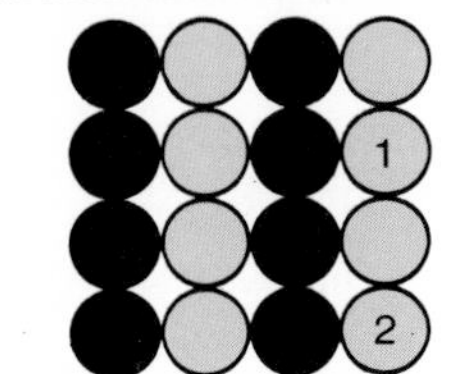

page 167. *Changing the Checkers.* Move pieces 1 and 2 alongside the two black checkers in the right-hand column. Push them left, to make this array.

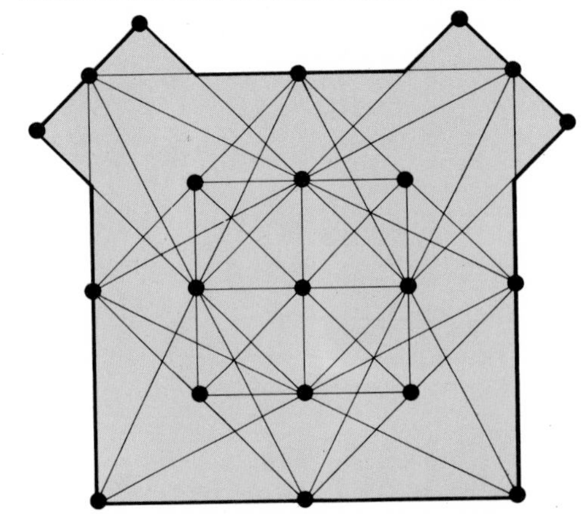

page 167. *Thirty Trios* — made from 21 checkers.

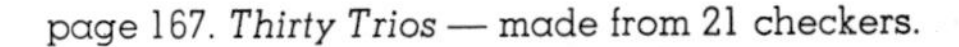

page 167. *A Rising Readership.* In the second month, four people take the magazine in each corner office, and one person in each other office. In the third month, two people buy a copy in each corner office, five do so in each of the others. In the fourth month, one person buys a copy in each corner office and seven do so in each other office. In the fifth month, no copies are sold in the corner offices, but nine are sold in each other office.

page 168. *The Four Couples.* In the table below, A represents Arnold, B is Bill, b represents Betty, and so on. The table shows the occupants of the boat on each trip, and the locations of all eight people between trips.

Near shore		Island		Far shore
ABCD abcd	ab →		→	
ABCD cd	←		← b	ab
ABCD bcd	bc →			a
ABCD d	← c	bc		a
ABCD cd	AB →	b	→	a
CD cd	←	b	← B	AB a
BCD cd	cd →	b		A a
BCD	← d	bcd		A a
BCD d	BC →	bc	→	A a
D d		bc	← a	ABC a
D d		abc	ac →	ABC
D d	←	b	← B	ABC ac
BD d	BD →	b	→	AC ac
d		b	← c	ABCD ac
d		bc	bc →	ABCD a
d	←		← c	ABCD abc
cd	cd →		→	ABCD ab
				ABCD abcd

page 168. *The Four Islands.* One possible route that begins on island B and ends on the land Y is:

B-3-Y-5-C-6-Y-8-D-7-C-4-B-2-A-1-Y

It is not possible to start from island C and finish on the land without retracing one's steps or omitting to cross at least one bridge.

page 168. *The Dog, the Goat and the Cabbages.* Here is one way the farmer can transport his charges. First he takes the goat to the far side, leaving the cabbages with the dog. Then he returns for the cabbages. He leaves these on the far shore while bringing the goat back to the starting point. Then he takes the dog to the far shore and leaves it with the cabbages while returning for the goat.

page 169. *The Six Bridges.* This journey must begin on island A and end on the lower bank, or vice versa. One possible journey is as follows:

A-1-Y-3-B-2-A-4-Y-5-B-6-Y

It is not possible to begin and end one's journey on shore without retracing part of the journey or omitting at least one bridge.

page 169. *The Detachment.* First the children row to the far shore. One stays there while the other returns. One soldier then rows across the river. The child on the far side brings back the boat. Both children row to the far shore, and one remains there while the other brings back the boat. A second soldier rows across and the child on the far side brings back the boat. They continue in this way until all the soldiers have crossed to the far shore of the river.

page 169. *The Nine Pipelines.* It is possible to connect each rig to all three refineries with two of the pipelines crossing but no fewer.

page 169. *Missionaries and Indians.* In the table below, a missionary who can row is represented by an M, while one who cannot is shown by an m. Similarly an Indian who can paddle the canoe is represented by an I, while one who cannot paddle it is shown by an i. Follow the table below to find the smallest number of crossings to get them all across the river.

Near shore	Boat		Far shore
Mmm Iii	Ii	→	
Mmm i	← I		Ii

Mmm Ii		Ii	→	i
Mmm	←	I		Iii
Mmm I		Mm	→	ii
m I	←	Mi		ii Mm
Mm Ii		MI	→	i m
m i	←	Mi		Ii Mm
Mm ii		Mm	→	I m
ii	←	I		I Mmm
Iii		Ii	→	Mmm
i	←	I		Ii Mmm
Ii		Ii	→	i Mmm
				Iii Mmm

Solutions to Solitaire Puzzles.

page 171. *The Latin Cross:* 43-23, 45-43, 53-33, 23-43, 42-44.

page 171. *The Greek Cross:* 45-47, 43-45, 64-44-46, 24-44, 47-45-43, 42-44.

page 171. *The Football Team:* a) 42-22, 43-63, 34-32, 51-53, 54-52, 31-51-53, 63-43, 22-42-44.
b) 45-25, 37-35, 34-36, 57-37-35, 25-45, 46-44-64, 56-54, 64-44.

page 171. *The Pyramid of Chefren:* 55-53-33, 35-55, 65-45, 44-46, 33-35, 25-45, 46-44.

page 171. *The Shrine:* 37-35, 57-55, 45-65, 47-45, 35-55, 65-45 (this forms a Greek cross), 44-46, 42-44, 63-43-45, 23-43, 46-44-42, 41-43.

page 171. *The Pyramid of Cheops:* a) 34-14, 43-23, 44-46, 54-56-36-34, 75-55, 15-13-33-35, 25-45-65-63-43, 42-44.
b) 34-36, 15-35, 54-56, 75-55, 36-34-54-52, 42-44, 56-54-34, 24-44, 45-43, 33-53, 52-54, 64-44.

page 172. *The Tiffany Lamp:* 32-34, 52-54, 57-55-35-33-53, 63-43, 47-45, 37-35-55-53-33, 41-43, 44-42, 23-43, 42-44.

page 172. *Center to Center:* 46-44, 65-45, 57-55, 54-56, 52-54, 73-53, 43-63, 75-73-53, 35-55, 15-35, 23-43-63-65-45-25, 37-57-55-53, 31-33, 34-32, 51-31-33, 13-15-35, 36-34-32-52-54-34, 24-44.

page 172. *The Davis Jump:* 51-53, 54-52, 56-54, 75-55, 45-65, 31-51-53-55, 33-53, 13-33, 25-45-43-23, 15-13-33, 37-35, 32-52-54-56-36, 73-75-55, 63-65-45-25-23-43, 57-37-35-33-53.

page 172. *Corner to Corner:* 51-31, 43-41, 62-42, 41-43, 44-42, 46-44, 26-46, 47-45, 32-52, 34-32, 54-34, 56-54, 31-33, 34-32, 22-42, 52-32, 54-52, 13-33, 14-34, 73-53, 74-54, 75-55, 34-36, 32-34, 37-35, 34-36, 54-56, 52-54, 57-55, 54-56, 66-46, 15-35-37, 45-47, 37-57.
Alternately: 51-31, 43-41, 53-51, 73-53, 22-42, 34-32, 31-33, 36-34-32, 54-52, 51-53, 56-54-52, 13-33, 14-34, 15-35, 74-54, 75-55, 34-36-56, 66-46, 54-56, 57-55, 32-34-54-56-36, 41-43, 62-42-44-46, 47-45, 26-46, 45-47, 37-57.

page 172. *The Octagram:* 55-57, 36-56, 57-55, 54-56, 74-54, 44-46, 56-36, 26-46, 47-45, 24-26, 45-25, 26-24, 66-64-44, 34-54, 14-34, 62-64-44, 52-54, 33-35, 54-34, 35-33-53, 41-43, 53-33, 23-43, 22-42-44.

page 172. *The Pentagon:* 55-57, 36-56, 57-55, 44-46, 25-45, 46-44, 65-45, 23-25, 43-23, 45-53, 53-33-35-15-13-33-31-51-53-55, 74-54, 55-53, 63-43, 42-44.

page 173. *The Five Crosses:* 64-66, 44-64, 74-54, 42-62-64-44-42, 41-43, 24-22-42-44-24, 14-34, 46-26-24-44-46, 47-45, 46-44.

page 173. *The Double Cross:* 54-56-36, 26-46, 35-55, 47-45-65, 74-54, 66-64, 43-63, 54-74, 62-64, 74-54, 33-35, 54-34, 35-33, 41-43-23, 14-34, 22-24-44.

page 173. *The Tilted Square:*
a) 64-62, 42-44, 62-42, 55-57, 41-43-63, 35-55-75-73-53-55, 57-37-35, 34-54-56-36-34, 33-13-15-35-33, 32-34, 24-44.
b) 53-73, 33-53, 46-44, 65-45-43-63, 35-33-31-51-53-55-57-37-35-15-13-33, 73-53, 74-54-52-32-34, 24-44.

page 173. *The Lonely Cross:* 24-44, 32-34, 53-33, 23-43, 35-33, 55-35, 25-45, 52-32-34, 75-55, 63-65, 55-75, 57-55, 36-56, 55-57.

page 173. *The Final Score:* 64-44, 56-54, 35-55, 54-56, 62-64, 42-62, 44-42, 24-44, 22-24, 42-22, 14-34, 26-24, 34-14, 46-26, 66-46, 64-66.

page 173. *The Twelve Guards:* 42-44, 23-43, 44-42, 41-43, 22-42, 24-44, 36-34, 44-24, 14-34, 26-24, 64-44, 52-54, 44-64, 74-54, 62-64, 46-44, 65-45, 44-46, 47-45, 66-46, 45-47, 34-14, 43-41, 54-74.

page 175. *The Tower of Brahma.* Let the peg on which the disks start be called a, and the other two pegs be called b and c respectively. Number the disks from 1 through 6, in order of increasing size. Then the transfer of disk 1 to peg b can be represented by 1b, and so on. Transfer all six disks as follows:

1b, 2c, 1c, 3b, 1a, 2b, 1b, 4c, 1c, 2a, 1a, 3c,
1b, 2c, 1c, 5b, 1a, 2b, 1b, 3a, 1c, 2a, 1a, 4b,
1b, 2c, 1c, 3b, 1a, 2b, 1b, 6c, 1c, 2a, 1a, 3c,
1b, 2c, 1c, 4a, 1a, 2b, 1b, 3a, 1c, 2a, 1a, 5c,
1b, 2c, 1c, 3b, 1a, 2b, 1b, 4c, 1c, 2a, 1a, 3c,
1b, 2c, 1c.

page 176. *Getting the Trains Past.*
Move C to the left, then onto the siding.
Move A and B to the right.
Move C to the left.
Move A, B, and D to the left.
Move B and D onto the siding.
Move B to the left.
Move A and B to the right.
Move C onto the siding.
Move C and D to the left.
Move A, B, and E to the left.
Move B and E onto the siding.
Move B to the left.
A leaves, pulling B.
C pushes D onto the siding and couples to E.
C leaves with D and E.

page 176. *Ordering the Engines.* In this puzzle engine number 5 is stationary throughout. The other engines move as follows:
7, 6, 3, 7, 6, 1, 2, 4, 1, 3, 8, 1, 3, 2, 4, 3, 2.

page 176. *The Giant Freight Trains.* Call the engine that is originally on the left L, and the one that starts on the right R. Then:
R takes 40 cars to the left.
R takes these 40 cars onto the siding.
L takes its 80 cars to the right.
R takes its 40 cars to the left.
L takes 120 cars to the left.
L pushes 40 cars onto the siding.
L returns to the left.
L moves to the right with the 80 cars it was originally pulling.
R pushes 40 cars up to the siding to couple with the cars already waiting there.
R moves off to the left, with its original 80 cars.

page 176. *The Line Gangs' Trains.* The engine that was originally on the left is labeled L, and the one that starts on the right is labeled R.
L goes onto the siding.
R takes its car to the left section of track, well past the switch.
L returns and couples to R's car.
L takes R's car to the right.
R goes onto the siding.
L pushes R's car to the left.
L takes all of the cars to the right.
R returns to the left, then goes to the right.
R takes all of the cars to the left.
R pushes the rearmost car (the one that R originally brought) onto the siding.
L goes to the left.
L departs pulling its own cars.
R reverses to the siding and couples to its cars.
R leaves to the left, with its car.

page 177. *The Double Siding.* To exchange the cars and finish facing the left, the engine:
moves past B, reverses onto BC and couples to the white car;
moves past B, reverses onto AB and uncouples;
moves past B, reverses onto CD, goes onto AC, and couples to the striped car;
moves past A, reverses onto AB, taking the striped car with it, and couples to the white car;
takes both cars past B, goes forward onto BC and uncouples from the striped car;
reverses past B, goes forward past A, reverses onto AC and uncouples from the white car, before going past A and reversing onto AB.

To exchange the cars and finish pointing in the original direction, the engine must:
go past B, reverse onto BC and couple to the white car;
push the white car onto CD and uncouple;
go past B, reverse past A, go forward onto AC and couple to the striped car;
push the striped car up to the white car so that the cars can be coupled;
reverse past A, go onto AB and uncouple the white car;
reverse past A, push the striped car onto CD and uncouple from it;
reverse past A, go onto AB and couple to the white car;
reverse past A, push the white car onto AC and uncouple from it;
reverse past A, go over AB and past B, reverse up to CD and couple to the striped car;
take the striped car onto BC and uncouple from it, before going on past B and reversing onto AB.

page 178. *The Perfect Hexagon.* To make this, move:
F to touch A and D.
E to touch D and F.
D to touch the lower sides of B and C.
C to touch D and E.

page 178. *Two Transformations.* First make the H into the O, by the following moves:
Move F to touch A and D.
Move H to touch E and F.
Move E to touch C and D.
Move D to touch G and H on the lower sides.
Move G to touch D and E on the lower sides.

To turn the O into the H:
Move J to touch N and O.
Move M to touch J and N.
Move J to touch M and N on the upper sides.
Move M to touch J and L.
Move N to touch I and M.
Move I to touch L and O on the lower sides.
Move O to touch K and P.

			8				
					7		
							6
	5						
						4	
3							
		2					
				1			

page 178. The solution to *The Eight Checkers* problem.

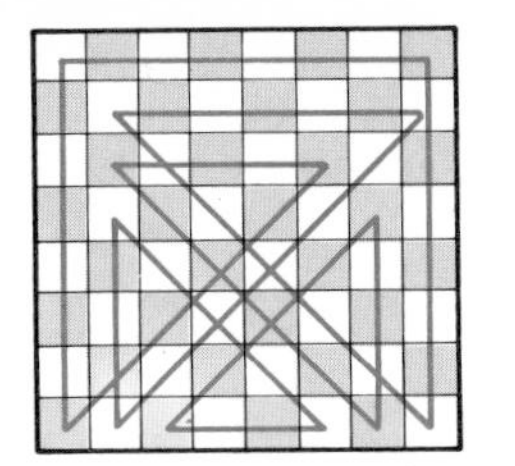

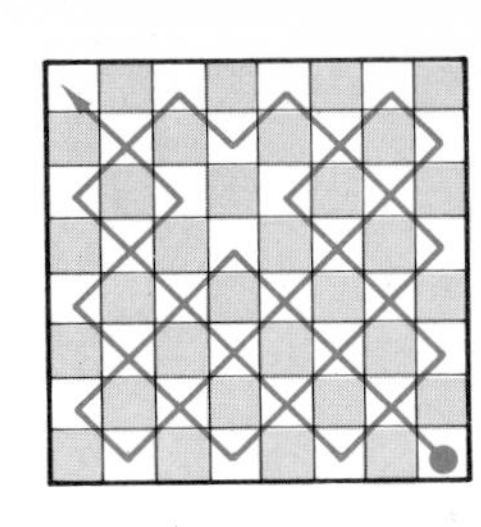

page 178. *The Queen and Bishop Go Touring.* For the *Queen's Tour*, move your piece as shown above (left) so as to cover the board in 14 queen's moves. Start at one end of any move shown in the figure.

The *Bishop's Tour* begins in the bottom right-hand corner of the board, and follows the pattern in the diagram (above right) to visit all of the white squares in 17 bishop's moves.

page 179. *Switch Sixteen.* The piece to be moved can be identified by the number of its square. There is only one vacant square to which it can move. Pieces move in the following order:

11, 7, 9, 8, 10, 13, 11, 14, 9, 6, 8, 5, 7, 11, 9, 10, 8, 2, 1, 6, 3, 5, 7, 4, 9, 12, 15, 17, 14, 16, 13, 15, 11, 7, 9, 14, 11, 13, 10, 8, 9, 6, 8, 2, 5, 7, 11, 9, 12, 10, 8, 9.

page 179. *The Square Dance.* If "A jumps over B and C" is represented by A × B × C, then one solution is:

E × F × C × A × G; B × D; I × H; B × I; E × B.

page 179. *Jumping Checkers.* The checker to be moved can be identified by the number of its square. There is only one vacant square into which it can move. Begin by transposing the checkers in the middle row, as follows:
19, 17, 16, 18, 20, 21, 19, 17, 15, 16, 18, 20, 19, 17, 18. Now move checker 25 into square 18 and exchange the checkers in the fourth row. (Add 7 to each number above and you will have the solution sequence.) Then jump checker 11 into square 25. Now exchange the checkers in the second row. Move checker 4 onto square 11 and transpose checkers in the first row. Jump checker 18 onto square 4 and checker 32 onto square 18. Now exchange checkers in the fifth row. Finally move the checkers in the central column in the order 25, 11, and 18.

page 179. *The Juggernaut.* To move the four black checkers to the left slots and the white checkers to the four right slots, move the following pairs of checkers, numbered from the left:
2+3 to 9+10, 5+6 to 2+3, 8+9 to 5+6, 1+2 to 8+9.

page 180-181 . *Sliding Block Puzzles.* On these pages the blocks of each puzzle are numbered, and these numbers are used in the solutions. If there are two directions in which a block can be moved, the correct way is indicated beside the number of the block by d (down), u (up), l (left), and r (right). Move the blocks in the order given.

The Flying Puzzle: 11+12, 10, 9, 7 (d+1), 11+ 12+ 8+13, 4, 1+2+3 +5, 6+7, 11+ 12+8+13+4, 3, 1+2+5, 7 (r+u), 11+2+9, 10, 1+ 8+13, 6+7, 11+ 12+9+10, 13, 8+1, 7 (d+1), 2+5, 3, 4+1, 7+6, 2+5+3, 4, 1, 7 (r+u), 8, 14, 1.

The George Washington Puzzle: a) to the top right; 15, 10+11+7+ 5, 3+4, 1, 7, 5, 3 (d+r), 1, 2+6, 8, 9, 12+13 (1+u), 7, 5, 3+4 (d+1), 1.
b) from top right to bottom right; 2+6+8, 9, 13 (1+u), 14, 15, 7+5, 12+13, 14, 5, 12+13, 14, 5+15, 7, 12 (d+1), 10+11, 4, 3 (r+d), 1, 2, 6+14, 13 (u+r), 12, 10+11, 3 (1+d), 1, 14, 12+13+10+11, 3+4, 1.
c) from bottom right to bottom left; 2+14, 6, 12 (u+r), 10, 11, 12+13, 10, 11, 12 (1+d), 14, 1, 3+4 ,7, 5+15, 14, 13 (u+1), 1, 4+3 (u+r), 7+15, 5+14, 12+13 (r+u), 1, 3 (r+u), 7, 15, 5, 14, 12 (d+1), 1, 3+4 (1+d), 7+15, 5+14, 12+13 (d+r), 1, 4 (1+d), 7, 15+5, 14+12+13, 1.
d) from bottom left to top left; 1, 13+12, 14, 5+15, 7, 4 (u+r), 1, 13+12 (u+1), 14, 3+4 (d+1), 10, 9+8+ 11, 13+12, 1, 8, 9, 12 (r+u), 1+14, 3+4, 8+10+ 9+11, 12+13, 1.

Ma's Puzzle: 9 (1), 8, 7, 6, 5, 9 (u), 8, 7, 6, 4, 2, 1, 3 (u), 9 (u+r), 5 (1+u), 6, 4 (d+r), 9 (d all the way), 5, 3, 1, 2, 5.

Credits and Acknowledgments

L = left; R = right; C = center; t = top;
b = bottom.

Puzzle Model Constructions
J. H. de Boer: 72-73; Jack Botermans: 5L, 6L, 7L, 11, 17, 22, 29-49, 54, 60-64, 67-70, 76, 80, 85, 98-115, 142, 144-155, 175, 177, 179; C. J. Bouwkamp: 165; Willem L. van der Poel: title page, 81, 82, 83.

Illustrations
Jack Botermans, Pieter van Delft, Otto van Eersel.

Character Illustrations
Henk Kneepkens: 6C, 7C, 7R, 28, 32, 37, 43, 48, 49t, 50bC, 56, 76tL, 117b, 146L, 159b, 161tC, 166R.

Puzzle Contributions
J. H. de Boer: 72-75, 166L; C. J. Bouwkamp: 165; Stewart T. Coffin: 66tL; Alan Fletcher, Pentagram Design: 140t, 141; Jenifer Haselgrove (Van der Poel collection): 83; Piet Hein International: 44; David Murley: 186bL; Prof. J. van der Poel Belasting Museum, Rotterdam: 93; Willem L. van der Poel collection: 1, 3, 8bL, 11t, 35b, 66R, 71, 81, 82, 84, 92b, 96, 97t, 106, 114; Tom Ransom collection: 180, 181L; Will van Sambeek collection: 5, 77; Inez Stodel, Antiquariaat, Amsterdam: 4, 12, 18-20, 20-21t, 24-26, 27.

Further Acknowledgments
Electro Galvanische Fabriek, Amsterdam; T.H. Bibliotheek, Delft; Universiteitsbibliotheek, Amsterdam.

Photographic Credits
ADM International bv: 14b, 15b, 62b, 65, 69, 170tL, 178L; Bibliothèque Nationale, Paris: 5, 57; Janet and Colin Bord: 124-125, 127b, 128tL, 131b, 132tR, 133, 136bR; Greg Bright: 139; British Crown Copyright — reproduced with permission of the Controller of Her Britannic Majesty's Stationery Office: 126t; British Museum: 128bL, 129tR; Cliché Musées Nationaux, Paris: 128-129; The Colonial Williamsburg Foundation: 136L; William Gordon Davis: 10t; Pieter van Delft: 168-169; Escher Stichting — Haags Gemeentemuseum: 10b; reproduced by permission of the Syndics of the Fitzwilliam Museum, Cambridge: back cover, center column, 137; Anton van der Gulik: 13t; Claus and Liselotte Hansmann: 8t, 8bC, 9; Mansell Collection; 124tL, 130, 131tL, 131tR, 132L, 132b, 135bC; National Museum of Ireland: 127t; Nordiska Museet, Stockholm: 97b; Beverley Ransom: 120R, 143b, 180, 181; Rijksarchief in Groningen: 134; Rijksmuseum, Amsterdam: 5, 87; Roger-Viollet: 126b; Alexander Turnbull Library, New Zealand: 116t, 116b; John White, West Air Photography (courtesy of Latimer New Dimensions Ltd.): frontispiece.

Photography of puzzle models, and front and back covers (left and right columns) by John Koopman.

Prints: AB Graphic and Photall.

Bibliography

Andrews, W. S. et al. *Magic Squares and Cubes.* 1917. Reprint. New York: Dover Publications, 1960.
Berndt, Frederick. *The Domino Book.* New York: Thomas Nelson, 1974.
Bord, Janet. *Mazes and Labyrinths of the World.* New York: E. P. Dutton and Co., 1976.
Bright, Greg. *Greg Bright's Fontana Mazes.* London: William Collins, Fontana Books, 1975.
———. *Greg Bright's Maze Book.* London: Latimer New Dimensions, 1973.
Dudeney, Henry E. *Amusements in Mathematics.* 1917. Reprint. New York: Dover Publications, 1958.
———. *The Canterbury Puzzles.* 1919. Reprint. New York: Dover Publications, 1958.
Elffers, Joost. *Tangram.* Cologne: M. DuMont Schauberg, 1973.
Fults, John Lee. *Magic Squares.* LaSalle, Ill.: Open Court Publishing Co., 1974.
Gardner, Martin. *Further Mathematical Diversions.* London: George Allen and Unwin, 1970.
———. *Mathematics, Magic and Mystery.* New York: Dover Publications, 1956.
———. *New Mathematical Diversions from Scientific American.* New York: Simon and Schuster, 1966.
———. *The Second Scientific American Book of Mathematical Puzzles and Diversions.* New York: Simon and Schuster, 1961.
———. *The Sixth Book of Mathematical Games from Scientific American.* New York: Charles Scribner's, 1971.
Golomb, Solomon W. *Polyominoes.* New York: Charles Scribner's, 1965.
Haddon, Kathleen. *String Games for Beginners.* Cambridge, England: W. Heffer and Sons, 1973.
Hoffmann, Professor L. *Puzzles Old and New.* New York: Frederick Warne and Co., 1920.
Jayne, Caroline Furness. *String Figures and How to Make Them.* 1906. Reprint. New York: Dover Publications, 1962.
Kordemsky, Boris A. *The Moscow Puzzles.* New York: Charles Scribner's, 1972.
Leeflang, K. W. *Domino Games and Domino Puzzles.* New York: St. Martin's Press, 1975.
Leeming, Joseph. *Fun with String.* 1940. Reprint. New York: Dover Publications, 1974.
Lindgren, Harry. *Recreational Problems in Geometric Dissections and How to Solve Them.* Rev. ed. New York: Dover Publications, 1972.
Loyd, Sam. *The Eighth Book of Tan: Seven Hundred Tangrams.* Rev. ed. New York: Dover Publications, 1968.
———. *Best Mathematical Puzzles of Sam Loyd.* Edited by Martin Gardner. New York: Dover Publications, 1959.
Matthews, W. H. *Mazes and Labyrinths: Their History and Development.* 1922. Reprint. New York: Dover Publications, 1970.
Minskin, E. *Pionerskaya Igroteka.* Moscow: Molodaya Gvardiya, 1966.
Read, Ronald C. *Tangrams.* New York: Dover Publications, 1965.
Schuh, Fred. *The Master Book of Mathematical Puzzles and Recreations.* New York: Dover Publications, 1968.
Tromholt, Sophus. *Streichholzspiele.* Leipzig: Otto Spamer, 1889.